Magnolia House

Angela Barton

Where heroes are like chocolate – irresistible!

Published 2021 by Choc Lit Limited
Penrose House, Crawley Drive, Camberley, Surrey GU15 2AB, UK
www.choc-lit.com

A CIP catalogue record for this book is available
from the British Library

ISBN: 978-1-78189-459-0

Printed and bound in Great Britain
by Clays Ltd, Elcograf S.p.A.

Magnolia House

Words are easy like the wind,
but faithful friends are hard to find.

William Shakespeare

For my dad, who I miss painfully.
A gentle man. A gentleman.

Acknowledgements

Thank you Choc Lit for publishing Magnolia House and for the incredible job of editing, designing, organising and helping to promote my book. Thank you to my small team of friends in Ampersands' Fiction Group, an off-shoot group in Nottingham Writers' Studio – Frances, Gaynor, Andy and Paul. Their positive critiques helped to improve every chapter. Thanks also to my anonymous reader in the Romantic Novelists' Association New Writers' Scheme who highlighted areas for improvement and praised what she loved. Thanks to my husband, Paul, and children Rosanna, Luke and Jack for encouraging my love of writing and a big hug to all my extended family and friends for their generous support. For my spaniels Harlyn and Brook who kept my feet warm during the cooler months of writing.

A thank you to the Tasting panel for passing my book for publication; Dimi E, Melanie R, Sam E, Debbie S, Jenny K, Anne E, Gill L, Joy S, Cordy S, Gillian C, Yvonne G, Kirsty W, Jo O, Alex T, Wendy S and Jenny M.

Chapter One

April's unexpected heat-haze danced as it levitated above broiled pavements. Shiny black slugs of melted tarmac dribbled into gutters, smelling as sickly-sweet as pineapple chunks. The news channels were proclaiming that it was going to be the hottest spring on record for the past seventeen years and the damp skin on Rowan's back was testimony to that fact.

Rowan and her husband, Tom, were in Clapham, standing across the road from Magnolia House and looking up at it in disbelief. It was a neglected and weather-worn building and its flaking central front door didn't bode well for the rest of the house. The sash windows looked rotten where paint had peeled and rain had drenched the exposed wood. The low parapet that was built around the edge of the roof was crumbling in parts and missing in others. Its only redeeming feature was a mature magnolia tree standing in the diminutive front garden.

Rowan unfolded the page from the newspaper that Tom had shown her at breakfast the previous morning and, after great excitement, they'd decided to drive to London for a viewing.

'It says here,' Rowan read, '*elegant semi-detached Georgian town house with basement accommodation. In need of some modernisation to bring it back to its former glory. Full of original features. Pretty courtyard to the rear of the property. Dated decor requiring attention throughout.*'

'Dated! I think they mean delapi-dated,' said Tom, rubbing the stubble on his chin. It was a nervous habit he'd developed since recently establishing his own photographic business, The Wider Picture.

Nearby church bells chimed half past the hour as the estate agent fidgeted impatiently next to the front steps.

'Do you still want to take a look?' asked Rowan.

Tom pulled a face and shrugged. 'We're here, I suppose,' he said, taking her hand and pulling her across the road.

'Tom and Rowan Forrester?' asked the agent as they walked towards her.

'That's us,' said Tom.

'Great. Let's get in out of this heat, shall we?'

As the woman turned a key in the lock, Rowan noticed that a line of perspiration had seeped through the back of the agent's olive dress, staining it dark green. Once inside the cool hallway, they gave a collective sigh of relief. Hues of red and yellow painted their skin like tribal markings as the sunlight shone through the stained-glass window in the front door. The smell in the dank entrance hall was musty and sweet, almost like a perfume.

They followed the woman into the kitchen where they discovered several cupboard doors hanging from their hinges, exposed pipework and an oven that had created its own biosphere of living organisms. Strange amorphous splodges were sprouting fungus and threading their way around each of the gas rings.

Tom and Rowan traipsed around tumbledown rooms where ceilings were decorated with damp patches, floorboards were broken and strips of ripped wallpaper hung like clusters of catkins. Although some rooms were in better condition than others, all had retained their ornate cornices, ceiling roses and wide floorboards that shone with an aged patina. They lingered on the top floor, taking in the view of rooftops and neighbouring manicured gardens, before moving to the next sash window that was littered with hollow husks of dead bluebottles.

'Look over there. Can you see the church spire?'

Rowan looked beyond Tom's pointed finger. The church's conical tower tapered towards the bare blue sky.

'Look, Clapham Common?' Rowan pointed, directing Tom's gaze towards patches of grass that were exposed behind the houses on the opposite side of the street. 'I didn't realise the house was so close to it.'

They followed the agent back downstairs to inspect the basement. It was surprisingly roomy and light, with lemon sunshine spilling in from windows set high in the walls. The glass frames were too high to see the front garden, but oblong strips of cyan sky filled the panes as street sounds filtered in through the loose casements. Occasionally, a disembodied passer-by walked past the house, the limited view from the basement revealing only their legs.

Tom grinned. 'This is perfect. I can even use one of these rooms as a dark room and expose some of my photographs the old-fashioned way. And there's so much storage space.'

Rowan knew that if any floor would hook his interest, it would be this one. She watched him stride from one basement room to the next, planning and imagining his new business. When he'd finished pacing and stroking the surprisingly dry walls, they trooped in single file back up the narrow staircase to the hallway and back into the dining room. Tom ran his hand over a wooden fire surround, tracing his fingers along the carved swags and shells. He crossed the room and stopped against the double doors, looking out.

'Can we go outside?'

'Of course. It's unlocked,' said the agent.

They stepped outside into a small courtyard garden, the glare of the midday sun making them squint. Aircraft droned above them, leaving white streaks slashed across the sky, criss-crossing existing contrails. The courtyard was full of pots containing withered brown plants, from which a handful of delicate yellow flowers gasped for life. The pale flagstones were decorated with star-shaped fans of dandelion leaves and at the far end of the modest enclosure stood a crumbling wall garnished with an overgrown wisteria. Despite its unkempt state, it was full of promise.

Rowan had loved everything about the house's ramshackle interior and envisaged a happy future living in it with the man she loved. The atmosphere was one of serenity and calm. Their four-year-old spaniel, Jet, would be safe in the enclosed courtyard and could run on the huge expanse of grass on the common. Rowan looked at Tom and saw a smile play on his lips and knew that he felt the same way.

'What do you think?'

He nodded slowly before answering. 'Potential. Lots of potential.'

Rowan clasped her hands together, as if in prayer. 'Shall we?'

'We should come back again on a dull day and have another look.'

'Tom, we're in the middle of an unprecedented heatwave. Forecasters are saying it could last for another fortnight. By the time a dull day comes around we'll have missed the auction.'

The agent interrupted. 'There *is* a lot of interest in this property.'

'See,' said Rowan.

Tom leant forwards and whispered in her ear. 'She would say that, wouldn't she?' He rubbed his thumb against his fingers to illustrate that there would be a commission to be had if she sold the house to them.

'But it's a perfect family home, isn't it?'

'Hmm. It's expensive and it'll need a lot of work.'

'But I told you, I want to invest Grandma's inheritance,' whispered Rowan. 'I know it'll still be a struggle for a while,

4

but I'm sure my jewellery designs will sell for more money in London and you said you'd have a lot of extra work if we moved here.'

'I know.' Tom's forehead furrowed in thought. 'If you're sure about your grandma's money and we stick to our limit at the auction, then perhaps ...'

'Perhaps we can?'

Tom smiled. 'Perhaps we should give it a go.'

Chapter Two

but I'm sure my ... ... for more money
to London and you said you'd have a lot of extra work if
we moved here.'

'I know,' Tom's forehead furrowed in thought. 'If you're

Tom's sister, Libby, lay prone on her double bed, resting her
chin on her cupped palms while staring at the screen of her
laptop. She'd arrived back from work ten minutes earlier,
having spent a boring day trying to avoid her bad-tempered
boss at the flower shop. She glanced at the alarm clock on
her bedside table. David wouldn't be home for another half
an hour, so she had time to fan out a plastic rainbow of
multicoloured credit cards on the pillow in front of her.

She typed in the account number from her red credit
card, added her password and waited until her account
details were displayed in front of her.

'Yes!' Libby clenched a fist in celebration.

Her credit limit had been increased. Rolling onto her
back she held the card above her head, smiling. Now she
could afford to buy Tom and Rowan a house-warming gift
if they were successful at the property auction. She kissed
the card and closed her eyes, resting it on her lips. Within
seconds her pleasure was replaced with a groan. Libby's
moods swung from elation to guilt as regularly as her
carriage clock chimed each quarter hour. She knew that she
owed thousands of pounds on her credits cards and that her
need to shop had worsened.

Why did a visit to Covent Garden or Oxford Street give
her a high she was unable to give up? She craved the buzz.
The anticipation of the journey. The bright colourful shops,
playing feel-good music. Shelves and rails full of tantalising
objects and clothes that would make her pain more
bearable. The purchase was the highlight. Her heart would
beat faster as she watched her bargain being wrapped in
tissue paper or rolled in bubble wrap. It would be carefully

placed in a pristine carrier bag and handed to her like a trophy.

The guilt usually kicked in before she'd even left the shop. She'd ask herself if she really needed more jewellery, make-up, another set of cutlery or any more baby clothes? She and David still hadn't conceived after three years of trying, so why she needed to start suitcase number three of tiny outfits was unfathomable. She just couldn't stop herself. Libby hadn't dared add up her accumulated debt. She only knew that David must never find out.

She sighed and sat up, rubbing her hands together to ease the pins and needles in her fingers. It was getting more and more difficult to hide all her new items from her husband. The suitcases were in the attic, hidden under an old rug. New suitcases had to be bought each time she filled one so David wouldn't notice that their holiday cases had gone missing. The spare room's divan bed was heaving with unpacked carrier bags, as was the back of their garage. Libby was dreading the day they would eventually move house.

She slipped the card into a purse and secreted it away in her Marc Jacobs's leather tote bag, another of her feel-good purchases. Picking up six more credit cards she shuffled them like a pack of playing cards. Libby dropped them into an overnight vanity case, zipped it up and turned the key on the miniature padlock. She then pushed the case back into its hiding place underneath her dressing table.

As she stood up, she caught her reflection in the mirror. Shame made her look away, unable to meet her own gaze. Shopping. What a ridiculous addiction to have. She could never go to her doctor and admit that she needed to shop constantly in order to feel better. The doctor would tell her that all she suffered from was an inability to keep her purse in her handbag. It was too embarrassing to contemplate.

Libby heard her mobile ringing in the kitchen and hurried downstairs to answer it. She saw David's shadow walking towards the house through the obscured glass window in the front door and opened it for him before scurrying down the hallway into the kitchen.

Her sister-in-law's name and photograph lit up her screen. 'Hi, Rowan.'

'Hiya.'

'Well, what do you think of the house? Are you going to bid for it?'

Rowan squealed down the phone, making Libby grimace and hold her mobile away from her ear. 'I'll take that as a yes. That's wonderful. I can't believe you're both going to live so close to us.' Libby grinned at David as he walked into the kitchen.

'*Hopefully* going to live close by,' said Rowan. 'We have to win the auction first, but fingers crossed it'll soon be goodbye drizzly Wilmslow, hello sunny Clapham.'

Libby laughed. 'It's been known to drizzle in London too, you know?'

'I don't care. I'm so excited and … hang on, your brother wants a word.'

'Hi, Libby.'

'Tom! You mad man. You're doing it then?'

'The auction's a pretty big hurdle but we're giving it a go.'

'I was telling Rowan, I can't wait to have you both close by. We'll be able to spend so much time together.'

'It's going to be an adventure, that's for sure. Is David there? I'd like a quick word.'

'Of course, hang on a minute. He's just uncorking a bottle of wine.' She turned and handed the phone to her husband. 'Tom wants a word.'

She walked over to the fridge to begin preparing dinner,

taking out a chilled packet of fresh penne pasta and a jar of tomato and basil sauce. When Libby turned, she was surprised to see that David had walked into the living room and was speaking in hushed tones. What could they possibly have to say that needed privacy? She moved a few steps closer and heard him whisper, 'You've got a nerve.' David was now hunched forwards sitting on a chair. Something was wrong. She walked towards him and saw him rake his fingers through his hair in an agitated gesture.

She rested a hand on his shoulder for comfort but startled him instead.

'Shit! No, no, it's Libby,' he said into the phone. 'I'll speak to you tomorrow. I've got to go. Bye.' He pressed the red button and handed it back to Libby.

'What was all that about?' she asked.

'Oh, nothing.' David stood up and walked towards the kitchen.

'David. You can't say it's nothing when you've just told my brother he's got a nerve.' She raised her eyebrows in question.

'Just football stuff. He's going to try out for our club when he moves.'

She frowned.

'We were bantering, that's all.' He smiled. 'Everything's fine.'

Libby wasn't convinced.

Chapter Three

Rowan had worked at Filigree Bridal Gowns in Manchester for four years having studied for a degree in textiles. Filigree had a workshop on the first floor above the shop, a room where wedding gowns were designed before being brought to life after weeks of cutting, pinning and sewing. It was here that Rowan was sitting at her workspace, sewing sequins onto a bodice.

'Ouch!' Rowan sucked her finger and then inspected it.

Her colleague, Chrissy, was standing at the ironing board pressing a garment. 'If you stop looking at your watch every two minutes then you'll stop stabbing yourself with the needle.'

'I can't concentrate. Tom's at the auction and I'm imagining new bidders increasing the price with every stitch I sew.'

'If it's meant to be, it'll happen.'

Rowan was sceptical. Chrissy grew anxious if the day's horoscope didn't turn out to be accurate and she'd feng shui-ed the life out of every incense-filled room of her apartment.

'This house you want in London,' said Chrissy, 'what's it like?'

'Old. It needs a lot of work but it's got so much potential.'

'Potential! Don't estate agents just love that word?'

'It's code for this house will eat your money and give you a nervous breakdown.'

Chrissy leant away from a cloud of steam. 'I love decorating. I'm actually quite good at wallpapering.'

'It's a long way off decorating. It's solid enough but the builder's quote is terrifying. It's a bit like a giant jigsaw;

it needs breaking up before putting back together again.' Rowan checked her finger again before she dared pick up the white material.

'Sounds expensive. Thank heavens for grandmothers, eh?'

Rowan carefully set the gown aside using her wrists and lifted a small first aid box off a shelf. 'Grandma's inheritance and the equity in our apartment have made it possible, but we still need a big mortgage. I'm just praying my new business takes off and Tom finds plenty of work or it'll be on the market again next year.'

Chrissy hung up the wedding gown she'd pressed. 'Have you made much jewellery since your silversmith course? It's a brave move to change career paths and move at the same time.'

'Now's as good a time as any.' Rowan wound a plaster around her finger. 'I love the freedom of designing and making my own pieces of jewellery.'

Rowan's mobile rang, interrupting their conversation. Flustered, she searched beneath swathes of lace and silk before finding it. Her heart was racing.

'Tom?'

He sounded ecstatic. 'Guess what?'

'My God, we didn't?'

'Oh yes we did. Magnolia House is ours.'

It seemed such a huge upheaval to move from Wilmslow to the capital, but Tom had been adamant that he'd find more lucrative photographic work in the heart of the city. Despite a little anxiety at leaving the North behind, the excitement of moving from the gentle buzz of Wilmslow to the deafening roar of London, filled her with excitement. The lure of a grown-up house close to the hubbub of the metropolis had smothered any sentimental regret she might have in leaving their first shared abode. To add to Rowan's excitement, Tom's sister, Libby, and her husband David, would live ten minutes away. Rowan and Libby had hit it off from the moment they'd first been introduced six years previously. Tom had almost needed to prise them apart in order to take his new girlfriend to the cinema as planned. Now Rowan couldn't wait for her sister-in-law to show her the sights and sounds of the city.

During the first few weeks of the renovation project, Tom spent many days away in London. He constantly drove backwards and forwards to do fashion shoots and check on progress at the new house, telling Rowan that he felt like he was attached to a piece of bungee elastic. The project manager had shown him what had been done, but for a long time progress was hidden behind plaster or beneath floorboards. Damp proof membranes were laid, pipework connected and crumbling walls were re-plastered. The basement staircase had to be replaced and the majority of the original sash windows needed extensive work in order to save them.

It had taken four long months, while living in rented accommodation nearby, but finally Magnolia House was ready. The teams of builders, joiners, electricians, plumbers and painters had left, having renovated it from a dirty stone in the ground to a polished gem. Windows gleamed, the crumbling parapet had been restored and the new front door shone with a high gloss finish.

Inside, the house had also been transformed. Smooth walls wore a fresh coat of pale pistachio, porcelain sinks sparkled, sash windows hushed smoothly open and shut. Oak floorboards no longer creaked, ceilings were no longer splattered with damp patches and the basement was now an all-dancing-all-singing photographic studio. Rowan had transformed the previously neglected courtyard and had converted it into a sanctuary of peace and serenity. Raised beds made from old railway sleepers were filled with fragrant herbs and glazed pots were full of brightly coloured pansies.

The biggest excitement of the following week had also been Rowan's biggest shock. She had put her recent headaches and nausea down to the smell of paint and wood varnish, but it was only when she'd hung a calendar on the kitchen wall that she realised she was late. The red star that predicted when she'd been due was etched onto a date ten days earlier. She'd been too busy to realise. A mixture of elation and fear flushed through her veins. It was what she had dreamed of since marrying Tom, but he'd set up his new business and a baby would certainly be a distraction. She could decorate a spare room as a nursery, but how would she tell Libby who was finding it difficult to conceive? And what about the expense? How could they afford a baby?

Her overriding emotion, however, was elation. The thought of having a baby to grow up in this beautiful house with them had made her hum silly tunes all day, despite her nausea. Libby and David were coming round for some dinner tomorrow after the men had been to football practice, so she'd keep it a secret until they'd left. She couldn't trust Tom not to mention it in his excitement.

The next evening, Rowan and Tom were lounging on their sofas opposite Libby and David. Having finished dinner, the French doors had been swung open to let the mild August evening air sigh into the house.

'I forgot to ask who won?' said Libby, turning to face Tom.

Tom was leaning back against the sofa deep in thought whilst biting his nails.

'Tom.'

He blinked and sat forwards. 'Sorry?'

'I was just wondering who won at football?'

'Oh. We did. Nice bunch of lads. I'd like to do it again. Would you excuse me a moment?'

Tom got up and left the room.

'Is he okay?' asked Libby.

'He's been a bit moody recently, but he's been so busy with the house and his new business. He's just a bit stressed. Has he said anything to you, David?' asked Rowan.

David fidgeted. 'Nope. As you say, he's been really busy lately.'

Tom returned a few minutes later and although he looked pale, alcohol and familiarity eased the friends through an evening of conversation. Despite being quieter and drinking more than usual, Tom joined in with the banter and good-natured gossip. It was nearly midnight before there was any sign of their guests moving.

'It's been lovely. Thanks so much,' said Libby, rubbing her stomach. 'I haven't eaten so much in ages.'

'And congratulations for staying sane over the last few months,' said David, raising his glass.

Rowan began collecting glasses. 'We could do this regularly. Friday night suppers after football.'

'Sounds good,' said David. 'Although I think that lasagne and garlic bread have cancelled out the exercise we've just done on the pitch this evening.'

Libby patted her husband's stomach. 'No one forced you to have three helpings.' She turned to Rowan. 'Have you given any thought to when you'll start your new business?'

Rowan was stroking Jet. 'Not yet, it's been too hectic. I'm going to spend next week emptying the last few boxes and then I'll visit a few gift shops to ask whether they buy direct from jewellery designers. Tom's going to make me a workbench for one of the spare bedrooms.'

Libby got up and began to collect screwed up paper

napkins and the odd plate. 'It might be tough as a newbie without a portfolio.'

'Everyone has to start somewhere. Charles Tiffany started out with a stationery store and he's sold a few pieces of jewellery since then!' Rowan laughed, then became thoughtful, resting her coffee mug against her lips. She was trying to think of a way of working alongside a demanding baby. 'I could even set up a website and start a mail order business.'

'I'm jealous. I hate working in the flower shop.'

Rowan stood up and followed Libby into the kitchen. 'Tom's in Scotland next week shooting some spring fashions for next year's *Petticoat* magazine. Are you free for a coffee sometime?'

'Of course. Give me a text. Anything to get away from the boss for half an hour.'

They wandered into the hall where Tom and David were standing next to the front door. They were speaking in urgent, hushed tones with their heads bowed towards each other.

'They look like naughty schoolboys plotting to raid the tuck shop, don't they?' said Libby.

'Definitely shifty.'

The men stood up straight and glanced back at their wives.

'Just discussing tactics for next week's match,' said Tom.

'Thank you for cooking, Rowan,' said David. 'It was great.'

'You're welcome. Same time, same place, next Friday.'

They waved until Libby and David's car lights had turned the corner, then wandered back into the lounge where Rowan wrapped her arms around Tom. Now was the perfect moment to tell him her wonderful news.

'Well, Mr Forrester, how does it feel to be the proud new

owner of a beautiful Georgian townhouse and the successful host of our first dinner party?'

'Good.' His voice was monotone.

She pulled back and looked at him. 'Just good? Is everything all right?'

'I'm fine.'

'You don't sound it.'

'Don't nag. I'm just exhausted. Leave the dishes and I'll do them in the morning. Night.'

Rowan watched him leave the room and heard him walk upstairs. The feeling of rejection and disappointment stung like a bed of nettles.

Chapter Four

Rowan had slept fitfully after Tom's blunt goodnight, but had finally fallen into a dream-filled sleep at four in the morning. She was woken up at half past eight when he brought her a cup of tea. He placed it on the bedside table before sitting on the edge of the bed, looking sheepish.

'Morning, darling. I've booked a table at Langan's tonight to say sorry for being such a moody little shit, lately.'

She rubbed her eyes and hauled herself to a sitting position. Tom leaned across and pushed a pillow behind her back. Immediately a wave of nausea enveloped her but she fought it by taking a sip of tea. 'Morning. That sounds lovely, but you didn't need to do that.'

'Yes I did. We need some time alone without builders, well-meaning friends or clients phoning and interrupting us. I'm taking you on a good old-fashioned date.'

She smiled. At that precise moment, the thought of eating dinner was making her want to run to the bathroom and retch. 'Where did you say you'd booked?'

'Langan's?'

He stood up and kissed her forehead. 'It's in Mayfair and apparently a celebrity hang out. I asked David and he recommended it. Sorry I've got to dash off so quickly, but I've a ten o'clock appointment across the city.' He walked into the en suite and checked his hair in the mirror. 'I've fed Jet so he just needs a walk.' He blew her a kiss before leaving the bedroom. 'See you later. Table's booked for seven.'

'Bye,' she shouted after him.

Rowan wrapped her fingers around the mug of tea and sipped again. What a perfect way to tell Tom that she was expecting their baby. She couldn't celebrate with champagne, but it would be a memorable evening.

They approached the red neon sign on the corner of Stratton Street just before seven. Rowan stepped inside the restaurant door into a long, golden dining room that was humming with laughter and friendly conversation. They were greeted warmly before being seated in between a table of elderly raffish gentlemen who were amicably poring over the wine list and a young couple who were cracking the golden toppings of their crème brûlées.

A waiter pulled out a red upholstered dining chair for her. She sat down, thanking him. There was a timeless glamour to the décor; walls were scattered with wildly different framed pieces of art, starched white tablecloths that lay like smooth icing on each table and heaving bookcases groaned under the weight of hefty tomes.

'Can I get you a drink?' the waiter asked.

'A brandy and a bottle of your house white, please,' Tom replied.

'Certainly, sir.'

'And a bottle of mineral water, please,' said Rowan.

The waiter nodded. She smiled at her husband. She would have to tell him the good news sooner rather than later because he'd wonder why she wasn't drinking her wine when it arrived.

'This is lovely,' she said.

'You're lovely.'

'Thank you, darling.'

Tom surveyed the room. 'You get the feeling that a lot of these people have been here since lunchtime, don't you?'

'Oh to have that much time to spare. I told Libby we were coming here and she said that Michael Caine was one of the original partners.'

'He was – in the seventies. Look, he's here on the menu.'

Rowan looked at the simple artwork that pictured three men, one of which was easily recognisable as the actor.

'I wonder if they'll let me keep it as a souvenir?'

She laid the menu on the table and looked up to see Tom checking his mobile.

'Are you expecting a call?' she asked.

He slipped his phone into his pocket, looked up and held out his hands to her across the table.

'No.'

She reached across and laced her fingers through his.

He took a deep breath and gave a long, drawn out sigh. 'I'm sorry. I know I've been working away a lot and been bad-tempered recently. I've got a lot on my mind, but you know I love you, don't you?'

'Of course. I love you, too. It's been a stressful few months what with the move and setting up your new business. It'll get easier.'

He squeezed her hands and sat back when the waiter returned with water, a brandy and a bottle of wine. A small amount of house white was poured into Tom's glass and he tasted it.

'Great, thanks.'

His glass was topped up and the waiter turned to Rowan.

'Not at the moment, thank you.'

'The garlic smells amazing. What do you fancy eating?' asked Tom. He raised his brandy glass and drank the amber liquid in one gulp.

Rowan watched him. He seemed tense. She looked at the menu. 'I might go for something light. This duck, pomegranate and blood orange salad sounds good.'

Tom looked up at the waiter who was waiting patiently. 'We'll have a duck salad and moules marinière with cream and garlic, please.'

Left alone again, Rowan asked, 'Are you all right, Tom?'

'Fine. Why?'

'You just seem uptight and a bit distracted.'

'I'm fine. Just tired.'

'Okay. As long as that's all it is. It's difficult to believe that we're sitting here in a fancy London restaurant, you have a new business that's keeping you busy and we have a wonderful house. How lucky are we?'

'I'm lucky to have you,' he said. 'You won't leave me, will you?'

Rowan pulled a face. 'What a thing to say! Of course I won't, silly.'

'I don't take you for granted, you know. I've made mistakes in the past but I love you and promise to work hard for us.' He took a large gulp of wine.

'Stop,' she said. 'If you're talking about the failure of your first idea in Wilmslow, it doesn't matter. We wouldn't be here now if the wedding photography business had taken off. It must be much more interesting to be doing fashion and sports shoots. Anyway, let's talk about something nice. Our new house. Decorating the spare room.'

'The spare room?'

'You never know who'll be joining us.'

'You mean your mother?'

'No. Maybe someone a little smaller.'

'Ronnie Corbett?' Tom gulped the remainder of his wine and poured a second from the ice bucket.

'You're being daft now.' She giggled. Rowan was enjoying herself. She'd tease him a little more before telling her secret. She subconsciously laid her palms on her stomach beneath the table, as if she and her baby were sharing a private moment. 'The chances are that the visitor will have no hair?'

'Matt Lucas?'

'Oh, I give up!'

'You're talking in riddles.' Tom poured another glass of wine.

'I'm just trying to have a light-hearted conversation with you.'

'Sorry,' said Tom. 'Who's coming? How do you want to decorate the spare room?'

'I was thinking of pink or blue.'

'Okay. You can choose which. I don't mind.'

Rowan looked at his face. He was beginning to slur his speech and was oblivious to her hints. She'd have to spell it out.

'I was thinking of decorating it as a nursery.'

Now she had his attention. He'd laugh and hug her in a moment. He was staring at her intently, trying to absorb this wonderful news. But he wasn't smiling. Why wasn't he smiling? The colour had drained from his face.

'Not yet. We will in the future but not now. I'm not ready for a baby.'

Rowan caught her breath. He thought she was suggesting trying for a baby. She immediately felt tears sting her eyes. 'But we've talked about it many times. You said we would start a family when we moved to London.'

'Christ, Rowan. We've only just moved into our new house. There's no rush. Can't you see how stressed I am at the moment?'

Rowan dabbed at her tears with a serviette. This wasn't how it was supposed to pan out. His phone beeped. He took it out of his pocket and read the message before emptying his glass.

'What's wrong, Tom? There's something you're not telling me.'

'It's just a fucking client that won't leave me alone.'

'Then cancel the job. You said you wouldn't work with stroppy, demanding people again.'

'I have a bloody big mortgage to pay for. Beggars can't be choosers.'

'We're not beggars. We've always worked hard.'

Their meals arrived and were placed in front of them. The waiter hesitated before asking if everything was all right. Rowan wiped away a tear and forced a smile.

'Yes, thank you.'

They ate their food in silence, both leaving the majority of it on their plates.

Chapter Five

The week passed in a busy blur. Tom had apologised profusely for his behaviour at the restaurant and once again Rowan assured him he was forgiven. She seemed to be accepting apologies these days like most wives accepted flowers.

Tom been away shooting a fashion assignment for the last couple of days and was due to return later that evening. Rowan had been hanging curtains and unpacking the last of the boxes all week. She had also distributed photographs of her jewellery to a handful of wedding boutiques and gift shops in the hope that something would turn up. All this was done without enthusiasm. Her pregnancy was still a secret. She felt as if she didn't know Tom any more. Gone was the funny, caring and attentive man. He was moody, quiet and spent long periods of time downstairs in his photographic studio listening to music. Perhaps she should suggest he see their local GP?

The following evening Rowan stood in front of the oven, cooking. She couldn't quite believe that it was Friday again so soon. Tom had returned the previous night and they had spent a pleasant evening eating dinner, watching a film and making love before falling asleep. Unfortunately the glorious weather of the previous week had moved south towards the Mediterranean, leaving behind high winds that were stripping the summer canopies of their leaves. It was as if the late summer storms had dampened the nation's mood as well as soaked the city.

Rowan dipped a teaspoon into the bolognaise sauce and tasted it before adding another squirt of tomato puree. The pregnancy test she'd bought from the chemist earlier in the day had confirmed what she already knew. Now she just needed to find the emotional strength to get through the evening with her friends.

The plan was that Libby would pick up Tom and David from football practice and then they were all going to spend another evening together, eating and drinking. She didn't quite know how she was going to hide the fact that she wouldn't be sharing the bottles of wine that would be opened.

She turned and checked the kitchen table. It was set with tea lights flickering in circular glass holders and had four freshly picked pansies standing in a miniature liqueur glass.

Remembering that the wine had to breathe at room temperature, she fetched a bottle of Brouilly from the cool pantry.

Fierce knocking on the front door startled her. The bottle slipped before she could catch it, spilling burgundy liquid down her jeans. Another barrage of hammering annoyed her.

'Okay, okay I'm coming. You don't have to knock the door down.'

Rowan reached for a tea towel and hurried to the door while wiping her jeans. She'd wanted the kitchen to look lovely for their arrival but now she and the kitchen floor were splattered. Her heels click-clacked on the Minton tiles as she hurried down the hallway, turned the latch and pulled open the front door. A gust of wind whistled inside.

David stood on the top step, his face white and his eyes wide and despairing. He was still wearing his football kit, his face smudged with mud and tears. He was panting, with one hand leaning on the doorframe for support.

'David! What's wrong? Is Libby all right?'

'It's not Libby.'

24

As Rowan listened to his words, she heard a wail that sounded like a wounded animal. Later she would be told that it had been her own voice.

Tom had died at 7.25 p.m. on that cool breezy evening. He'd been playing five-a-side football at the leisure centre and according to David, had just collapsed. Another player had performed CPR until the ambulance had arrived, but there'd been nothing anyone could do for him.

David ushered Rowan into the car where Libby was waiting for her, also in a state of shock. Libby held out her arms as Rowan collapsed into them.

'Where is he?' cried Rowan. 'I want to see him.'

'The ambulance took him.'

David bent down and looked into the car. 'Rowan ... Rowan. I need your keys?'

'Which hospital did they take him to? He needs me.'

'Rowan, your keys? I'm sorry, but I need to lock up before we go.'

'The kitchen ... in the kitchen. I'm cooking Tom's dinner ... it'll spoil ...'

Libby gripped Rowan's hands in her own, tears streaming down her face.

'What happened?' asked Rowan. 'Maybe it's not Tom. They could be mistaken. Tom's strong. I'm making his dinner.'

Libby hunted in her handbag and pulled out some tissues. She handed one to Rowan before blowing her own nose. 'It was Tom.'

'What did he say? How did he look?'

'Nothing. Asleep.'

'Maybe he is. Maybe he's asleep. He's been travelling and working too hard and moving house. He's stressed and exhausted. It can do that, you know? The body just shuts down so it can recover. To protect itself.'

Libby slowly shook her head and squeezed Rowan's hands. 'No.'

'But how do you know?'

'I just do. Shhh,' said Libby, stroking Rowan's hands.

Rowan snapped them away. 'How? I need to know. Did you see him?'

Libby nodded, her tears mingling with mucous that oozed from her nostrils. She blew her nose again. 'His eyes were half open. David closed them.'

Rowan stared back at Libby, her lips trembling. Her body began to shake in silent, helpless sobs. Her sister-in-law had a look of complete desolation that told her as surely as a thaw follows a hoar frost, that Tom would never be coming home.

Rowan learned that Tom had died from sudden death syndrome. It appeared that he'd had an undiagnosed heart arrhythmia. For the first two days following Tom's death, Rowan and Libby clung to each other in shared sorrow at the loss of someone they'd both loved deeply. Rowan had stayed with Libby and David for a week and her dog Jet had mysteriously appeared in their house on the second day. During that week, spasms of grief gave way to numb moments of clarity for Rowan. Sleep was fitful and dreams were cruel, but it was more the awakening from them that caused the anguish.

She'd pull her duvet close to her body, imagining that the scrunched bedding was Tom. She made deals with God to be a better person if only He would turn back time. Her body contorted and convulsed with longing, tears soaked the bedclothes and swelled her eyes. Jet had been hugged and cried on for many hours and never once tried to pull away.

The early September morning of Tom's funeral was mild, but drizzle fell softly. Tom was to be laid to rest in Sevenoaks, close to where he was born and where his parents still lived. Rowan's parents had arrived from France where they now lived, full of grief and concern for their daughter. Rowan had insisted on driving Tom's car to Kent because she said she needed to concentrate on the roads. The thought of sitting as a passenger, gazing out of the window as they drove closer to Tom's final resting place, was too much to contemplate. Libby, David and her parents travelled with her.

Rowan was leaning against Libby as they walked up the path of Saint Mary's, their bodies forming an A-frame of support. Once inside, the smell of waxed wood and candle smoke made Rowan's stomach churn. She swallowed hard and raised her head to look down the aisle. A coffin was mounted on a stand in front of the altar. Tom. Her husband. Her best friend. Her baby's father. She stumbled and Libby's grip tightened.

The church was two-thirds full. David was now on her opposite side, his arm gently supporting beneath her elbow. They walked down the aisle and when they reached the front of the church, Father Martin ushered the family into the reserved seats. She could hear Tom's mother sniffing. She turned. Tom's father was offering her a cotton handkerchief. Dear Sylvia and Bryan. They looked older than she remembered.

During the service, Rowan felt like a sheet of cling film had been draped over her thoughts and vision. It was if the day was a shadow of reality; not believing he was gone but knowing it was true all the same. She felt guilty for only half listening to the readings and the eulogy because David had been amazing at organising everything with Tom's parents. In the car on the way there, David had told her not to worry about feeling strange; it was nature's way of protecting her.

Rowan was relieved to get back out into the fresh air. The church had become airless and oppressive. Everyone had followed the pallbearers back down the aisle, the men's arms raised in support of the coffin that was resting on their shoulders. The drizzle had stopped and weak sunshine spilled light and warmth on the guests. They walked a short distance to where a grave had been dug in the church's cemetery.

Father Martin spoke a few more words before each of them took a handful of earth and threw it into the grave. The soil and stones echoed off the coffin. It was so final. Rowan's tears now fell. Where had so many tears come from? She couldn't see any more. Her whole face was wet. Her nose was blocked. She couldn't breathe. Tissues were handed to her. Arms comforted her. But nothing altered the fact that Tom had gone.

Rowan wasn't sure how long had passed. Perhaps five minutes, perhaps half an hour. She embraced Tom's parents and promised she wouldn't be long before she drove to their house for the wake. She hugged and thanked some old school friends of Tom's for coming and smiled when one of them shared a funny anecdote about him. She exchanged pleasantries with Tom's distant relatives, many who she hadn't met before. She wasn't quite sure how she was putting one foot in front of the other, but the love of family was supporting her through the day.

Family and guests were slowly walking out of the churchyard and towards the car park. Rowan said a final farewell to guests who couldn't make the wake and thanked Father Martin who was waiting at the lychgate. Libby was still there, not having left her side all day. They were holding hands as if they were schoolchildren in the playground, as they walked to Tom's car.

'We got through it,' said Libby.

'Somehow. I couldn't have done it without you.'

'Nor could I without you and David.'

'Where is David?'

'He travelled with both our parents in the hired people carrier. Lots of people are leaving their car here for an hour or two. There's not much space for parking at my parents' house.'

They reached the car and Rowan walked round to the driver's side.

'Do you want me to drive?' asked Libby.

Rowan didn't answer.

'Rowan? What is it?'

Rowan was staring at the driver's door. Tom's name had been scratched in large, jagged lines deep into the paintwork.

Chapter Six

Following Tom's wake, Rowan's parents, Bill and Grace, travelled back to Magnolia House with her to help settle her into some semblance of a routine and organise a few necessary bits of paperwork. Rowan hadn't been at home for a fortnight, having stayed with Libby and David since Tom's death.

'I'll put the kettle on,' said Grace. 'Bill, can you turn the heating on please. Just for an hour or so.'

Rowan went upstairs to the bathroom. She flushed the toilet but before washing her hands, she noticed Tom's dark whiskers decorating the porcelain sink where he'd last shaved. His toothbrush lay in dried bubbles of lather, its bristles splayed like thirsty tulips. A ribbon of dental floss hung from a dripping tap, one end swinging as each water droplet knocked it. He's such a messy man, she thought.

Was a messy man. The change of tense felt like an obscenity.

Rowan glanced up into the mirror. Dark circles shadowed her eyes and her make-up-smudged face had lost its glow. Her eyes were expressionless as she stared back at her reflection in this mirror for the first time since the news had been broken to her. It seemed an appropriate expression, she thought. Everything else had been broken since she'd answered David's knocking on the front door. Her concentration. Her routine. Her heart.

Looking back at Tom's usual chaotic detritus in the sink, she couldn't bring herself to clean it. Not yet. Rowan washed her hands over the bath and dried them on the soft towel that had last been touched by Tom, just before he'd left the house for the very last time. She held it to her face and inhaled, hoping her mind would swell with images from his scent. It smelt of washing powder and toothpaste, both of which evoked no meaningful images.

Her mother called up to her. 'Dad's put the heating on. Are you all right?'

Rowan walked downstairs where her parents were waiting in the hall. 'Tom's left a mess in the sink.' Rowan's face creased before her hands covered her face. Grace reached out for her and they held each other.

'I'll clean it for you?'

'No, it's okay.' Rowan breathed in deeply and let out a shuddering breath. 'It's funny. If he were still here, I'd be moaning about his mess. Now, it's almost comforting.'

Bill gently rubbed Rowan's upper arm. 'It's going to take time, darling.'

'I can't stop thinking about Tom's car, either. Who would do that?'

'Try not to think about it,' said Grace. 'The police are investigating and you have a crime number for the insurance. Like I said in the car, it was probably a client with a grudge who'd heard where the funeral was being held.'

Bill clasped his hands together decisively. 'I'll tell you what we're going to do. I don't know about you, but it's mid-afternoon and I'm in need of a drink. What have you got in?'

'I thought you'd put the kettle on.'

'I'm not sure tea will hit the spot at this moment in time. Do you have any wine in? We always have a glass in France with our lunch. It's one of the many French traditions we've embraced.'

'There's red in the pantry and white in the fridge.'

'Chilled white it is,' said Bill.

He strode purposefully down the hall towards the

kitchen, chose a crisp Sauvignon Blanc, took out three glasses from the cupboard and carried them to the kitchen table. Rowan noticed that someone had cleaned away the spaghetti bolognaise since she'd last been in the house. She must ask David who had done it and thank them.

'Right. No time like the present. Let's get some things organised to keep our minds busy,' said Grace, unscrewing the bottle and pouring it into the glasses. 'Have you got a pen and paper?'

'Yes.' Rowan fetched a magnetic shopping list from the front of the fridge and pulled a pen out of the letter rack.

'Give it to your father.' Her mother patted the seat of the pine chair next to her to encourage Rowan to join her, while her father settled himself opposite.

'Now, tell me to mind my own business, but organising you and your finances will keep my mind occupied as well as yours. I don't want to know specifics, just that you have enough to live on until you find another job.'

Rowan wiped her eyes with a crumpled tissue and watched her father write *Options* at the top of the first page.

'Take a glug,' ordered Grace, kindly.

Rowan obeyed. The cold liquid refreshed her mouth and cooled her throat.

'Do you have any savings?' asked her mother.

'A little, but most went on the deposit, renovations and setting up Tom's photographic business. I'll be okay for a bit.'

'And of course there's Tom's ...' Bill paused. 'Tom's life insurance.'

Rowan nodded, unable to trust her voice.

'And what about mortgage protection insurance? Sorry, love. I know it's soon after Tom's ... I know it's early days, but I'm sure knowing you're financially secure, to some degree, will give you peace of mind as well as us.'

'Yes, the mortgage will be paid off. The paperwork is in Tom's filing cabinet along with his company receipts and invoices.' Rowan wiped another tear from her cheek.

'It'll be all right, love?' said her father, reaching across the table and squeezing her hand. 'But things need to be organised too.'

'But I haven't got an income. How will I manage to live in this stupid big house?'

'It'll never be just a stupid big house. Too much love went into getting it just right,' said Bill. 'You've got to look after yourself and not rush things. You've got to give yourself time to recover from the shock.'

'It *is* stupid. I hate this house.' Rowan's chin trembled. She felt as if she'd regressed into childhood and despite knowing she sounded like her ten-year-old self, she couldn't stop. It was as if her parents were sitting her down and persuading her to organise her homework as they'd done two decades earlier. 'How could he leave me with all this?' She swept an arm in a semi-circle in front of her. 'He took care of all the renovations. I couldn't tell you where the fuse box is or who our utility provider is. Tom said I should concentrate on setting up my own business and finding new friends. He said he'd handle all the mundane bits.' Rowan's nails dug into her soggy tissue. 'What am I going to do in this huge house by myself?'

Rowan folded her arms across her stomach, subconsciously protecting her unborn child. It was still her secret. She wasn't totally alone.

'I know,' said Grace. She wrapped her arm around Rowan's shoulder.

'I'm sorry. I'm being so pathetic. You lost Grandma last year and were so brave.'

'It's okay. I've got your dad and, besides, it's our job to look after our little girl no matter how old she gets.'

They gently rocked backwards and forwards, until Rowan sniffed and chuckled.

'What would Tom say if he saw us sitting here crying over him?'

'He'd probably suggest we get a plumber in to mop up all those tears,' said Bill.

They pulled apart and smiled.

'Right,' said Rowan, decisively. 'Where were we?'

Grace sipped from her glass and shuffled back to face the table.

'I was saying that you mustn't rush things,' said Bill. 'You should just take a couple of months or so before even thinking about a job.' He looked at his daughter. 'You can do that when you're feeling a little stronger.'

'Another option is that you could sell Magnolia House if it doesn't feel the same now,' said Grace. 'Perhaps find somewhere a little smaller. But you'll need structure. A plan. It'll keep your mind occupied.'

Rowan ran her fingertip around the rim of her glass. 'It's all feels so strange.'

'I know, love. It's only been a week or so.'

'I meant London. This house. I don't know anyone here, apart from Libby and David. Do you think I should move back to Wilmslow and try and get my old job back?'

'Only you can make those decisions, darling. My advice would be to take time to think things over. You've got wonderful support with Libby and David.'

'I know.'

Bill tapped the pen against his teeth several times then suddenly stopped. 'What if …'

'Go on.' Rowan was far from enthusiastic.

'How about sharing your house?'

Rowan frowned.

'Flatmates.' Her father held out his hands, palms

34

upturned. 'This house is far too big for just you. You could have one or two people to share Magnolia House with you and they can pay for the privilege. Who knows, you could make some good friends. You could do with some support and money.'

Rowan sank her head into her folded arms on the table. 'I want Tom, not strangers.'

'I know, darling. We all do. But we've got to be strong,' said Grace. 'Dad's not suggesting you put an ad in the paper today. You've got a good financial cushion, so leave it a bit. It was just a thought anyway. Something else might turn up.'

Chapter Seven

November arrived bringing with it insipid skies and half-hearted attempts at foggy mornings. It had been ten weeks since Tom had died, leaving Rowan and Jet to fall into a monotonous but comforting routine. At times when she felt she had no energy or inclination to get out of bed, Jet's impertinent disturbances reminded her of her responsibilities. She loved her dog and he in turn enabled her to keep her broken heart unlocked by letting her hold his warm body for comfort without wriggling away. He reminded her that instead of fighting her feelings, she must submit to them like coastal trees bend in submission to the ocean gales. Tom used to say they should *go with the flow*, and that's what she endeavoured to do.

She and Jet would wake at seven and go for a walk on the common, followed by breakfast and a couple of hours watching dreary morning television. She'd normally skip lunch and retreat to her dressing table where she'd fiddle around with silver findings and semi-precious stones, convincing herself that she was working. Most afternoons consisted of a nap, another dog walk followed with a bowl of soup and yet more television. But Rowan discovered that solace could be found in repetition, even if the cost was becoming more isolated from the world beyond Magnolia House and Clapham Common as each day passed. But it was precious healing time. She'd needed the silence. She needed to pause and temporarily withdraw from the bonds of friendship. She'd had to halt the collective dinner parties, gossip and endless carousel of noise.

Today was going to be different because she was meeting Libby on the common during her sister-in-law's lunch break. Rowan left the house with Jet, turned and locked her front door. She was heading to one of the common's bandstands where they'd arranged to meet. Libby had rung her earlier that morning to say that the next few days were going to be unseasonably warm for early-November and they should make the most of the sunshine. They'd been like a pair of bookends since Tom's death, propping each other up over cups of tea or with telephone conversations, each supporting the other when they struggled to cope, each sharing the weight of grief.

Flashes of dewy silver sparkled on the grass as Rowan and Jet marched purposefully across the common. It was a sunny day with occasional clouds scudding across a pale grey-blue sky. Rowan was wearing one of Tom's woollen jumpers over a pair of jeans, her long dark hair tied into a ponytail. She could feel it swishing from side to side as she strode along the tarmacked path. As she and Jet got closer, they could both see Libby leaning against the rails inside the circle of the bandstand. Jet's tail wagged faster in recognition. Libby waved.

'Have you been waiting long?' Rowan asked.

'Only five minutes. There's no rush. The old witch doesn't know when I finish my deliveries.'

Rowan hugged her sister-in-law. 'Still not enjoying work then?'

'No. I'll escape one day, but I can't afford to yet.'

They began to wander arm in arm along the path towards the children's park. Jet walked obediently on his lead, taking great interest in a small flock of birds that soared off in sallies of flight accompanied by a crescendo of cawing.

'It's gorgeous, isn't it?' said Libby, gazing up into the sunshine. 'Seventeen degrees in November.'

Rowan just squeezed Libby's arm a little tighter in reply.

'I'm glad you came out to meet me,' said Libby. 'How've you been this week?'

'Okay I suppose. I just can't find the motivation to do anything. How are you?'

'You know …'

Rowan nodded.

'Why don't you visit your parents in France for a break?' said Libby.

'I'm okay at home with Jet. We've got into a sort of routine. Walks, television and sleep.'

'David and I are worried about you.'

'Don't be. I'm fine. I'm sure it's perfectly normal to feel a little cut off from reality when you've lost your husband.' She smiled weakly at Libby. 'How about you? Have you got a stitch? You're holding your stomach.'

'I've had a nagging pain on and off for months now. Maybe even over a year. I'm sure it's nothing. I'm just unfit I think. Too much driving and not enough jogging.'

'And how's David?' asked Rowan. They stopped at the railing to the park and watched several children in the play area.

'He misses his best mate and seems to stay in his office upstairs a lot. I don't think either of us wants to worry or upset the other, so we're keeping out of each other's way. As much as I hate working at Tea Rose, it does keep my mind occupied.'

'Despite seeming to lounge about on the settee all day, I'm doing a lot of thinking. I can't seem to get Dad's idea of converting the house out of my mind. He seems to think a couple of tenants will give me company as well as an income.'

'He's right. And besides, you can't stay lying on the settee watching daytime television with Jet all day long.'

Rowan glanced across at her sister-in-law. 'I know. I've a few ideas for jewellery designs and I'm planning on setting up a website I can sell from next year.'

'Next year!'

They started to amble towards the dry deserted lido. 'Next year is only seven weeks away, you know?'

'Bloody hell. You're right. That's crazy.'

'Time flies when you're having fun,' said Rowan, sadly. 'What are you planning for Christmas? Are you having your parents to stay like last year?'

'No. They've been invited round to some neighbour or other. I think they play cards and dominoes together a couple of times a week. I think that ... without Tom, they want to do something completely different this year. What about you? Are you visiting your parents?'

'No. I think I'll just stay at home this year. I feel safe with the door shut and snuggled up with Jet.' She sensed Libby looking at her and turned towards her. 'What?' she asked, wide-eyed, the pitch of her voice an octave higher.

'It's not good for you locking yourself at home. You'll become a recluse.'

'No I won't. I'm just not ready yet. I'm not sure what I'm not ready for, but I feel as if I'm healing during the hours I'm spending on the settee.'

'Hmm. If you say so.'

'I'm here, aren't I? If I was becoming reclusive I wouldn't be here with you now.'

'I suppose not. Have the police been back in touch about the vandalism to Tom's car yet?'

'Yes. I've had a letter confirming the crime number and a telephone call informing me that nothing more can be done because there was no CCTV in the church's car park and no evidence to work on.' Rowan shrugged.

'Unbelievable. Is it fixed?'

'It's had a new driver's door. Whoever did it pressed so deeply that the metal was dented in places.'

'Bloody hell, Rowan. If I knew who did it ...'

As they walked amiably around the common, Rowan found herself thinking about her unborn baby. She was three months pregnant now so her baby's tiny fingers and toes would be developed. In six months' time, a part of Tom would live on and share the house with her and Jet. It gave her great comfort to know that she carried his baby around inside her body. She'd still kept the secret to herself, feeling that this was her time with Tom's baby. Precious time to feel, absorb and think before life became a pantomime of mess, noise and visiting friends and relatives. Perhaps she should consider starting the building works before she got too big and exhausted to cope with the chaos.

They passed the domed clock tower of The Holy Trinity, the austere grey and white church perched by the roadside on the edge of the common. The trees surrounding it swayed gently to and fro as if conducting the bird song. Rowan watched a mother and father teach their son how to ride his bike without stabilisers for the first time. The child's father passed the small supplementary wheels to his wife before holding the seat beneath the child's bottom. As she watched them share this momentous wobbly rite of passage, a deep sadness weighed heavily inside her belly. Her unborn child wouldn't have its father to help it through life's challenges.

'Look, an ice cream van.'

Rowan snapped out of her maudlin thoughts and followed the direction of Libby's finger towards a brightly coloured van parked near one of the gates to the common.

'C'mon,' called Libby. 'I fancy a cone with a chocolate flake stuffed in the top.'

After an hour, Rowan walked back home embracing the weak warmth from the sun while relishing the sweet taste of ice cream lingering in her mouth. Libby had driven back to work, but not before Rowan had pointed out to her sister-in-law that she had strawberry sauce around her mouth. It'd been nice to laugh at such a silly thing and feel almost normal again.

She passed under the skeletal magnolia tree in her front garden, stopping at the porch. She turned, scanning the vista of houses and spiky hedges opposite that marked out the neighbours' boundaries. Mr and Mrs Matthews were shepherding their children into the car, the postman whistled to himself and further up the road a neighbour was cleaning her bedroom windows. Looking up she saw contrails, thin lines of vapour making patterns across a sky as blue as the Virgin Mary's robes. Life continued. Everyone carried on as normal, smug in the knowledge that death hadn't paused at their garden gate. Rowan sighed and turned the key.

Despite having had an enjoyable hour, Rowan felt relieved to close the door on the world once more. Small doses of life outside the safe confines of her home were enough at the moment. She bent to pull Jet's harness over his head and hung it over the stair post. She was thinking of sitting on her bed and attempting to sort through some beads while she was feeling invigorated, so began to walk upstairs. Halfway up, she remembered seeing the postman and decided to check whether any letters had been delivered into the cage behind the letter box. Turning to go back downstairs, she suddenly caught sight of Jet directly below her on the stairs. She tried to step down two stairs to avoid him, but lost her balance.

Everything went black.

Rowan felt Jet's wet tongue lick her cheek before he settled down beside her and whimpered. It occurred to her that it wasn't normal to be lying at the bottom of the stairs in the hallway. She looked at the cornicing above her and thought how funny it was that some corners of the house were overlooked daily. She scanned the painted ceiling, the intricate ceiling-rose and the blue pendant light shade, remembering the day she held the ladder still while Tom climbed to hang it. A small grey cobweb nestled among the contours of the ceiling-rose like a delicate lace napkin. She became aware that her foot hurt and her head ached. But what was she doing lying on her back with her right leg resting on the second stair? Groaning in pain, she remembered falling. Although she had no recollection of landing, she recalled the momentary terror she'd experienced as she'd toppled over her cowering dog. Jet was now trembling against her body. She stroked him, feeling his flanks shaking in spasms.

Rowan tentatively sat up and grimaced at the pain from her ankle. She rubbed it, surprised to see that it was twice the size that it should be.

'It's okay, Jet. There's a good boy. I didn't mean to frighten you.' She felt his legs and paws and rubbed his tummy. 'I don't think you've hurt anything.'

She grabbed hold of a spindle and tried to stand so she could hobble to the kitchen to call Libby, but as she flexed her stomach muscles an agonising pain stabbed at her stomach causing her to cry out.

Chapter Eight

Christmas Day dawned in gentle grey increments. Rowan lay in bed watching the hues in the bedroom grow paler and colour seep into the room, breathing shape into its interior. She'd opened the curtains earlier when she'd gone to the bathroom but although she'd climbed back into bed again, sleep had been elusive. Lying on her back, Rowan rested her hands on her stomach, painfully aware that her once slightly swollen stomach she'd grown to love, was now flat.

Last month, following her fall downstairs, Rowan had managed to struggle into the kitchen. As she drank a glass of water, she'd felt a warm flow leave her body and dampen her underwear. She'd put her hand inside her knickers to check what had happened and had stood shaking as she'd stared at her bloodstained fingers. The ambulance had arrived within quarter of an hour. They'd wrapped her in a blanket, helped her into a wheelchair and had taken her to hospital. She'd rung her sister-in-law later that evening after a doctor had confirmed her miscarriage and sprained ankle. Libby had driven to the hospital to be with her and the pair of them had wept and talked until a nurse had politely asked Libby to leave an hour past visiting time should have ended. After a small operation on her womb, Rowan had been allowed home the following day and had gone to stay with Libby and David for twenty-four hours.

The bedside clock's digital face shone 07.50. Rowan stretched. She thought of the day ahead and felt quite relieved that she didn't have to talk to anyone or socialise until teatime, when Libby and David had insisted on visiting her.

'I'm not listening,' Libby had told her. 'It's not right to spend the whole of Christmas Day on your own. We're coming round even if we have to break in.'

Rowan smiled as she thought of her sister-in-law; a vital strand in her woven lifeline of support. As she lay there listening to a neighbour's car door slam and the engine start, she was glad that Libby had insisted on visiting her.

The only outward signs in Magnolia House that alluded to Christmas was a small tree in the lounge, from which she'd hung a few baubles and lights, and a row of Christmas cards from family and friends on the fire surround. A turkey dinner from Marks & Spencer's was waiting in the fridge and she planned to find *Serendipity*, her favourite festive film, on Amazon Prime.

Rowan pulled on her dressing gown and slid her feet into her slippers. She opened the bedroom door and padded downstairs towards the kitchen, with only a hint of a limp from last month's twisted ankle. Jet jumped out of his basket and greeted her as he did every morning, his whole being ecstatic at seeing her once again. He writhed, wagged and wound himself around her legs as if she'd been out of sight for a month instead of one night. Rowan bent to fuss him. His unconditional love had been a balm for her heavy spirit. He was another unyielding strand to her support network.

The day passed much like any other, which suited Rowan. This was her first Christmas without Tom and it didn't deserve to be highlighted in any way. If she could have cancelled the festive season and all its forced jollity, she would have done so. She and Jet had walked in the drizzle to the bandstand and back, before sitting in front of an open fire that crackled and hissed in the hearth like a poorly tuned radio. She listened to a carol concert on Radio 4, ate her ready meal while Jet slept at her feet and watched *Serendipity*. As snowflakes fell in Central Park at the end of the film and John Cusack was reunited with Kate Beckinsale, she always cried. That afternoon, her tears lasted longer.

Following a doze in front of the dying embers of the fire, Rowan woke with a start when a glowing log slipped and settled among the pale ash. The carriage clock on the mantelpiece showed it was five o'clock, leaving her just enough time to jump in the shower and wash her hair that had been flattened by the earlier drizzle.

Libby and David arrived just before six. Their arms were full of gifts, bottles and nibbles, but Rowan noticed that their smiles didn't reflect in their eyes. Like her, they too must be going through the motions of celebration this year. The least she could do was make an effort for her dear friends.

'Merry Christmas. Come in out of the cold. Brrr!' They greeted each other with kisses and lingering hugs full of unspoken words. 'Let me take your coats. I'll just put them here to keep warm.' Rowan draped the coats on either end of the hall radiator. 'Come through,' she said, leading the way through the hall and into the lounge. 'The fire's roaring and the wine's waiting.'

David put down two carrier bags and Libby stood warming her hands in front of the flames. *The Snowman* was turned down low on the television while the snowman flew over snow-covered rooftops.

'I love this animation,' said Libby, still in front of the hearth. 'Ooh! That's better. You can't beat a real fire.'

'How's your day been?' David asked. He took two bottles of wine, a round box of Turkish Delight and a small Christmas cake out of a carrier bag.

'Okay,' said Rowan. 'We've had a walk, watched a romantic film, had some dinner and a nap.'

'Sounds like our day, except Libby made me watch the

Queen's speech and a ridiculous film about an elf who was really a man.'

'That's the whole point of the story, silly. A baby crawls inside Santa's sack while he's delivering presents, then Santa takes him back to the North Pole by accident. The little boy is then raised as one of his elves, but he grows up. It's sweet.'

'If you say so.' David looked unconvinced. 'Sounds to me as if Father Christmas needs locking up for kidnap.'

'You just didn't enter into the spirit of the film,' said Libby. 'You slept through most of it anyway.'

'What do you expect?'

Rowan looked from David to Libby, wondering if they were teasing each other or having a minor domestic. They settled themselves on separate settees and Rowan went to warm some mulled wine that had been infusing. She dipped a finger in the burgundy liquid and sucked it. It was warm, aromatic and sweetly spiced. Pouring it through a sieve, Rowan separated the cloves and cinnamon sticks and filled three glasses. She carried them through on a tray and within five minutes, all three were sipping in front of the fire, smiles bravely in place even though Tom's absence was glaringly obvious.

'Presents!' exclaimed Libby, reaching for a carrier bag she'd bought in with her. She lifted it onto her knee and delved inside it. She brought out two packages wrapped in ivy-decorated paper and tied with red raffia. 'This one's for Jet and this one's for you.' She handed the two parcels to Rowan.

'Thank you. I told you not to bother this year and—'

'As if we're not going to buy you a Christmas present,' said Libby.

'Hang on then,' said Rowan, placing the gifts on the cushion beside her. She walked to the tree and took two presents from beneath it. She gave one to David and one to Libby. 'I hope you like them.'

Everyone gave a good show of being excited and began to open their gifts. Rowan un-wrapped an exquisite tan Kiki James Tuscan leather-bound photo album. It was so soft and tactile that she couldn't help but stroke the cover before undoing the leather tie. Inside each page was interleaved with parchment tissue paper as delicate as dandelion seed heads.

'I love it. Thank you so much.' Rowan stood up and kissed them both. 'I'll treasure it.'

Libby slid her gift from its box. She held up the intricate Willow Tree wooden carving of a man and a woman linking arms. An engraving beneath them read, Brother and Sister. Libby hugged it to her chest and closed her eyes. She tried to speak but her chin wobbled as she leant sideways and hugged her sister-in-law. 'Thank you.'

The girls then turned to David who pulled away the last piece of tissue paper. He gently unfolded a leather strap that revealed a second-hand watch that he'd admired many times. Tom's watch. He silently fastened it to his wrist and laid his fingers on top of it, pausing as if absorbing its history through the pores of his skin. He looked up.

'Thank you. I can't tell you what this means to me.'

Rowan nodded her head in reply and smiled, lips pressed tightly together with emotion.

Chapter Nine

Rowan tried not to raise her hopes too high as she trudged through an icy shower. She was on her way to a gift shop near Covent Garden, the first business meeting she'd felt strong enough to cope with since Tom's death and her miscarriage. Hunched beneath her umbrella, she listened to the tapping raindrops on the taught material. The shops were decorated with red hearts and flowers, heralding the imminent arrival of Valentine's Day. A day for loved ones and yet another first celebratory occasion she'd have to spend on her own. She'd already struggled through Christmas and Tom's birthday.

She passed a coffee shop, spilling out a heady aroma of coffee beans, and lowered her umbrella. If Libby's directions had been correct, the gift shop should be halfway down the next side street. She turned into Dempster Street, her eyes scanning for The Blue Moon gift shop. She saw it across the road, a turquoise orb hanging from a bracket above the front door of the shop.

Rowan pushed the door open, a tinkle of a bell welcoming her inside and alerting the staff to her presence. A man stood behind a desk, muttering as he wrote in a notebook. Rowan wasn't sure what she'd expected Nick to look like, but she knew it wasn't the short balding man who looked up at her. On the telephone he'd sounded younger.

'Morning, how can I help you?' he asked, pushing his rimless glasses further up his nose.

'I'm Rowan Forrester. I have an appointment with Nick.'

'Oh yes. Nick said he hoped to be back before a Miss Forrester arrived.'

'Mrs,' said Rowan. Rowan presumed she'd keep her married title. Surely you don't lose your husband *and* your title? Before she could continue this train of thought, the elderly man continued.

'I don't actually work here. I'm Nick's accountant. I called in to pick up some paperwork for the quarterly VAT and somehow I got lumbered here to watch the shop for half an hour.' He chuckled, his belly wobbling like strawberry jelly in his red jumper. 'Not that I mind. I missed the shower and I get to chat with attractive young ladies.' He chuckled again, seemingly pleased with his attempt at flirting.

Rowan was beginning to wish that she hadn't come. She could feel anxiety squeezing her chest. Thankfully Nick's accountant gave her an opportunity to take a moment to gather her emotions.

'Why don't you take a look around? Nick shouldn't be long.'

Rowan wandered around the small shop floor, gazing into glass cabinets full of gemstone necklaces and earrings. Amber and aquamarine dazzled as they lay on black velvet, their silver findings twinkling under the spotlights. Gifts of carved wooden jewellery boxes lined the shelving, along with decorated jewellery stands, their metal twisted into hearts and flowers. As she was admiring a selection of cloisonné-beaded bracelets, the shop door opened, surprising her with its force.

'Made it! It's just started bloody pouring again.' The man who'd rushed into the shop hadn't seen her behind the door and didn't give his accountant time to speak. He rubbed the raindrops from his hair. 'She's not here yet then?'

The accountant didn't answer but pointed towards Rowan. The younger man turned and laughed.

'Sorry, I didn't spot you there.' He stepped towards her, wiped his hand on his trousers and held out his hand. He shrugged. 'It's raining. Hi, I'm Nick. Have you met Clive, my accountant and stand-in assistant?'

Rowan shook his damp, warm hand. He was tall and slim and although not traditionally good-looking, he had a strong jaw and smiling cornflower-blue eyes. His mousy brown hair was sticking up on end, having been rubbed free of raindrops.

'Hello. Yes, I have. I've been having a little browse. You have some lovely gifts here.'

'Thank you. Do you think your pieces would fit in with the displays?'

'I'd like to think so.' She patted her handbag. 'I've bought a small selection with me.'

'Let's take a look then,' he said, rubbing his palms together in anticipation. 'Follow me and we'll pop into the back.' He looked sheepishly at Clive. 'Do you mind hanging on for another ten minutes? Charlotte's not back from her lunch break until half past.'

'Take your time,' said Clive. 'I might as well take a look at your books here rather than take them away.'

The back room was as small as a box room in a modern house. It had a sink, a filing cabinet and a table with two chairs. A microwave oven and a kettle were pushed against the back wall on the table.

'Not much room, I'm afraid. I'd take you upstairs to a bigger room I use for storage and packing gifts, but I left those keys at home.'

'It's fine.' Rowan took out a purple velvet roll that was tied with a black ribbon. She laid it on the table and slowly unrolled it to reveal delicate twisted silver bangles, each decorated with a single glass bead. She unrolled the velvet further, unveiling exquisite drop earrings and beaded necklaces.

Nick picked up a bracelet and stroked its smooth twists. 'Beautiful. Delicate.' He looked up and held her gaze.

Rowan looked down at the velvet wrap. She had no intention of flirting with this man. Her mind had been invisibly bubble-wrapped to protect it from unwanted attention. Her heart had been deep-frozen to preserve it for the future. No one could even begin to thaw it just yet.

'Thank you. They're all made from silver so they're tough and non-allergenic.'

Nick carefully laid the bracelet on the velvet and picked up a necklace. He draped it onto the back of his hand and rolled the glass beads between his fingers.

'The beads are exquisite. Do you mind me asking where you buy them?'

'I make them myself.'

Nick raised his eyebrows. 'You make them?'

Rowan felt at home talking about glass beads. Here she was in a world she understood, a world that made sense and held no anxiety. 'I heat glass rods with a little oxygen-propane torch then gently rotate the glass rod,' she said, twisting her fingers in the air as if holding an imaginary rod, 'and a blob of glass forms. I keep rotating until it forms the shape and size I'm trying to achieve, and them I cut it off. It's called lampwork.'

'But how do you get these the different colours on the beads?'

Rowan was delighted that he seemed genuinely interested. 'The hot glass becomes the consistency of thick honey. It's easy to decorate the beads while it's so malleable. I can even make leaves and tiny flowers out of glass. Look here, on these earrings.'

Nick picked up the earrings and shook his head in awe. 'You're not just a pretty face, are you?'

Rowan decided that if they were going to become business partners, she should make it clear that she wasn't interested in him or having a relationship with anyone. His attempts at flirting had to stop.

'I'm glad you like them. I'm recently widowed so I'm hoping to set up my own business by selling my work to a few outlets. I'd be delighted to supply you with my jewellery, but I'm afraid I can't make it exclusive to The Blue Moon. I'd have to do business with other retailers in order to make my business viable.'

'I'm sorry ... about your husband. I hope you don't think I was ...'

'Thank you. I just think it's only fair to let you know a little about myself if we're talking business. Do you think you'd be interested?'

Nick became more professional and no longer tried to search out her eyes with his own. 'I have just the place for your collection.' He picked up an earring with two pink glass beads suspended from a silver hook and held them up to the light. 'I don't think I'll have any trouble selling everything you've shown me today. There are about ten pieces here. Let's talk money over a cup of tea, shall we?'

Pleased that Nick now understood this would purely be a business relationship and that she'd sold her first collection of jewellery, she smiled and nodded.

Back at home, Rowan snuggled into a corner of the settee with Jet curled on her feet. Sipping tomato soup, she smiled to herself as she wrapped her fingers tightly around the warm mug. She'd sold her jewellery and had plenty more pieces packed away upstairs. She'd have to unpack her lampwork equipment and start designing and creating again if this was now to become a new business. And she'd need a company name and had to source some more gift shops. There was so much to do now. It was almost a relief to concentrate on something other than her grief.

She placed her mug on the coffee table, disturbing a sleeping Jet as she moved. He stood up, wobbled and dropped back down to sleep again when he realised that Rowan wasn't getting up. She'd picked up her mobile phone and dialled Libby.

Her sister-in-law had worked for Tea Rose, an upmarket flower shop, for almost a year. She either created beautiful displays and bouquets, or delivered them, depending on which members of staff were working that day. Their clients included powerful companies who needed conference rooms brightening up, rich men wanting to treat their wives or impress their mistresses, and, of course, churches, cathedrals or castles where spectacular no-expense-spared weddings were to be held. Her colleague, Marion, had been sacked last month for delivering two-dozen red roses to someone's wife instead of their mistress. If it hadn't been for the attached message that read, '*Can't wait to search out that little freckle again*,' then the irate freckle-less wife would have been none the wiser.

'Hi, Libby. What're you doing?'

'David's not home yet, so I'm running a quick bath to warm myself up. I've had to traipse up long driveways in the rain and I'm soaked and cold. Is everything okay? How are you?'

'I've had a good day, thanks. The Blue Moon has bought ten pieces of my work and I'm going to start making jewellery again. And guess what?'

'What?'

'I've decided that I *am* going to take in lodgers. I feel a bit stronger and I think selling my work and having someone come on to me, gave me a bit more confidence.'

'Who came on to you?' asked Libby.

'Oh, just the guy who owns the gift shop. He was only flirting a little bit and I made it clear that I wasn't interested, but it made me feel, I don't know, human again, I suppose.'

'That's great, Rowan. Tom would be very proud of you, you know?'

Rowan was quiet for a moment.

'Rowan?'

'I'm still here.'

'Sorry. I didn't mean to bring you down when you've had a good day.'

'It's okay. It's just that I feel guilty for feeling happier. It's as if every step I take forwards, I'm leaving Tom further behind.'

'Just accept the good days for what they are. Do you really think that Tom would want you to turn into Miss Havisham? I'm his sister, so I can say with great authority that he would have been so proud of you for being strong.'

'Thanks. Have you had a good week?'

'I'm working overtime to earn a bit more money. You know what it's like … bills to pay.'

'Yes. I'm sure I'll be receiving a lot more of those in the future because I'm going to ring some building contractors tomorrow.'

'Good for you. It'll give you something to focus on.'

'It's all going to be all right, isn't it, Libbs?'

'It's all going to be just fine.'

Chapter Ten

Six weeks later, Rowan was sitting with her elbows on the kitchen table and her hands covering her ears. It sounded as if the builders were demolishing the whole house and every now and then the vibrations would make the glasses chink against each other in the kitchen cupboard. She groaned and looked once more at the advert she was trying to write.

Magnolia House
*2 newly-renovated one-bedroomed apartments
to let in beautiful Georgian townhouse.
Two minutes from Clapham Common.
Underground Station nearby. Cable TV and
wireless internet.*

What should she charge? And was she really doing the right thing by inviting strangers in through her front door? Rowan was beginning to doubt her decision and had bitten the nail on her finger so low that it was now throbbing. She pushed back her sleeve to check the time and wondered whether to phone Libby while she was at work.

Rowan decided not to take the chance of phoning, just in case she should get her sister-in-law in trouble with her strict boss. She yawned and glanced under the table for Jet, knowing that he'd be lying by her feet even before she looked.

'This is boring, isn't it? Can't have a cuppa, can't go to the loo and can't leave the house.' She stood up and walked to the kitchen window, looking out at the fine drizzle that seemed to linger in the air. It was strange how the elements played a significant part in a person's mood, she thought.

Rowan turned when she heard someone knock on the front door. 'Not another workman,' she said, under her breath. She walked down the hallway towards the front door.

'David! Come in, come in.'

Rowan was delighted to see her brother-in-law. He wrapped his arms around her waist and lifted her feet off the Minton tiles as he hugged her. He gently lowered her back down.

'How are you doing?' he asked, following her into the kitchen.

'So, so. Sometimes I feel good, even happy. Then I feel guilty that I feel happy. Do you know what I mean?'

'Of course and it's perfectly normal. I was playing football last week and scored a goal. I was laughing and showing off like an idiot until I saw the bloke who helped Tom on the night he died. This chap was sitting on the subs bench clapping, but I felt bad that I was celebrating when Tom wasn't there. So yes, I know exactly what you mean. It's an awful cliché, but the show must go on.'

David bent to stroke Jet who had climbed into his basket. He then joined Rowan at the kitchen table and leant forwards on his forearms. 'So how are things going here?'

'I'm having a few jitters,' she said, pointing up to the ceiling at the noise above them. 'Am I doing the right thing? Do I really want strangers living with me? I don't feel as if I can make decisions without asking Tom for his opinion.'

'Now listen to me,' said David, resting his hand on Rowan's. 'Firstly, you aren't going to have strangers walk in and live with you. You're going to *choose* who moves into your home and I'm sure you'll only agree to have nice people move in. Secondly, they aren't going to be living with you, because you know that each floor has been designed to have their own front door. Thirdly, these so-called strangers will probably become good friends and you won't have time for us in the future. Fourthly, think of the money and—'

Rowan laughed. 'Okay, okay, I get the idea.'

A loud crash rattled the glasses in the cupboard again.

David feigned fear and held his arms over his head. 'Anyway, I think the workmen have gone too far in converting your house now. I don't want to be the one who has to tell them to rebuild the walls they've knocked down.'

'I don't want them to stop and I know I'm being silly, but everywhere is so messy. It's too noisy to concentrate on making jewellery, the water's been turned off and I forgot to fill the kettle first, so the builders are a bit narked that I can't make them a hot drink. *I'm* a bit narked because I can't flush the loo and I'm desperate *and* I don't know how much to charge these so-called new friends of mine.' She turned her laptop to face David.

'Will you stop stressing and let an agency deal with it all? They'll put an ad in the paper and they'll advise you about suitable rates to charge in this area. Why are you heaping all this extra pressure on yourself? Anyway, that's why I'm here.'

'To help me sort out the rates?'

'No. To show you this.'

David pulled a newspaper cutting out of his inside jacket pocket and laid it on the table. He ran his palm across it to smooth it flat. It showed a 'crazy low price offer' on flights to Bergerac.

'Why don't you escape the mess and noise for a week or so? Visit your parents. It should be warmer there and you need to relax and recharge your batteries. Libby spotted it last night and asked me to call round with it.'

The thought of relaxing in Aubeterre without living in chaos appealed to her, but what about Jet? Rowan looked over to his basket where he was curled nose to tail in a deep sleep. But it wasn't only Jet. She felt guilt weighing her down as heavily as a wet winter coat. Libby had lost a brother at the same time she'd lost a husband. How could she go away to France while Libby dog-sat?

'I am tempted, but I've got Jet to think about.'

'You're just making excuses. You know Libby and I would love to look after him.'

'But what about Libby? And you? She lost her brother and you lost your best friend. It wouldn't feel right going on holiday while you're checking on the builders here and taking care of my dog.'

She didn't like to mention that she knew that he and Libby were going through a tough time at the moment. Libby had confided in her that David had asked to look at the bank statements and had questioned her about the amount that was being spent. Libby said she'd become defensive, they'd had a row and she'd thrown the paperwork away because she'd had a recent splurge at the shops.

'Don't think of it as a holiday,' said David. 'Look on it as a method of healing. Give yourself some time and space to think. Libby and I have each other to talk to and she adores Jet. We'll get away later in the year for a break somewhere. We think this is the perfect opportunity for you to escape for a week or two before you start supplying the gift shop and organising tenants.'

'You're both wonderful. I'll think about it.' She leant over and hugged his wide shoulders. 'You've both been so supportive. I couldn't have managed without you.'

'We'll all get through this together.'

There was a comfortable pause in the conversation. 'I'd make you a cup of tea but as I said, the water's been turned off.'

'It's okay, I can't stay anyway. I have a lunchtime meeting with the art directors about a pitch we've got to put together. We're meeting at The Windmill down the road.'

'It's a lovely pub. Tom and I ...' She smiled weakly and shook her head. 'We called in for some lunch the first day we came to view the house. We had a wonderful steak there.'

David winked kindly before checking his watch. 'I'd better make tracks. Please give the idea of visiting your parents some serious thought.'

'I will.'

David stood up and hugged Rowan before walking back down the hall, his shoes scraping on the plaster dust that covered the tiles. 'I think it'll do you good to see things from a distance and escape this mess and noise. You've been through a lot.'

'I promise to think about it and thanks for calling round.'

'Bye. See you soon.'

She waved as she watched him walk down the short garden path and climb into his car. He beeped as he pulled away.

Rowan walked back into the kitchen with a wry smile on her face. She sat back down and rested her head on her forearms, leaning on the table. Seriously, what would she have done without David and Libby? She smiled again into her blouse sleeve and thought of having a break in Aubeterre. She envisioned being spoilt by her parents, visiting the Sunday market and the monolithic church with its twisting stairs hewn from solid stone. Visions of beautiful chateaux and the local river beach filled her mind with memories and happier times, until she fell sleep.

Rowan awoke bleary-eyed to the sound of the workmen leaving for their lunch break. Glancing at the kitchen clock on the wall, she couldn't believe that forty minutes had passed. She'd slept badly during the night yet again and was now exhausted. Barely awake, Rowan fumbled her way across the kitchen, her slippers shuffling on the floor. She yawned loudly before reaching into the cupboard and lifting a mug from the shelf. She carried the kettle to the sink and turned the tap on. When nothing happened, her shoulders slumped as she remembered the water had been turned off. Tears pricked at her eyes as she wearily replaced the kettle.

She needed to get away.

Chapter Eleven

It was Saturday morning and the house appeared calm and quiet when Libby woke up. Rowan was leaving for France that morning so Jet had been collected the previous evening.

Libby climbed out of bed and walked downstairs, hoping that David had already left for his weekend football practice. She couldn't face any questions about their finances over breakfast. As she walked into the kitchen, David looked up from his newspaper while sipping a steaming mug of tea. Libby hoped her face didn't reflect her disappointment.

'Morning,' he said.

'Morning. Any tea in the pot?'

'Sorry, I just dunked a tea bag in some hot water. I thought you'd stay in bed for a while.'

'Why would you think that?' asked Libby, filling the kettle again. 'I don't usually lie in bed at the weekend.'

'It wasn't an accusation. I just thought I wouldn't disturb you.'

Libby plugged in the kettle and took a mug from the cupboard. She hovered near the sink, looking out on to the garden that was now blooming with spring flowers. She didn't answer but felt a wave of anxiety spread through her body. Palpitations interrupted her heart rhythm at the thought of him bringing up this month's expenditure over breakfast.

The kettle clicked and Libby made herself a cup of tea. She felt too nauseous to eat anything. Replacing the milk in the fridge, she decided to sidle past David and drink her tea in the lounge to escape any questions. As she walked across the kitchen, David folded his paper noisily, leant back against his chair and stretched.

'Any plans for today?' he asked.

'I'll take Jet for a walk this morning and then maybe wander round the West End and have a cup of tea in Fortnum's.'

David whistled. 'Sounds expensive.'

Libby's eyes studied his face trying to discern what emotion he was feeling. His new haircut, which was cropped short, made him look sterner.

'It's only a pot of tea. I'm not buying shares in the company,' said Libby, in defence of what she presumed was the first shot in the next battle about finances.

David's voice was flat. 'There's no need to jump down my throat. I was just making an observation that there are hundreds of cheaper places for a drink.'

Libby clutched the mug of tea tighter, letting the heat scald her palms for a few seconds. She wanted to retort that there were also hundreds of mothers wheeling their babies around London too, but she wasn't harping on about not being one of them. Why should she be made to feel so guilty about buying little things to cheer herself up? 'I don't want to argue again. I know you're going to tell me not to spend any money and I won't unless it's necessary. I only buy little things for the house or personal bits.'

'It's not what you buy, Libby, it's how often. Every time you go out, you come back with a little bag of this or that. It all adds up over the month. I'm sorry. Go and have a nice time.'

Libby felt tears balancing precariously on her lower lashes. She looked at the ceiling, as if by defying gravity she could stop them from falling. She knew that she wasn't upset because David was asking her to be careful with her spending. After all, the little bags that he saw her bring home each day were just pebbles compared with the mountain of bags she hid in the car until he'd left the house. She felt ashamed, alone and helpless. Her addiction had hold of her as tightly as bindweed clings to a flower.

That afternoon, Libby tucked her credit card back inside her purse and accepted the gift-wrapped box with a smile.

'Thank you.'

She walked through the store towards the exit, her heart beating quickly, euphoric that she now owned a Mikey necklace with matching earrings. It didn't matter that she already had a shoebox full of unworn dress-jewellery, because she didn't have anything quite as exquisite as these.

Weaving through the oncoming crowds, she clutched her new purchase to her chest with a determined frown etched on her forehead.

Quarter of an hour later, as Libby was being rocked and jostled in her seat on the tube, the gloss of her shopping euphoria had inevitably tarnished into guilt once again. Remorse prodded her conscience. When and where would she ever wear these diamante jewels? She and David never went anywhere that required her to wear earrings that resembled crystal chandeliers. Even on New Year's Eve they preferred to spend a cosy evening with Rowan and Tom playing board games and drinking games, while Jools Holland partied away in the background.

Libby looked around the carriage. Everyone seemed to be either lost in the *Metro* newspaper or pretending to read the adverts above the windows for somewhere to look other than at each other. Did all these other commuters have hidden secrets from their loved-ones? Did she look like a guilty obsessive shopper to them? What did one look like, anyway?

Libby closed her eyes to block out the blank faces and artificial lighting. That was another fifty pounds she'd added to her debt. Yet more interest to pay and more unnecessary junk to hide when she got back home. But even as she sat there regretting that particular purchase, deep inside a little bubble of anticipation was brewing. She was on her way to Fortnum and Mason's for afternoon tea. What if there was the perfect pair of shoes waiting for her on the second floor?

Chapter Twelve

Moments earlier Rowan had watched as the steps were wheeled into place for passengers to disembark onto the airport tarmac. She stepped out of the aeroplane's door at Bergerac, paused at the top of the steps and squinted in the sunshine. The heat felt good on her skin and the sweet coconut smell from someone's sun cream added to her feeling of escapism. The dust and noise from Magnolia House seemed a long way away.

Rowan walked down the steps, a mild breeze blowing her hair across her face. A snaking line of garrulous passengers followed one another towards the baggage reclaim hall. She half expected to turn around and see Tom waiting for her, a smile on his lips and luggage in his hands, but common sense prevented her from turning; that and the knowledge that confirming his absence would stab more keenly. Rowan stepped forwards to collect her case from the conveyor belt. Once she'd been allowed through passport control, her eyes scanned the small crowd waiting for family and friends to arrive.

'Over here, Rowan.'

Rowan turned to see her mother waving frantically at the back of the throng. She hurried around the bulk of the waiting crowd and fell into her mother's arms. She hugged her, breathing in the comforting mix of Dior perfume and sunscreen.

'Hello, darling,' said Grace. 'I'm so glad you decided to come.'

Rowan stood back and smiled, unable to immediately trust her voice not to croak with emotion. She noticed that her mother had allowed her short bob to grow greyer and was now long enough to touch her shoulders. She was slim, tall and feminine, looking a decade younger than her sixty-two years.

'It's good to be here.' She linked her mother's arm while dragging her case behind her as they walked towards the car. 'Where's Dad?'

Grace chuckled as she unlocked the boot. 'He's broken a bone in his foot. He was walking to the lake to spend a few hours fishing. His foot sank into a rabbit hole and he's been hobbling about and moaning for a week now.'

Rowan heaved her case into the empty boot.

'Poor Dad. I bet he's a nightmare being stuck in the house.'

'You know your dad.' Grace sighed. 'Always has to be on the go. After the first two days I couldn't stand it any more. I remembered Monique who lives above the butcher's had some crutches from her bunion operation last year. She was happy to lend them to your dad, so at least he can walk around the village, buy a paper and natter to his friends in the square.'

Grace started the engine and navigated her way out of the airport. She glanced at her daughter. 'How are you?'

Rowan twisted her lips and shrugged. 'I'm okay. One minute I can be talking to someone, dry-eyed, thanking them for their kind words and then I can be in the supermarket or on the tube or washing the dishes alone at home and I just dissolve into tears. I think bereavement's a little like losing your mind.'

Grace patted her daughter's hand. 'Grieving is a long slow process, darling. You just need to relax and let me look after you for a week or two. Try not to think about the renovation work or Jet. David will keep a close eye on Magnolia House and Libby will spoil Jet something rotten at their house.'

'She's being so strong. Do you know she hates her job, is still struggling to conceive as well as coping with the loss of her brother and she's *still* there for me? I just don't know how she does it.'

'I'm sure David is a tower of strength for her.'

'Hmm,' replied Rowan, thinking about the difficulties her best friends were going through. She hoped that having Jet in the house with them would bring them closer together. Dogs had an uncanny knack of encouraging conversation and making people laugh. Hopefully Libby and David would have long walks with Jet together and talk things over. It was such a relief to know that he was being looked after. Poor thing had been getting stressed with all the noise and disruption.

Rowan lay back against the headrest, her face turned to look out of the window. As they passed the miles of the thick dense trees of Le Grand Bois, the ephemeral trunks began to hypnotise Rowan and her eyelids slowly closed as the car weaved its way south towards Aubeterre-sur-Dronne.

'Wake up. We're here.'

Rowan opened her eyes and rubbed the ache in her neck where her head had lolled forwards on the journey. The early spring sunshine shone brightly through the copse of trees surrounding her parents' house which was situated on the edge of the village; close enough to the heart of the community to feel included, but far enough away from the hustle and bustle to be peaceful. Its painted wooden shutters matched the colour of the blue April sky and had been thrown open to air the rooms, giving the small house the impression that it had opened its eyes now that winter was a chilly memory. The car crunched to a halt on a small pea gravel drive. Rowan saw her father lift an arm and wave from the swing seat on the veranda. He was reading a newspaper with a glass of wine on the table beside him.

Rowan opened the car door and hurried up the set of four steps leading to the veranda that ran the width of the cottage.

'Dad, I've missed you.' She bent to hug her father whose plastered left foot was resting on a wicker chair. 'Honestly, Dad, I can't turn my back on you for a minute.'

Bill hadn't been referred to as William since his schooldays. Now aged seventy-one and a retired headmaster, he was fulfilling his dream of living in France. Since Rowan's earliest memories of sitting around the table to eat each evening back in Manchester, she remembered the dreams and stories her parents would tell of their future dream house and life in France. They'd been living that dream for nearly six years now.

'It's wonderful to see you, love,' said Bill. 'Sorry I can't get up but Roger Rabbit's got it in for me and set a trap near the lake.' He pointed with his thumb in the general direction of the fishing lake to one side of the cottage.

Grace laughed. 'Your father can't accept the fact that he's getting on and he's not as steady on his feet as he used to be. He's fabricated some story that the wildlife is out to get him. The locals haven't a clue who or what Roger Rabbit is and think he's lost his mind as well as his balance.'

The three of them laughed, relieved to be back together again.

'Come on in. Let's put the kettle on.'

'It looks like Dad's on the hard stuff already.'

'When in France, my love, when in France,' called her father. 'It's tradition to take a glass of grapes with your lunch. It'd be rude to go against the country's customs. Besides, it makes a cheap and tasty painkiller.' He raised his glass to his foot and chuckled.

The day of the accident started innocently enough the

following week. Rowan slowly became aware of voices and laughter seeping into her dreams, trickling into her sub-conscious and dragging her from sleep into a new day. She blinked her eyes open and stared into the darkness, luxuriating in the knowledge that she was still in France. Stretching, she smiled to herself. She'd been half dreading returning to Aubeterre without Tom, but had found it incredibly healing. Memories had flowed like warm syrup. She'd immersed herself in their exquisiteness but kept guard for fear of being enveloped by something more painful. As the fortnight was nearing its end, Rowan felt that her visit to this little jewel of a village in the middle of Charente, had, if not altogether healed her emotional turmoil, had certainly formed a protective layer over her grief. Better to remember the times when they'd been at their happiest, rather than concentrate on his absence.

The friendly banter continued outside her bedroom window. The French shutters blocked out a huge amount of light so Rowan shuffled towards the window in darkness, arms outstretched in front of her. She opened the gauze-draped windows and pushed the shutters wide open. Instantly the glare of the sun rising above the treetops made her squint as light and colour flooded into her bedroom.

Rowan leaned on the stone ledge outside her window. From her first floor vantage point, she heard the distant noise of the Sunday market buzz into life in Le Place Trarieux at the end of the lane. She breathed deeply, savouring the aroma of fresh coffee drifting up towards her room from the kitchen.

Le Place Trarieux was the village square, surrounded by small shops, cafés and tall, centuries-old houses. A narrow road ran around its perimeter with alleyways and narrow lanes snaking off in different directions like veins on a leaf. The square itself was lined with sweet smelling Linden trees and huge stone containers filled with flowers. Rowan could hear the market stalls being set up for that morning's trade beneath the lush broad-leafed canopies.

'Bonjour, Rowan,' called a cheerful voice.

Rowan looked down to see the upturned face of Fabrice, the local baker, smiling up at her. He'd worked in the square for many years and had become good friends with her and Tom. Her mother was standing beside him holding two freshly baked baguettes.

'Morning, Fabrice,' she called.

'*Mais non, parlez Français.*'

'Sorry – er, *pardon. Bonjour. C'est une belle journée.*'

'*Mais pas aussi belle que vous!*'

Rowan blushed at the compliment as she waved and turned back towards her little sink in the corner of her room. He'd told her that the day wasn't as beautiful as she was. Looking in the mirror she noted a constellation of freckles that had appeared on her sun-kissed face and a lack of puffy bags under her eyes. She was certainly sleeping better here.

Following breakfast on the veranda, Rowan decided to drive into Riberac. Her mother was working part time at Fabrice's *boulangerie* and her father was still hobbling around on crutches, so she borrowed her parents' car and set off on the twenty-minute drive. Farmland gave way to deep forests of oak, sweet chestnut, bracken and broom. Miles of dense trees bordered the road, framing the deserted country lanes. Rowan wound the window down, embracing the cool breeze and inhaling the sweet spring scents. She saw a buzzard soaring ahead of her, gliding on the thermals. Occasionally she passed a group of cars huddled together in a man-made clearing. She recognised them as wild boar and roe deer hunters who had parked up to join La Chasse. Her father had often regaled her about stories of this proud and ancient hunting tradition.

Having arrived at the old market town, Rowan manoeuvred the car into a parking space. The kiosk haled the new month in bright red letters alongside the tariff. She paused, mentally ticking off having survived her first March without Tom. Heat invaded the car as soon as she opened the door. Pushing her sunglasses further up her nose, she reached for her mother's wicker basket and bought her ticket.

Rowan spent the morning exploring the street market and occasionally calling in to small knick-knack shops which she adored rummaging through. Modern life seemed suspended as a myriad of stalls lined the pavements along the lovely old streets, selling local goods and produce. Red, white and blue bunting danced in the light breeze while locals and tourists searched out the crustiest bread, sweetest fruits and ripest cheeses. Tables groaned with the weight of brightly coloured fruit and vegetables. Beautiful hand-painted pots, that had been lovingly fashioned by a local potter, were stacked and lined up in front of a war memorial. Fresh fish lay on beds of melting crushed ice, staring sightlessly back at the crowds. Paintings of sunflowers and lavender fields were propped up on easels and summer dresses hung from rails like forgotten marionettes.

Rowan bought a straw hat and a baguette, inhaling the heady smell of grilled meat. She followed the sweet spicy aroma as if in a trance and found an old man squinting against the smoke, cooking merguez sausages. She fought the temptation and continued to saunter along the stalls with her basket tucked into the crook of her arm. Her new hat gave her a little protection from the midday sun but the sun's rays bit into her pink shoulders.

With her basket full of fat pink-tinged garlic bulbs, a wedge of Camembert cheese, a bag of cherries and three icing dusted almond croissants, she set off back to Aubeterre.

Driving into the village, Rowan spotted a vacant space on the edge of the elevated parking area. On impulse, she decided to stop and admire the stunning view before continuing down the winding hill to her parents' house. Tom had always said that the vista of rooftops, verdant countryside and the silver streak of the river that snaked through the landscape were wasted on a place to park boxes of metal. The car shuddered to a standstill with gravel from her tyres whipping up sun-baked dust like spirals of smoke signalling her arrival. Reaching across the seat she retrieved the basket and her sunglasses before pulling the keys out of the ignition. She pushed the car door wide open with her elbow a second before a shadow, a high-pitched squeal and a crunching of metal frightened her rigid for a few seconds. Rowan opened her tightly squeezed eyes, her heart pounding in shock. She was horrified to see a crumpled figure lying on the floor wrapped around a distorted bicycle.

She jumped out of the car, the bag of cherries dropping to the floor and scattering in the dust like beads falling from a broken necklace.

'Are you okay?'

She crouched beside the man and asked again. 'Are you okay? *Est ce que ça va?*'

She grasped his shoulder making him cry out.

'Ow! Sunburn.'

Her hand shot back to her chest where she clutched it, fearful of hurting him again. At least he spoke English, she thought. 'I'm so sorry. I should've looked before opening the door.'

The man slowly unwound one leg from the handlebars and pushed himself into a sitting position. He looked up at her with a pained expression on his tanned face. His hat had fallen off to reveal a short crew cut and a stubbly hint of a beard. His eyes were so unnaturally blue that she was

72

sure they were coloured contact lenses. As he grimaced, she saw blood seeping through the small cracks between his teeth, giving the impression that he'd drunk a cheap glass of red wine. Was that glitter in his lip salve?

'Do you need an ambulance?' she asked.

The man looked down at his jeans which were rolled up to mid-calf and slapped them a few times to remove the dust. His flip-flops hung from his toes at an odd angle and a rip in his jeans gaped like an open mouth.

'My Armani's are ruined. It's taken me weeks of washing on a hot cycle to get them faded to perfection.'

'Sorry?'

'They were too dark, but they were a perfect fit.'

'But are you all right?'

'Let's just say I have a bruised ego. I spotted a gorgeous man walking his dog so I freewheeled to catch his attention. Then this.' He grunted as he struggled to his feet.

Fabrice came running towards them, his long fringe and white baker's apron flapping in time with each stride. He threw a Gauloises to one side on reaching Rowan.

'*Mon Dieu! Qu'est-ce qui s'est passé, Rowan?*'

Rowan watched the cyclist sigh theatrically and lean against her car. She watched open-mouthed as the bloodied man flirted outrageously with Fabrice.

'I think I need the kiss of life,' he said.

Rowan suppressed a giggle. He was now hamming up his injuries so that he could lean on the baker's shoulders.

Fabrice looked concerned. 'I ask my wife if you need the 'elp. She call 'ospital for you.'

The cyclist pursed his lips, let go of Fabrice, stood up straight and cleared his throat. 'No thank you, I'll be absolutely fine.'

Fabrice looked at Rowan questioningly and she raised a hand to reassure him.

'*C'est bien, merci. Il n'est pas blessé.*' She looked back at the cyclist. 'You're not hurt, are you?'

'Only from rejection, dah-ling.'

Fabrice left, shaking his head in confusion as he walked back to his stall.

'You deserve an Oscar,' said Rowan, laughing. 'That was award winning.'

'I've only got four days left in France and I still haven't found my handsome French *je ne sais quoi*.'

'Maybe you should stop looking and let them find you. I'm Rowan by the way.'

'Mason. Mason Oakland.' He extended an arm and shook her hand. 'Call me Ace.'

'Can I give you a lift somewhere?'

'I'm staying down the road so it's just a short walk. I'm desperate for a drink though. My throat thinks I'm giving it the cold shoulder.'

Rowan smiled. She liked Ace instantly and was relieved that he wasn't badly hurt. 'My parents live around the corner. Please come back with me and I'll get you a drink.'

'You don't have a gorgeous brother by any chance, do you?'

Rowan helped Ace to haul his dusty bike off the floor. 'Sadly not.' They pulled it into an upright position and stared at the protruding spokes and twisted handlebars.

'Think it's bitten the dust, literally and metaphorically,' said Ace.

'I'll buy you another one. I insist.'

'Don't worry. It's hired and I paid an arm and a leg for the insurance. I'm sure it happens a lot around here. The French drive on the wrong side of the road and crazy Englishwomen open car doors into the road.' He winked at her.

'Do you want a tissue?' Rowan pointed to his mouth.

She watched him suck the blood stained saliva from his teeth before feeling around his mouth with his tongue.

'Just bitten my tongue, I think. I'm told I must learn to do that more often in conversation.'

They walked side by side down the cobbled hill, the bike squeaking alongside them.

'What about your car?' asked Ace.

'It's dad's. I'll take a look later.'

The two of them struggled to the bottom of the hill with Ace hobbling and Rowan trying to keep him and his bike upright. Once at the bottom, she directed him along a little lane off the square to the right. Several hundred yards further along, she stopped.

'This is where Mum and Dad live.'

She leant the bike against their small front wall and led him along the front path that curved like a smile through the lawn. The stone house sat in a generous plot surrounded by fruit trees and huge Cyprus trees that afforded her parents some shelter from the hot summers and bitter winter winds. The two-storey building had five windows on the front elevation, each flanked by shutters and surrounding a central front door; similar to a child's drawing of a house. A front veranda spread the whole width of the house as if it was underlining the drawing. They walked up the steps where she pointed to the swing seat.

'Take a seat there and I'll fetch you a drink. Won't be a sec.'

Once inside, Rowan hurried to the sink where she filled a small mixing bowl with warm water and ripped off several sheets of kitchen roll.

'Dad! Dad, are you home?'

Rowan waited for an answer that didn't materialise. She bent to retrieve a glass jug from a cupboard and filled it with orange juice from the fridge and ice cubes from the freezer. Balancing the bowl, jug and two glasses on a tray, she gingerly made her way back outside.

'Don't know where Dad is. He's probably hobbled off somewhere.'

'Hobbled? You haven't nearly broken his legs too, have you?'

'No.' Rowan grinned. 'Dad had an argument with a rabbit hole.' She placed the jug and glasses on the ornate metal table and then stooped to place the bowl of water on the decking.

'Thanks,' said Ace, pouring two glasses of orange juice.

'So tell me, what's a gay Englishman doing cycling around Charente by himself?'

'Trying to find a handsome *homme* to pay *homm*-age to.' Rowan knelt at his feet and chuckled as she dipped the paper towels into the warm water. 'But why so early in the season and why France?'

'I sell vintage clothing in London but … ouch.' He flinched as Rowan dabbed at the graze on his knee. 'I'm moving retail space from Stanmore to Wandsworth but the new shop isn't ready yet. My landlord's giving my flat a lick of paint so I decided to escape the mess and escape for a week. I didn't fancy Ibiza or Ayia Napa because the music scene hasn't started yet, so here I am, having crossed the Channel on a whim.' He frowned. 'Why are you looking at me like that?'

Rowan sat back on her heels. 'Because I can't believe you're moving to Wandsworth. It's just around the corner from where I live in Clapham. We're almost neighbours.'

'Seriously?'

'Honestly.'

He shook his head. 'It might be a cliché but it's a small world.' Ace hooked a piece of ice from his juice using a bent finger and crunched on the frozen cube. 'What do you do?'

'I used to work in textiles but at the moment I'm designing bespoke pieces of jewellery to sell on to gift shops.'

'Fantastic! I know where to come when I need a new nipple ring.'

Rowan sat next to him on the swing seat. 'Sorry, can't help you there. But I can make you a rather fetching anklet if you're in the market for one.'

Ace stuck out one foot showing his broken flip-flop. 'Have you seen these hairy toes? They're the last thing I want to draw attention to.'

Rowan pulled her maxi skirt down to cover her legs. 'Snap. I can't remember when I last shaved my legs.'

She sensed Ace look sideways at her. There was a pause in their conversation before he spoke.

'Holidaying alone, unshaven legs, not paying attention when opening car doors and a deep sadness hidden quite well beneath a golden tan and friendly conversation. Fancy talking to a stranger?'

Rowan was taken aback. Gone was the camp facade and humorous bravado and in its place was a genuine concern in his voice and etched on his features.

She stuttered. 'I ... maybe ...'

Ace immediately held up his hands as if surrendering, his camp intonation returning.

'You don't have to say anything. Like I said, I'm trying to bite my tongue in conversation. My ex used to say that I don't know when to close my mouth.' He gave her a wink.

'Whoever he was, he was mad to leave you.'

'He didn't leave me. Well, he did, but ... he died. My husband died last summer.'

Ace gave a dramatic intake of breath, placed his glass on the table and covered his mouth with his hands. His eyelashes fluttered as he blinked away tears and wafted a hand in front of his face to fan himself. 'That's too tragic.'

He cupped his cheeks with his hands. 'What happened?' He shook his head and held up a palm to her face. 'No, don't tell me. I've done it again. You don't have to tell me.'

Rowan shrugged, a pain in her throat feeling like a hot knife stabbing her. 'His heart stopped while he was playing football. We were told it was sudden death syndrome.'

Ace's eyes glistened. 'We?' He grabbed her hands. 'Don't tell me you have a little one still waiting for Daddy to come home.'

'No.' Rowan smiled, surprising herself that she'd seen the humour in Ace's dramatic reaction. 'I live close to his sister Libby and her husband. It was her husband, David, who was playing football with Tom when he died.'

Ace bit his bottom lip and made a small whimpering sound. 'Sorry, but I'm useless with a sob story. I blub every time someone gets voted off *Strictly* or exits *EastEnders* in a taxi.'

Rowan slid her hands from beneath his and patted his clenched fists. 'It's getting easier. Let's change the subject, shall we?'

'Yoo-hoo!'

They looked up and saw Grace waving at them as she walked in through the garden gate.

'It's Mum,' said Rowan, standing up.

'The *poissonier* was in the market and I just couldn't resist buying some oysters for a treat and some salmon for the freezer.' She stepped on to the veranda and saw Ace struggling to stand up. 'Hello.'

'Mum, this is Mason. He likes to be called Ace. I knocked him off his bike.'

'Good Lord,' said Grace, looking horrified. 'What speed were you going?'

'It's okay, Mum. I was parked. I opened my door without checking.'

Grace looked at Ace. 'Are you all right, dear? What on earth has she been feeding you? You're lips are sparkling.'

'That'll be my Dior lip balm. Nice to meet you,' he added, holding out his hand.

Without batting an eyelid, Rowan watched her mother shake his hand and reply animatedly. 'Oh, I love Dior. I wear Addict. Here, smell.'

Rowan's mouth fell open as her mother stuck her wrist under Ace's nose.

Ace sighed. 'That's divine. A classy choice for a classy lady.'

Grace giggled like a schoolgirl. 'Don't be silly.' She batted the air as if swatting a fly. 'Anyway, I won't disturb you any longer. It's lovely to meet you. Rowan, would you mind putting the fish in the fridge for me while I nip upstairs to the little room?'

'Would you like to stay for some dinner?' Rowan asked Ace.

'Thank you, but I must be getting back for a long soak before I go out. I can't miss the opportunity of maybe getting some sympathy from a handsome Frenchman tonight.'

'We must stay in touch when we get back to England.' She bent down to where she'd left her bag on the decking and rummaged inside. Pulling out a pen, she ripped the back sheet from her diary and scribbled her phone number down. 'Give me a ring when you're settled back in London and we'll meet up for a bite to eat.'

Ace took the piece of paper. 'I was hoping to take home a phone number, but I never expected it to be a woman's!'

Chapter Thirteen

Back in London, Rowan arrived first at Harrods' Tea Rooms and was sitting at their reserved table waiting for Libby. After a few minutes she spotted her sister-in-law, who appeared to be stuffing something into her handbag. Rowan waved and silently mouthed 'hello', not wanting to disturb the pianist who was playing gentle airs for the diners. Libby joined her and forced the zip on her bag to close. They greeted each other with a hug.

'I've missed you,' said Libby. 'The weather was obviously good.'

'It was lovely and I missed you too. Thank you so much for looking after Jet for me. I'd missed him so much that I let him sleep at the bottom of my bed last night.'

'Careful, he'll get used to it.'

'What've you been buying?' said Rowan. She pointed to Libby's bulging handbag.

'Nothing much. Just a cheap necklace. I might take it back.'

'Let me see, let me see,' said Rowan, rubbing her palms together in anticipation.

'I must order first. I'm starving.'

Rowan watched Libby bury her head in the menu and wondered why she seemed on edge.

'Are you okay?'

'Me? Yes of course. I'm fine. David and I just had a few words this morning, but it was nothing. Now, what shall have?'

A waitress came to their table with pen and pad in hand.

'I'll have an assortment of sandwiches with fruit scones, clotted cream and blueberry jam, please,' said Libby.

'Make that two, please.'

The waitress jotted down the order, smiled and retreated.

'So, how was France?'

'Bittersweet. It brought back so many happy memories and it's such a beautiful place, but everything seemed different without Tom.'

Libby laid her hand on Rowan's forearm. 'It's only been eight months.'

'I know.'

Libby changed the subject. 'How did the builders get on while you were away? David said he called round several times and they were doing a great job.'

'It looks amazing. They've put in a door at the top of the basement steps and converted Tom's studio into a one-bedroomed apartment. It's only small, but just perfect. It's got a little kitchenette and bathroom and a surprisingly spacious lounge. It'd be great for a young couple.'

Libby laughed. 'You sound like an estate agent. What about the rest?'

'They've used some of the first floor landing to put up a stud wall, so I've got my own front door at the top of the stairs. Thankfully the Georgians gave their houses generous proportions to work with. I had a walk around it and it's quite big compared to the basement rooms. They've done a lovely job converting each floor. I can't wait to show you.'

They stopped talking and leant backwards as the waitress brought their teapot and a jug of milk.

'And what about your apartment?' said Libby, as she poured out their teas.

'I love it. I feel safe upstairs and the builders have been really helpful by moving furniture for me. The landing has been used to create a bigger lounge.'

'So you're happy with your decision?'

'Very. I just need to find the right people to be my neighbours. That'll be a bit scary, but it'll be good to have company – and an income.'

The plate of triangular cut sandwiches arrived on a gold-edged plate. The waitress wished them an enjoyable meal, before disappearing back into the kitchen.

'Tell me how you've been and why were you having words this morning?' asked Rowan.

'David's just a bit grumpy, but so am I. I'm fed up with work and my miserable boss. I get there bright and early in order to create beautiful bouquets in pink or blue to celebrate the birth of a baby, meanwhile I'm busy keeping the tampon industry in business every month.' Libby looked up guiltily. 'I'm so sorry. That was insensitive. I just forgot for a moment.'

Rowan swallowed a mouthful of sandwich with some difficulty. She would have been almost due to give birth to Tom's baby if she hadn't fallen down the stairs.

'It's okay. I'm coping.' She tried to lift the atmosphere. 'I met a wonderful man on holiday called Mason. Everyone calls him Ace and he's so funny. It's a shame I met him towards the end of my stay.'

'Was he French?'

'No, from London, would you believe? We're going to meet up. You must come so I can introduce you both. Oh, how could I have forgotten?' Rowan delved into her handbag. 'I want to show you something strange that came in the post this morning.' She pulled out a sheet of paper and passed it to Libby. Libby read the few words that had been spelt out with small square cuttings from a newspaper and stuck on to the sheet. It read,

YOU'Re EXPOSEd NOW!

Libby studied the paper. 'What does it mean? Who sent it?'

'I don't know. That's all that was in the envelope.'

'Who cuts letters out of newspapers? Someone's been watching too many old detective films,' said Libby.

'It was either posted as a joke or to the wrong address. I'd hate to think that it was genuinely meant for me.'

Libby handed it back. 'Weird. Shall I ask David to show it to his mate who's a policeman?'

'No. As I said, I think it was meant for someone else; maybe the person who lived there before we bought it.'

'I'd just throw it away. Perhaps it's from the postman and he's seen you naked.'

The two of them laughed and continued to catch up on news. An hour later, they left the restaurant and took the lift to the ground floor where sumptuous displays beckoned. Rowan felt Libby slip her arm through hers and pull her towards the perfumery department. She watched as her sister-in-law picked up several bottles, removing the lids and sniffing each one in turn. They moved from counter to counter with Libby seemingly mesmerised by the exotic packaging and bright colours of hundreds of expensive fragrances drifting invisibly through the vast space.

Staying on the ground floor, they proceeded through the arches to the Food Hall where Rowan feasted her eyes on the glorious art deco ceilings, skylights, chandeliers and marble counters where food was presented like works of art. Customers moved trance-like from display to display, the air saturated with the tantalising aromas of coffee beans, chocolate and exotic ripe fruit.

Libby gave a theatrical sigh. 'Oh, I just *love* it here!'

Rowan smiled at her, noticing the change in her mood. Libby seemed impassioned and excitable. Her cheeks were flushed with a grin stretching her mouth wide.

Picking up a box, Rowan studied the pale pink colour of a sugared almond pictured on the top of the lid. It was the perfect pale hue of pink she wanted for her new bedroom. She knew that machines could mix paint by scanning a shade taken in by a customer, so she decided to take this box along to B&Q. She could indulge in the sweet-coated nuts as she was rolling her walls with paint.

She followed Libby who had wandered across the floor, seemingly drawn by sensory colours and smells pulling her this way and that. Rowan looked at her watch.

'Libbs, do you know what time it is?'

Libby turned and blinked, seeming a little confused. 'Sorry, what?'

'You're in a world of your own. I said, do you know you've had over a two-hour lunch break?'

'Bloody hell, I'd forgotten I should be at work!' Libby looked disorientated. 'I'll have to think of a good excuse. Damn, I was enjoying myself too.' She hurriedly kissed Rowan on the cheek. 'I'll call you later. Bye.'

Rowan watched her sister-in-law weave around shoppers before disappearing into the next room. She subconsciously shook her head, wondering why Libby had been behaving so oddly.

Stopping to admire a display of cakes that resembled toys rather than baking, Rowan tucked the box of sugared almonds under her arm and secured the strap of her handbag more securely on her shoulder. There was a fairy castle, a steam train and a teddy bear all covered in coloured icing, enticing customers to buy and spoil their loved-ones with such magnificent designs. A white cake caught Rowan's eye. It had beautifully crafted marzipan decorating its top, in the shapes of a baby's bottle, bib and bootee. Next to the miniature objects were written the words, *On the Birth of Your Baby*.

She was surprised to find that tears had blurred the words. Next month she would have been able to hold a miniature Tom in her arms and in the months to follow, she would have recognised his smile again on the lips of their child. She could have hugged a part of her husband once again. Embarrassed that she was now sobbing noisily and unable to stop, Rowan stumbled towards the exit. She struggled to find a tissue in her handbag as she pushed through the glass doors onto the pavement. She breathed in the fresh air as if she'd surfaced from deep water. Rowan blew her nose and was wiping her eyes when a hand touched her shoulder.

Thinking it was Libby returning to ask her something, Rowan turned immediately and was shocked to be confronted by two uniformed security guards.

'Sorry,' said Rowan, making to sidestep the men.

'Excuse me, madam. Would you mind coming with me?'

Rowan frowned. 'Me? Why?'

'We have reason to believe that you have left the shop without paying for something.'

Rowan stared back, angry that they'd made a mistake while she was obviously upset. She looked down at her hands that were empty, except for a soggy tissue.

'You've made a mistake. I only have my handbag on my shoulder and ...' Rowan realised that she had something else nestled beneath her right arm, her elbow bent to keep it in place. Removing it, she was horrified to discover that she still had the box of sugared almonds.

'No, it's a mistake. This is ... so ... embarrassing,' stammered Rowan. 'I liked the colour of this almond here. I was going to buy some paint in the same colour. Then I saw the cakes and got upset. It's just a silly mistake. I'll pay for it.'

She realised that her story didn't sound very convincing,

but she was also acutely aware that shoppers had stopped and were straining to hear what was being said.

'You can explain everything to the police in the manager's office, madam.'

'The police? But I'll pay. It was just a silly mistake.'

'It's procedure, madam. If you'll come this way.'

Rowan was escorted back through the main doors with a security guard holding each elbow. Her face was aflame with shame as she was led through a side door and down several corridors. As she entered the manager's office, she heard the final words of a telephone conversation.

'Yes please, sergeant. Security has caught the shoplifter and she'll be here when an officer arrives. Thank you.'

As Rowan sat down in the office to wait for the police, she realised that she had another unwanted label.

Firstly, widow. Now, shoplifter.

Chapter Fourteen

The following Friday evening, Rowan was struggling to open the front door to her apartment. She'd spent a busy day making earrings, finalising the 'to let' advertisement for the paper, hanging Roman blinds in the two new apartments and walking Jet on the common. It was only when he'd needed feeding that she remembered she'd used the last of his food.

Having dashed to the local shops before closing time, she clenched the handles of a carrier bag between her teeth, squeezing a large box of dog food under one arm while trying to unlock the door with her other. She grimaced as she pushed it open and carried the shopping bags into the kitchen. She heaved the bags onto the worktop, wondering why she hadn't thought to live on the ground floor? Jet sprang to greet her.

'This is all your fault,' she moaned, light-heartedly.

Jet wound his way between her feet as she stumbled out of the kitchen, trying to avoid him and a selection of dog toys that he'd scattered on the floor.

Once in the lounge, she sprawled out like a starfish on the settee. Lying on her back, gazing up at the ceiling light, Rowan wondered for the hundredth time whether she was doing the right thing by inviting strangers into her house. She now had The Blue Moon as a client, which earned her some money and kept her busy making her jewellery. If only she could find a few more customers, then she wouldn't have to share her front door. She rubbed her forehead, dragging her hand up through her hair. Too late now, she thought. Magnolia House had been separated into three apartments that had been washed, painted, dressed and made ready to be introduced to their new tenants.

Adding to her stress was the knowledge that she'd taken something accidently from Harrods. She felt as if her life was spiralling out of control. Thankfully, when she'd explained everything to the policeman and the manager, and the police computer had verified that her name had never been reported for a crime before, they all agreed that a verbal warning would be adequate for a first offence. Despite the fact that her explanation had been believed, it still didn't stop her cringing every time she thought about it.

Having got her breath back, she noticed that her answering machine was flashing. She sat up and pressed the button. A voice immediately shouted from the machine from a noisy bar.

'Bonjour, Rowan, it's Ace. Where are you? I need to talk. My landlord has decided to put the bloody flat on the market. That's why he was decorating it. Thought he was just being nice. I'm in The Pink Feather with some friends. Can you call me back later? I hope you haven't rented your rooms yet.'

Rowan grinned. How wonderful would it be to have Ace living in Magnolia House with her? He'd be the perfect remedy to the shameful self-pity she'd been feeling recently. She immediately punched out the dial-back number and waited impatiently, jiggling up and down on the edge of the settee. Jet thought this was a new game and crouched down, bottom and tail in the air, wanting to play.

'Ace! It's Rowan.'

'Hey! How's things?'

'Fine, thanks. Busy. I've been hanging blinds today.'

'Who's gone blind?' he shouted. 'It's so noisy here ... wait a minute.'

Rowan could hear a muffled crackling.

'Hello, is that better?'

'Much better,' said Rowan.

'I'm sitting on the loo in the gents so I can hear myself think.'

'Too much information.'

'No, just sitting on the lid for the peace. Now, tell me that you haven't rented out your rooms yet.'

'The advert's going in the paper on Monday.'

'Well stop the press. I want it.'

Rowan laughed. 'I've got two apartments, so the ad can still go in. Don't you want to come and see what they look like first?'

'No, I've met the landlady and she'll do. When can I move in?'

'Whenever you like. Both apartments have one double bedroom, a lounge, bathroom and kitchen. The ground floor flat is bigger than the basement flat so the rent's a little more, but both are fine for a single person or a couple.'

'Stop. I've already said I want to come and stay. You don't need to sell it to me, but as I'm the first to rent, I'll take the bigger ground floor.'

'I can't believe it. We're going to be neighbours.'

'Just make sure you don't try and kill me again. One near miss is enough.'

'I promise.'

'I think we have a deal then.'

Ace moved in a fortnight later. It had rained during the night and the air smelt of wet tarmac and sweet blossoms. Rowan had felt a bubble of excitement in her stomach all week at the prospect of her new friend moving in with her. Ace and his friend Kevin had been lugging boxes, clothes and furniture in through the front door for the past two hours and now the van's horn beeped before disappearing onto the main road. Now she wouldn't be rambling around Magnolia House by herself. Ace would only be a flight of stairs away.

'Last few things,' said Ace, carrying a cactus through his new front door.

'What on earth is that?' said Rowan, pointing at the spiky plant. 'It's a bit … phallic.'

'This is Dick and you'd better not be laughing. He's been a good friend to me and helped me out of a depression last year.'

Rowan covered her mouth with her palm, not knowing whether to laugh again or take the news of his recent depression more seriously.

'How?' she asked, narrowing her eyes.

Ace placed the plant pot reverentially on his kitchen table. 'When I was feeling low last year, my boyfriend bought Dick for me. And before you start questioning its name, it's because my boyfriend was called Richard, okay?'

Rowan smirked and nodded.

'He was sensitive and supportive when I couldn't be bothered to get out of bed, wash or eat. We're talking my boyfriend here by the way, not the cactus.' Ace rubbed his short blond hair as if scrubbing away the memories of his depression and pulled himself up to sit on the worktop. 'He bought it for me and explained that this little cactus struggled to survive against all the odds. It lives in harsh conditions. Heat. Drought. Isolation. But it not only survives, it flourishes and flowers and grows spikes to protect itself from whatever is thrown its way. It's a metaphor for life and it worked. It really worked. It took some weeks but every time I glimpsed Dick sitting on my bathroom shelf, bulbous and proud – the cactus, not my boyfriend – it would make me smile.'

'He's very welcome. Any friend of yours is a friend of mine.'

'I just knew you two would hit it off,' said Ace. He sprang down from the worktop and hugged Rowan.

Rowan wrapped her arms around Ace's waist, her cheek resting on his shoulder. She could smell his cologne and the warmth and strength of his body. Although she knew this was a brotherly hug, it felt wonderful to be held tightly after nine months with only Tom's pillow to embrace.

'What happened to your sensitive and supportive boyfriend?' she asked.

'He dumped me for an air steward.'

Chapter Fifteen

James Oakland peered inside his brother's marshmallow-pink fridge and frowned.

'You're out of milk?'

Ace breezed into the kitchen while dancing to the strains of 'I Should Be So Lucky'. 'Not out, never had it in.'

'Since when?'

'Since I read that dairy plays havoc with your waistline.' Ace patted his flat stomach and shimmied. 'On the wagon. Not touched a drop for four months.'

James took a carton of orange juice out of the fridge and clicked the door shut. 'You might have your stomach back, but your teeth will fall out if you don't have calcium in your diet.'

'Thank you, Nigella, but I take supplements.' Ace waved an envelope in the air as if he was fanning himself. 'I've got to post this letter before twelve or it won't go today. I'll pick you up a pint of the white stuff. Oh, and don't make a noise. I haven't told the landlady you're staying yet.'

James drank the remnants of his glass of juice then licked the fruity pulp from his lips.

'I won't. I'll get a quick shower while you're out.'

'I'll only be quarter of an hour. Look after Kylie for me and don't you dare scratch her. That's a limited edition LP.'

James rolled his eyes at his brother. Ace's obsession for Kylie was legendary.

'Don't worry. I'll give her my full attention.'

Ace looked back over his shoulder and winked as he left the apartment. 'You should be so lucky.'

James grimaced as he placed his glass in the sink. He still had jet lag from his flight home from Los Angeles, forty-eight hours earlier. Rubbing his fingers backwards and forwards through his hair, he walked into his brother's bedroom and fell on his bed. It was so much more comfortable than the sofa bed where he'd been spending the last couple of nights. But it was good to be home again. Los Angeles was a wonderful place to work for a couple of years, but even the Californian sunshine couldn't persuade him to sign another two-year contract.

James had been teaching carpentry at Inglewood College of Design and Fabrication for the past two years. He hadn't exactly been running away from a broken heart, it was more a case of making a statement. *I don't care that you left me*. Of course he had cared, painfully so. As far as James was concerned, Helen had been *the one*. They'd only dated for eighteen months, but he'd fallen in love. He'd envisaged a future with her and was planning to propose on her birthday in June, but she'd unexpectedly ended their relationship. James had spotted an advert offering an opportunity to teach students current and cutting edge techniques for designing and making wooden furniture in California. Maybe if he applied for a job on the other side of the world, Helen would realise that she'd made a terrible mistake and change her mind.

As leaving day had loomed closer, James rented out his small apartment, bought his Virgin Atlantic ticket and shut down his small carpentry business, Oakland Joinery. There had still been no word from Helen. The day before he'd been due to leave, he'd sent Ace round to her parents' house with the excuse to collect a few unimportant belongings that James would probably throw out anyway. Ace's secret mission was to find out if Helen was regretting her decision and having second thoughts. As it turned out, Ace didn't even get as far as knocking on the door. As he'd pulled up opposite her parents' house in his old Fiat Punto, Helen had opened the door and stood to one side to let a man leave. The man had turned to face her and the kiss they shared wasn't a thank-you-for-servicing-my-boiler type of kiss. Ace had turned the ignition and returned to tell James that she'd moved on.

Within a month of landing at LAX, James had been teaching, socialising, surfing and developing a golden Californian tan. He was having such a fulfilling and carefree life, that Helen began to fade from his memory as if she were being slowly erased from a page.

That previous romance played no part in his thoughts as James lay on his brother's bed. Now that he was back in England he'd have to restart his business and quite liked the idea of taking on an apprentice. He'd really enjoyed teaching and had been told that he had a knack for it. However, one problem needed solving first. In the rush to pack up, wind up his business and rent out his apartment two summers ago, James hadn't read the rental agreement properly before signing it. A couple of months ago, after he'd emailed the letting agency to give three months' notice of his return to his tenants, he'd been reminded that they'd signed a tenancy for three years, not two. So now James was back in London and his flat, which was only a few miles away, was occupied by a professional couple. He was effectively homeless and jobless.

Groaning with effort, James dragged himself off the bed and into the bathroom. He turned on the shower's boost button and looked at himself in the mirror while the water was getting up to temperature. Despite feeling sluggish and sleep-deprived, his skin glowed the colour of warm honey, testimony to his frequent beach trips. He stretched out his hand to test the heat of the water, stepped out of his

Abercrombie & Fitch pyjama bottoms and stood beneath the pummelling jets.

In the apartment above him, Rowan was also looking in the bathroom mirror, checking her lipstick before going for an informal interview for the post of seamstress. Diamante Brides had answered her job enquiry and had emailed her a time for calling in for a chat. It wouldn't hurt to do some sewing to help pay the bills, she'd thought. Squatting next to Jet's basket, she ruffled the curls on the top of his head. 'Be a good boy and no chewing.'

He gazed back adoringly then settled his chin onto his crossed paws.

After surveying her floral top, dark skinny jeans and sandals, Rowan had a quick spray of Jo Malone perfume. She fetched her portfolio from the settee and left her apartment. At the bottom of the stairs she decided to call and see if Ace was in. She hadn't seen him for a few days and had been meaning to offer to cook for him one evening that week. It would be good to have a gossip and as she had a few minutes to spare, she decided to see which day would suit him best.

Rowan knocked and waited. She could hear Kylie Minogue 'spinning around' through the closed door and wondered if Ace had heard her knock. Then she heard a man's voice shout, 'Just a minute.' It was a deeper voice than Ace's. She hoped she hadn't disturbed an intimate moment. The handle turned and the door was pulled open. In front of her stood a half naked man with one towel wrapped around his waist and a smaller one over his head. He was taller than Ace, over six foot, and there was no doubt that he worked out because his rigid oblique muscles curved from his hip to down inside his towel. His skin glistened with droplets of water as he rubbed his hair with the towel, an aroma of spice and bergamot wafting into the hallway.

'You took your time. Lost the use of your hands?' said his muffled voice, from beneath the towel. He stepped to one side. When no one answered, he stopped rubbing his hair and looked up from beneath his towel.

Rowan felt a blush spread across her face. His skin was tanned and his questioning eyes were the colour of bonfire toffee. A curtain of dark tousled hair fell forwards over them before he pushed it back with a sweep of his hand. His face had a couple of days' beard growth and although his teeth were white, when he smiled she noticed that one tooth was very slightly crooked.

'I'm sorry. I was after Ace,' said Rowan.

'Sorry. I thought *you* were Ace. He said he wouldn't be long.'

Why hadn't Ace told her that he'd found a new boyfriend? she wondered. 'I'll call back.'

'Can I tell him who called?'

'Just say Rowan popped downstairs.'

'Ah! So you're the landlady.'

'You make me sound middle-aged and frumpy, but, yes, I suppose that's what I am.'

'I'm James.' He held out his hand. 'I'm staying for a bit ... er ... if that's okay?'

Rowan took his large warm hand and shook it. 'Of course, I don't mind who my tenants have to stay. Within reason. I wouldn't want him to befriend a rugby team and bring them back. Oh, I didn't mean ... I mean, I'm sure he wouldn't ...'

She knew she was rambling now, but thankfully Kylie came to her rescue by stuttering in the background as the track became stuck. James looked over his shoulder towards Ace's beloved vintage record player, giving Rowan the opportunity to appraise his body for a few brief seconds: a tanned and toned body, a broad chest with a light covering of chest hair and a small tattoo of a bird just above his right hip. Her eyes returned to his face just as James turned back to her.

'Kylie's having a strop. I'd better sort her out. It's Ace's favourite LP. I'll tell him that you called round.'

He closed the door having smiled widely and said goodbye, leaving Rowan staring at the paintwork. She chewed her lip, struggling with a strange amalgam of emotions that left her feeling confused. Then it dawned on her why she felt so unnerved. She was feeling guilty for having found another man physically attractive for the first time since Tom's death.

Thank goodness he was gay.

James closed the door and exhaled. He hadn't been expecting to open the door to a pretty face with wide searching grey eyes. He smiled to himself as he lifted the needle from the record and retraced his steps to the bathroom. As he searched in Ace's cabinet for the deodorant, he remembered that his brother had told him that Rowan had recently been widowed. Enveloped in a mist of spray, James clicked his teeth in disappointment. For a second he'd believed that he might have found an attractive distraction from job hunting and boredom until he'd sorted himself out. He heard the apartment door open and called, 'Is that you?'

Ace stopped at the bedroom door brandishing a pint of milk. 'Who do you think it is?'

'Your landlady just knocked on the door.'

'Oh God, you didn't open it like that, did you?'

'I thought she was you and that you'd forgotten your keys.'

'What did she want? Was she okay about you staying here for a bit?'

'She was lovely. You never said she was a stunning brunette.'

Ace looked levelly at James. 'Don't go there. Seriously, she's had a tough time and will be vulnerable to a sympathetic, predatory ear.'

James looked hurt. 'What do you take me for? I'm not a predator. I'm just capable of acknowledging a pretty face.'

'I'm just saying, that's all.'

James raised his arms in mock surrender.

Chapter Sixteen

Several days after meeting James, Rowan was in her kitchen trying to salvage a moribund vase of flowers. She was throwing away wilted chrysanthemum heads while rescuing vivid orange Gazanias that looked like they might last another few days in fresh water. The intercom buzzed making her jump. She kept forgetting that she'd had it installed and its shrill call continued to take her by surprise. Hurrying towards it, she pressed the answer button.

'Hello.'

A voice crackled back. 'Let's just wipe your nose.'

Rowan stared at the little speaker, half expecting to see an explanation in its fine silver mesh. 'Pardon?'

'It's Nora. Nora Chambers. I've come to see the apartment.'

'Oh, hi, I'll come down. Won't be a sec. Come on in.'

Rowan pushed the button to let Nora into the hallway, put the catch on the lock and ran downstairs to greet her. Nora had telephoned her the previous evening because she'd seen the advertisement stuck on the ground floor window.

Rowan slowed her pace as she neared the bottom of the stairs and took in the scene. She guessed that Nora was a little younger than her, perhaps in her late twenties. Her hair hung in long loose russet spirals, the colour of autumn leaves just before they fall. Like a Pre-Raphaelite oil painting, she was fair and curvy, her face scattered with a constellation of freckles. Her striking features looked guiltily at Rowan, one hand clutching her coat across her chest while the other held the hand of a small child.

'I'm sorry, but I didn't think you'd let me take a look if you knew I had a little girl.'

Rowan walked down the remaining steps to the hallway and held out her hand. Nora hesitated before letting go of her coat and shaking hands.

'It's not that I wouldn't have let you. It's just that the empty apartment is in the basement. If you've got a little one with a pushchair and goodness knows what else, then maybe it wouldn't be suitable.' Rowan looked down at the child.

'Her name's Primrose,' said Nora. 'She's fifteen months old now. I've left her pushchair outside.'

Rowan bent down and squatted on her heels so that she was closer to the little girl.

'Hello, Primrose. What a pretty name.'

Primrose looked like she'd stepped out of the pages of a Baby Gap catalogue. Her hair was the same as her mother's along with her shock of tight curls. As Rowan raised her hand to stroke Primrose's hair, the little girl removed her thumb from her mouth with a pop and buried her face into her mother's coat.

'She's beautiful,' said Rowan, standing up.

'Thank you. She's very good. She sleeps through the night and only cries when she's poorly.' Nora stroked her daughter's hair. 'Could we still have a look?'

'Really, it's not a problem. Even if she did cry, no one would be disturbed. It's a very solid old house.'

Rowan walked to the back of the hall and opened a door leading down to the basement.

'We've had a new staircase put in,' said Rowan. 'It's wider and stronger than the old one. This used to be my husband's photographic studio.'

'Really?'

On reaching the bottom of the stairs, Rowan opened a door that led into the small basement apartment. 'He passed away last year.'

'Oh, I'm sorry.'

'Thanks. Working helps. It's getting a little easier.'

The light shone in from the casement windows perched high on the walls facing the road. It had been transformed from a functional studio into a warm inviting cream living space.

'I'm afraid you can't see much out of the windows but it's light enough.'

'It looks perfect,' said Nora, wandering through the small rooms. She ran her fingers along the painted brick walls. 'I thought it might be dark and damp, but it's not.'

'Before Tom died we renovated the whole house.'

Nora let go of her daughter's hand and turned to Rowan. 'Do you miss him?'

Rowan blinked at the unexpected question.

'How do you keep going? How do you move on?' Nora continued.

Rowan was perplexed by the personal questions until the penny dropped. Of course, she thought, Nora's a single mother looking at a one-bedroom apartment. She must have been through an ordeal too.

'I keep busy. I have good friends and although I always hated the cliché when people used to say it to me last year, time's a great healer.'

Nora seemed to mull this over but didn't reply.

Rowan hesitated before taking a deep breath and forcing herself to smile. 'I was just putting the kettle on upstairs. Would you like a coffee?'

Nora raised her eyebrows in question. 'Are you sure we won't be intruding?'

'Of course not, come on.' Rowan looked at Primrose. 'And I bet if I look, I might find some biscuits.'

Once upstairs, Nora carried her daughter over to the lounge window while Rowan switched on the kettle in the kitchen.

'The view's amazing,' said Nora. 'I didn't realise you could see Clapham Common.'

Rowan stuck her head around the kitchen door. 'I think the view was the deciding factor when Tom and I decided to buy the house. You can just make out the children's park and the bandstand. How do you like your coffee?'

'White, no sugar thanks.'

'How about Primrose? Would she like some juice?'

'No, thanks. I think she's dropping to sleep on my shoulder.'

Rowan returned to the kitchen. What if she hadn't lost Tom's baby? Would it have made life easier or more difficult? She imagined a little boy with Tom's cheeky smile and love of sport, sleeping in his own half-sized bed. She turned and removed the carton of milk from the fridge and absent-mindedly poured some into their mugs. She could have passed down all Tom's expensive photographic equipment to their child instead of selling it. She stood still for a few seconds, lost in her private reverie.

She silently admonished herself. You're going to frighten off a new tenant if you start to sound miserable. Rowan smoothed down her knee length skirt and fixed a smile in place. Carrying the mugs into the lounge, she placed them on the coffee table. Nora had moved to the sideboard where she'd picked up a photograph of Rowan and Tom.

'I'm sorry, I'm being nosey,' said Nora, putting the frame back in place.

'It's okay, I don't mind.'

'It's lovely. Where was it taken?'

'We were playing Scrabble at my parents' house in Auberre-sur-Dronne.'

'I've never been to France.' Nora didn't move from the sideboard as the conversation slowed.

'Coffee's here,' said Rowan.

'Thank you. I think this little one has fallen asleep.'

'Here, lay her on the settee.'

Nora came round to the settee and gently laid Primrose on several cushions. She sat down beside her and picked up her mug.

'I'd like to rent the basement if it's okay about Primrose.'

'Why don't you tell me a little about yourself? Where have you moved from?'

'I'm originally from Bristol but moved to London five years ago to do some modelling.' She pulled a face. 'I was a lot thinner then. I've put on a bit of weight since having a baby and I've been comfort eating since Primrose's father left us.'

'I'm sorry, that's awful. Do you have any contact with him?'

'No. It's just the two of us. She helps a lot when I'm feeling low because I have someone else I'm responsible for. And she makes me laugh now she's getting older.'

Rowan looked towards the sleeping titian-haired toddler. She wondered how Nora earned a living and would be able to pay the rent, so she broached the subject.

'What do you do now that you're not modelling?'

'I still model. I'm a size fourteen so I model plus sizes. Primrose has also earned us some money with some baby modelling too. She's perfect when magazines want a curly-haired red head.'

'Is a size fourteen really considered a plus size?'

Nora chuckled for the first time. 'A size twelve is too large for most magazines. Sadly you still have to look like you're in need of a good hearty meal before you'll get on their books. I don't mind any more. Primrose is worth the extra pounds in weight.'

Jet squeaked as he yawned and stretched out on the carpet before standing up. Licking his lips, he tottered towards Rowan who was now sitting in the armchair. He dropped on the floor and began to doze once more, his chin resting on her feet.

'Where do you live now?'

'When I moved to London to work, I shared a house in Tower Hamlets. I wasn't happy there but when I met Primrose's father he helped me move into a small place in Putney. The problem was that although it used to be a nice area, it's now dirty and rundown with a high street full of burger joints, bookmakers and kebab shops.' Nora paused as she touched her daughter's small feet. She took a deep breath. 'When he left I couldn't work for a while. I was in a bad way. Baby blues they said but it was more than that. I loved him. I was evicted for not paying the rent.' Nora looked up quickly. 'That won't happen again. I'm feeling much better and I have a job.'

'It's okay. I'm not judging you. It sounds as if you've both had a tough time.'

'We've managed. We stayed at a wonderful refuge run by the Church Housing Trust. I met other single mothers there and stayed until I started to model again. Then I could afford to rent a bedsit in a large Victorian house in Lambeth. It's just one room but it's ours. But now Primrose is getting older and walking, I feel it's time to rent somewhere with a little more space. Somewhere with our own kitchen and bathroom. The basement looks perfect.'

Rowan nodded, having listened to Nora's brief sad history. 'I'm so glad you've come through the worst of it and it's great that you're modelling again.' She hoped that she didn't sound patronising. 'Who looks after Primrose while you're working?'

'Well, depending on where I'm working, I can either take her with me or pay for a private nursery to have her for a day here and there. Normally there are always willing hands wanting to cuddle her while I'm getting ready on set.'

Satisfied that Nora had a job, organised childcare and seemed like a nice lady, Rowan smiled. 'The basement's yours if you don't think it's too small. There is also a small, shared courtyard garden, where you'll find a washing line and the wheelie bins. You'll love Ace who lives on the ground floor and I know that he'll adore Primrose with all those red curls and freckles.'

'Thank you. You won't regret it.'

Chapter Seventeen

Ten days had passed since Rowan agreed to let Nora and Primrose rent out the basement floor. She'd struggled at first with the notion that someone would be living in the small rooms that Tom had found so perfect for his photographic studio. He'd chosen his own pieces of furniture and had spent days painting walls and positioning equipment to his exacting standards. But Rowan knew she needed to overcome her reluctance and she achieved this by viewing the basement as a different space. It was no longer the place where she'd find him hunched over old-fashioned negatives with a small magnifying glass, having chemically developed some prints. Nor was it the same place where they'd shared a passionate encounter in the dark room. The rhythmical throb of his favourite bands no longer echoed up the stairs and the smell of strange developing fluids had long since faded.

No. It was now a freshly decorated living space. They were rooms that Tom had never stepped inside while they looked as they did now. He'd never seen the cappuccino-coloured Roman blinds, or the new beige carpet with its flecks of cream. He'd never sat on the Ikea sofa or placed his mug on the coffee table. It was now Nora and Primrose's home.

Upstairs, Rowan was sitting at her new workbench gazing out of her bedroom window, ruminating over the basement and drumming her fingers distractedly. With the help of Ace and James, they'd made the bench out of a left over length of kitchen worktop that they'd placed on top of two identical bedside tables. With their drawers facing outwards, the bedside tables gave the overall appearance of a sturdy desk. Now all she had to do was get on with some work. But maybe they'd positioned it in the wrong place. Sitting by the bedroom window gave her too many opportunities to procrastinate by daydreaming through the glass. She remembered her old colleague, Chrissy, in Wilmslow. She could do with her now to practice her feng shui on her bedroom furniture.

Rowan's tools, silver and gold findings and beads were labelled in boxes and stacked up next to the bench. Glass rods and her lampwork torch were pushed against the wall under the window and a sheet of A4 paper lay on the table, highlighted by an anglepoise lamp. A circular beam of light shone onto the paper, spotlighting it as if an audience was waiting for entertainment; pausing for something dramatic to happen. Maybe a design, an idea or a colour scheme would miraculously appear, colouring the empty page. But creations weren't forthcoming.

Downstairs, James was scraping the last crumbs of toasted bagel and scrambled eggs onto his fork. Swallowing the last of his breakfast, he rubbed the back of his neck with his palm, elbow raised at right angles as he stretched his neck right and left, trying to relieve the ache from having slept on the sofa bed for several weeks.

It was Monday morning and Ace had gone to work leaving strict instructions for James to get out and find a job so he could contribute to the food bill. What does a carpenter do, having just come back from two years teaching in California? He'd had a lazy few weeks adjusting to the new time zone and getting to know the immediate area, but he couldn't get away with doing nothing for much longer. Not that he wanted to do nothing. He was bored and starting to suffer from cabin fever.

James supposed he could look in last night's newspaper

at the jobs' section. He was sure that he'd seen Ace reading the obituaries and giggling at the *desperate pages*, by which Ace meant the lonely hearts columns. James searched in the toilet and en suite first, the obvious places to look in a male household. Not finding it there, he scoured the kitchen and lounge. James stood in the middle of the immaculate apartment that Ace had straightened before he'd left to work in his vintage clothing shop for the day.

'Why are gay men so bloody tidy?' James asked, out loud.

He reached inside his pocket to retrieve his mobile and punched out his brother's number.

'You better not have locked yourself out, because I'm not coming back yet,' said a voice at the other end.

'Good morning to you, too,' said James.

'My good morning started at seven thirty. It's now quarter past ten, you layabout. What do you want?'

'Yesterday's newspaper. It's done a disappearing act.'

'No it hasn't. I hate to see them lying about for days, so I leave them outside Rowan's door so she can read them.'

'Why would she want an out of date newspaper?'

'Something about *best buys* in skin care.'

'Oh, okay. Maybe I'll borrow yesterday's back again.'

'Remember what I said. She doesn't need a lumbering joiner coming on to her.'

'Carpenter. And I don't lumber! I'll be polite and charming.'

'That's what I'm afraid of.'

'Seriously, I'll behave. God, you remind me of Dad with your nagging?'

'I'm your older brother. It's my job. No flirting. She's still grieving.'

James heard the shop bell ring on the other end of the phone. 'Get back to work then Gok! Sell those smelly original Levi's and seventies woolly tank tops.'

'They're not smelly. They just contain vintage dust from a bygone era.'

'You mean they need a bloody good wash. I'm going. See you later.'

'Heathen. You wouldn't know vintage if it jumped out at you. Get a job.'

Rowan noticed that her fists were clenched tightly, a habit she'd become aware of recently. Libby had told her it was anxiety and that she should go to the doctor, but Rowan didn't want to have her emotions dulled by medication. She wanted to feel the searing pain of loss when she thought about Tom. Although to her shame, her feelings of late were of anger and frustration. Why had he left her? Why hadn't he made a new patient check at the doctor's surgery when they'd moved? If he'd made the appointment when she'd suggested it, then maybe … She sighed and closed her eyes. She should have made the appointment for him and just told him when he had to go. But would he have gone?

Rowan looked down at the red half moon indentations made by her nails on her palms. She rubbed them before resting her head on her forearms and leant on the desk. Her mind usually reeled during quiet moments in the house. Her thoughts would rage like a violent undercurrent liberally sprinkled with unanswered questions. Maybe she'd feel better if she took Jet for a walk on Clapham Common. Blow the cobwebs away, as her late-grandmother used to say.

Before she had chance to stand up, Rowan heard someone knocking on her apartment door. Ace would be at work at this time so she wondered if Nora needed something. Jet barked and scampered from the bottom of her bed and out of the bedroom. Subconsciously smoothing her hair with her hands, she pushed the chair away from the workbench with the back of her knees and went to answer the door.

She felt the heat rise on her cheeks when she pulled the front door open and saw James standing there. He wore loose jeans, an oatmeal T-shirt and a sheepish smile. He pushed his hair out of his eyes.

'Morning,' he said, bending to stroke Jet.

'Is everything okay?'

'Fine, thanks. I'm just after the newspaper that Ace left outside your door this morning. It had a jobs page in it and I've been threatened with eviction if I don't find work.'

'Come in and I'll see what I've done with it.'

James stepped inside the lounge. 'How's your new workbench? Ace is still complaining of backache since we carried it upstairs. I've told him he should get to the gym but he thinks he can get fit by cutting out carbs and dairy.'

Rowan smiled. 'The bench is wonderful but it doesn't help if the creativity isn't kicking in.' She crouched to look on the shelf under the coffee table. 'Here it is.' She pulled out the newspaper, dropping it before handing it to James. Why was she so flustered?

'I know the feeling. Just because I have a circular saw at my disposal, doesn't mean a table will make itself.'

Rowan stood in front of him, arms folded through shyness. It unnerved her to have such an attractive man who she didn't know very well, standing so close. He didn't give the impression of being a gay man. His mannerisms and sexily dishevelled appearance didn't fit with her preconception of a well-groomed homosexual, like Ace.

'I was wondering if having the workbench in front of the window was such a good idea,' she said, making small talk to break the silence. 'I seem to be doing more daydreaming and curtain twitching than anything else at the bench.'

'Well, the time to worry will be when you start facial

twitching,' he said, tapping the folded newspaper against his cheek. 'Can I give you a hand moving it somewhere else?'

'Oh no, thank you. You've already been such a great help getting it upstairs. I think it's me that's the problem. I can't seem to get motivated despite feeling lucky to have found someone who wants to buy my work. It doesn't help that the weather can't make its mind up what it's doing.'

Rowan cringed inwardly. Was she really standing here discussing the weather and her lack of motivation? She'd have him backing out of the doorway in desperation to escape from her and her maudlin conversation. 'I'm sure I'll feel a lot better when I've had some fresh air. I was just about to take Jet for a walk.'

'Want some company?'

Rowan was taken aback. She'd been expecting him to use the dog walk as an excuse to leave. How could she say no without appearing rude and ungrateful?

'Are you sure?'

'Of course. What's to mind about a stroll in the sunshine? It's called delaying tactics.' He grinned, holding up the newspaper and shaking it. 'Putting off the inevitable. I'll just drop the paper downstairs and meet you at the front door.'

With that, he ran downstairs leaving Rowan to put Jet's harness on. How had that happened? One minute she was sitting down to try and design a piece of jewellery and the next minute she was preparing Jet for a walk accompanied by Ace's new boyfriend.

The sun appeared from behind a cornucopia of clouds as Rowan and James crunched along one of the gravel paths that ran through Clapham Common. The warm rays lit up the expanse of grass, now decorated with shifting shadows. Normally Rowan found that quiet contemplation during long walks calmed her thoughts. The birdsong, the distant squeals from delighted children and the soothing hum of the traffic, all gave her other things to focus on. But uncharacteristically, she was feeling ill at ease and hesitant walking alongside James.

'Do you ever let him off the harness to run free?' he asked.

'No, I daren't. He might run away.'

'Shall we live dangerously and give it a go?'

Rowan looked at James and pulled an anxious face. 'What if he runs away?'

'He looks like an intelligent spaniel to me. Besides, I'm here and I won't leave this common until I've found him.' He winked mischievously. 'Go on, let him have a run.'

Rowan held her breath before saying on an outbreath, 'We could give it a go, I suppose.'

James knelt down and unfastened the harness. Before he slipped it over Jet's head, he gently held the spaniel's jaw and looked directly into his eyes. 'Now don't let me down, Buddy. I've put my neck on the line here.'

Jet looked at a pigeon that flew nearby and landed on the grass. 'Are you listening to me?'

He pulled the harness over Jet's glossy head, but surprisingly Jet didn't move.

'Let's walk on a little and see what he does. I don't think he knows he's free.'

Rowan and James walked along the path calling to Jet. He took a few tentative steps towards them before realising that he was without the restraint of his lead. Bounding with the joy of freedom, he ran around them in large circles, occasionally stopping to roll on his back, legs dancing in mid air.

Rowan laughed, realising that the majority of occasions she'd laughed in the last ten months, was when Jet was with her. He was an invaluable comfort.

They approached the weatherworn bandstand. It was deserted except for a solitary pigeon pecking at the floor. Usually children swung from the barriers or chased each other in circles, but due to the earlier rain, it was empty. Now the drizzle had passed and distant cumulus clouds looked like erupting volcanic mountains amidst a blue ocean.

They sat down on a bench and Rowan wrapped her jacket tightly around her body. Not so much from the cool shaded air beneath the trees, but more for comfort from her unexpected bashfulness. She stretched her legs out in front of her and looked down at her dusty jeans. She'd lost weight. The pale denim material hung in small folds around her thighs and she'd had to force another notch into her leather belt the previous week.

'How are things?' asked James.

Rowan looked sideways at him, his attractive face shadowed in profile. His shoulder length hair had been swept back away from his face, revealing cheekbones and a day's worth of fine bristles. The image of the messy sink that she'd found after returning home following Tom's death sprang into her mind. Looking at James, Rowan had a powerful urge to touch his face. Just to feel the touch of unshaved warm skin once again. Just for comfort.

She looked away suddenly as James turned towards her. She shuffled self consciously, bending her legs beneath the bench and leaning forwards. 'Sorry, I was miles away. What did you say?'

He smiled kindly at her, lips together and eyes creased in the corners. 'I asked how you're feeling. Are you glad you made the decision to have lodgers in your home?'

She faced him once more, noticing his brown eyes were the colour of strong coffee and his lashes were thick and long for a man. But it was the softness in their depth and the way fine lines radiated from their corners when he smiled, which Rowan noticed most. 'It's been one of my better decisions. It's lovely to have company instead of rattling around the house by myself. In fact, I was thinking of cooking dinner for everyone soon. I'd like you and Ace to meet my sister-in-law Libby and her husband David; and Nora could get to know everyone too.'

'That sounds good. Nora seems like a nice person. I've bumped into her and her daughter a couple of times in the hallway and I'd love to meet Libby and David.'

'Great. I'll organise it then.'

Rowan looked towards the bandstand where Jet was sniffing about its edges. He lifted a back leg and sprinkled on a large dandelion. She shivered involuntarily.

'Are you cold sitting here, out of the sun? Shall we order a coffee from the café and sit over there in the sunshine?'

Rowan glanced over at the café bathed in dappled sunlight. It resembled a large glorified shed and was built beneath a horse chestnut tree, its lush leaves proudly revealing pink pyramids of blooms. 'Good idea,' she said, leaning forward to stand while still keeping her hands in her coat pockets.

James followed her across the expanse of concrete seating area, whistling to Jet who scampered obediently towards them. The warmer air enveloped them like a duvet as they sat at a small table in direct sunlight.

'I told you he'd be a good dog. What would you like to drink?' asked James.

'A latte, please.'

'Coming up.'

Jet continued to sniff among the shock of wild flowers that were growing around the tables. He occasionally jumped as a bumblebee moved on to another flower. Rowan leant back against the chair, lifted her chin, closed her eyes and breathed in the sweet air. When she opened her eyes, verdant young leaves were shaking in the canopies, highlighted with lemon and gold rays of sunshine. Jigsaw shapes of blue sky colour-washed the backdrop as a breeze rustled through the branches. Images of green, gold and blue jewellery projected on to her mind's eye. Nature's hues for a summer jewellery collection.

James came out of the café balancing two mugs and one large Danish pastry on a tray. He placed it on the wooden table and sat down.

'They only had one pastry left, but it's huge so I thought we could share it.'

'It looks amazing.' Rowan rubbed her palms together eagerly.

James placed a mug of coffee in front of her and another in front of himself. Holding a serviette in each hand, her tore the crumbling pastry in half and placed the slightly larger piece next to her mug.

'Thank you. Apple's my favourite.'

They sipped their drinks and delighted in the sweet sticky pastry.

'Ace told me that you've spent some time in California,' said Rowan.

'Two years. I taught carpentry in a school over there.'

'That sounds exciting. What made you go?'

'My heart. Or rather my broken heart.'

'Ah!'

James nodded as he chewed and swallowed another mouthful. ''Fraid so. But like most things, it happened for a reason. Looking back, I can see that the relationship was too one-sided. Mine unfortunately.'

'Unrequited love is a cruel emotion. I remember Billy Withers at school. I was ten and had made up my mind that Billy was going to marry me when I was sixteen. Sadly he was more interested in grubbing about for bugs in the soil at playtime, than meeting me at the tuck shop.'

James laughed. 'It's such a shame that girls mature so much sooner than boys. I bet he's kicking himself now.'

'He'll be thirty-two now. That's incredible. It can't possibly be twenty years ago.'

James sipped his coffee, leaving the mug resting against his lips as he looked up at Rowan from beneath a strand of hair that had fallen over his eyes. 'So you're in your early thirties?' He grinned. 'They don't call me Sherlock for nothing. You look much younger.'

The intensity of his gaze sent a frisson of goosebumps up Rowan's arms. She wished he wouldn't look at her like that. She swallowed and mumbled her thanks into her coffee mug.

James sat up straight. 'Sorry, that sounded a little corny. It wasn't meant to. I'm thirty-four, so you'd think it'd be about time I got my act together, wouldn't you?'

Rowan lowered her mug and glanced down to check that Jet was still there. He was dozing on a sunny patch of grass beside her chair. 'You'll never hear me complaining about a compliment. Where did you live before you moved to America?'

'I've got a small place in Clerkenwell, near Shoreditch Park. I made a bit of a cock-up when I signed the lease agreement for my tenants. I thought it was for a two-year period, but apparently it was for three. Now I'm homeless while strangers live in my flat across the city.'

'But it must be such a relief to know that you could move back into your own place next year if things don't work out with Ace.'

'Yeh, I'll definitely move back anyway. I'm sure Ace doesn't want me hanging about for too long. I think I stifle his social life.'

'But don't you go out together?'

'Let's just say we appreciate different types of nightlife. He has his clubs and parties and, to be honest, I'm happy with meeting friends in a local pub or nice restaurant.'

Rowan frowned but didn't pry any further. People's relationships were all as different as the people themselves. If they like to socialise separately, it was their own business.

'What job are you looking for?'

'I'm torn, really. I loved teaching kids in California, but I don't know whether to look for a job in a school or whether I should set up my own business again.' He scratched his head. 'I'll probably have to take on something local just to earn some money for the time being. Maybe I could do a few days in Ace's second-hand shop.'

'Vintage, dah-ling!' said Rowan, mimicking Ace's voice.

James threw his head back and laughed. Rowan's eyes were drawn to his pink glistening tongue, making an unexpected erotic wave loop in her stomach. Immediately she felt ashamed and shocked by her reaction. She lowered her head and pretended to study her fingernails.

'Yeh, he's great. He loves that shop and has worked really hard to make a go of it. I can't bear the smell of the old musty clothes but I'm proud of him. He's built the business up from a grubby market stall to a successful shop which has a loyal customer base.'

'I'm just thankful that his previous landlord decided to sell the flat above his shop,' said Rowan. 'Otherwise I probably wouldn't have heard from him after France.'

'It's a lot healthier in every way that he's not living above his work any more. Not only can he escape the temptation to work late, but he gets some exercise getting there.'

Rowan pushed her empty mug into the middle of the table. Glancing around the common she watched as a flurry of pigeons took flight, flapping their wings like sheets drying on a windy day. The sun highlighted delicate white daisies that trembled in the slight breeze and a warm ray of sunlight embraced her shoulders.

'The sun's wonderful, isn't it? It just makes everything seem so much more positive,' she said.

'Yes. I missed the seasons when I was away. It's even sunny at Christmas over there. It's just not the same spending Christmas Day surfing with Santas in Speedos.'

Rowan laughed.

'Has the fresh air cleared your thoughts a little?' asked James.

'It really has. I looked up into this canopy and have been inspired to make a collection of jewellery using those summer colours as a theme.'

'That's great. I've enjoyed it.' Jet appeared from beneath the table and rested his chin on James' knee. 'We'll have to do it again, won't we, boy?'

Rowan didn't know how to feel about that. On the one hand she'd had a wonderful time. But there was something about James that unsettled her. Surely she couldn't be developing a schoolgirl crush on a gay man at her age, and so soon after her husband's death?

That was just asking for trouble.

Chapter Eighteen

The following Saturday Rowan stood in her kitchen mixing a jug of Pimm's and lemonade. She added chopped mint to a mound of cucumber and strawberries and stirred them into the amber liquid, before pouring herself a glass. Nursing her drink between her palms, she surveyed her dining table. It was set for six people with two short church candles flickering in the middle of the settings. She hoped that the evening would go well and her friends could get to know each other a little better over a home-cooked meal.

Hearing a gentle knock on the door, Rowan put down her glass, stood up straight and took a deep breath. She smoothed her knee-length red shift dress over her hips and pushed her hair behind her ears. Here goes, she thought.

Nora was standing at the door, proffering a bottle of wine.

'Come on in. You're the first to arrive,' said Rowan, stepping to one side.

Nora walked inside and hugged her, the bottle of wine now hanging down Rowan's back.

'I told you I'd help,' said Nora. 'You look tired.'

'I'm fine. It was the onions. I've been rubbing my eyes and blowing my nose.' Rowan took the wine from Nora. 'Thank you, that's kind. What would you like to drink?'

'I see you've made some Pimm's. I'd love a glass, please. Do you mind if I pop this here on the table?' Nora was holding a baby monitor. 'If Primrose wakes up I'll hear her and nip downstairs.'

'Of course you can. How is she?' asked Rowan, turning to fetch a glass.

'She's suffering a bit because her molars are coming through, but she went off to sleep after a bottle of milk and a dose of Calpol.'

Rowan returned with a drink and handed it to Nora. 'You must be a very proud mum. She's an adorable little girl.' Rowan secretly hoped that the evening wouldn't contain too much baby talk in order to protect Libby.

The intercom buzzed and after releasing the lock, a sharp knock at the door swiftly followed. David poked his disembodied head around it. 'Room for two little ones?' Libby walked into the lounge followed by her husband who was clutching a bottle of champagne. Rowan and Libby hugged each other tightly.

'This is my new tenant. Nora. She's moved into Tom's studio with her daughter. Nora, these are my best friends, Libby and David.'

Everyone shook hands and smiled.

'I love your dress,' said Nora to Libby. 'Where did you get it?'

'Oh, it's just something I picked up in the sales.'

'I keep telling her that even if it's in the sales, it still costs money,' said David.

'I'll put this bottle in the fridge.' Libby took it from him, non-too gently.

David leant forwards and kissed Rowan's cheek, whispering, 'Sorry, we've had words in the car.' He stood up and breathed in deeply. 'This *is* civilised,' he said, pointing to the table decorated with gold and black placemats and napkins.

'I thought I'd go to a bit of effort as this is my first dinner party since my new tenants moved in.'

They both knew that it was also the first one since that disastrous evening. Ten months had passed since Rowan had been cooking supper and David had disturbed her by hammering on the door with the worst possible news. Neither of them mentioned it.

Libby came out of the kitchen. 'I've poured myself a glass. Hope you don't mind.'

'You know the rules. Help yourself,' said Rowan.

'Don't worry about me, Libbs, I'll get my own.' David's comment was clipped with sarcasm. He shook his head at Rowan and rolled his eyes.

Rowan's heart sank. All still wasn't well between her old friends and they were about to spend the evening socialising with her new friends.

'What can I get you?' she asked David.

'Beer, please.'

'I won't be a minute.'

Libby frowned. 'Don't forget it's your turn to drive.'

Rowan saw David's shoulders slump. She exchanged a concerned look with Nora, who pulled a face in response. Rowan sighed heavily and went to grab a can of beer from the kitchen.

After five minutes of polite conversation, footsteps could be heard running up the stairs. Ace and James knocked and entered. Rowan went to greet them, glad to escape from the tense atmosphere on the sofas.

'Mama Mia!' said Ace, dumping a bottle of vodka and a carton of fresh orange juice in James' hands. Taking Rowan's hands, Ace held her at arm's length so he could see her more clearly. 'You look divine, dah-ling.'

She kissed his cheek. 'Thank you. You're very sweet. Are you going to be on your best behaviour tonight?'

'Aren't I always?'

James stood beside her. 'Ignore him. He's been like that all day; ever since he bought Kylie tickets online.'

Rowan laughed. 'That explains *everything*.'

James leant forwards and kissed her cheek, causing

her to catch her breath as she inhaled his aftershave. It reminded her of a balmy, citrusy, summer's evening in the Mediterranean.

'You look amazing. Red suits you.'

'Thank you.' She felt her cheeks blush. 'Let me introduce you to my best friend Libby and her husband David.' Rowan pointed with an open palm to each of them in turn. They each shook hands and exchanged pleasantries. She turned back to James. 'What can I get you to drink?'

'A beer would be great, thanks. Here's Ace's obligatory vodka and these are for you.' He held out a bunch of purple lisianthus flowers.

'Thanks, both of you. They're beautiful.'

'You're welcome. Can I help with anything?'

'No, just relax with the others and I'll get you both a drink.'

Rowan walked into the kitchen and put the flowers and vodka on the worktop. She leant her back against the upright fridge. She was beginning to think she wasn't prepared for this evening.

Everyone was sitting around the table chatting when Rowan carried the starters to the table. She'd placed a tomato and onion bruschetta in front of each of them and then took a seat herself.

'Tuck in and help yourselves to dressed salad.'

'So, Nora, I hear you're a model,' said Libby.

Nora swallowed before answering. 'Yes, I'm lucky that I can still work despite having Primrose. I'm heavier these days, but my hair gets me jobs.' She laughed as she tweaked her long auburn spirals. 'I'm modelling for lots of autumn fashions at the moment. My hair matches all the imitation russet leaves they use.'

'Who has Primrose while you're working?' asked Libby.

'I usually take her with me, but now she's walking I'll have to enrol her in a day nursery for the odd day.'

'Don't forget to check their credentials. Make sure they have a good Ofsted rating.'

'I won't be sending my daughter to some backstreet mothers' meeting room,' said Nora. 'Anyway, Rowan's also kindly offered to help out with babysitting now and again which will be an enormous help.'

All eyes turned to Rowan.

'It'll be no trouble. I can work at the bench when Primrose has her sleep. It'll be fun for me and Jet to have some company.'

'Where is the old boy?' asked James.

'He's asleep in my bedroom. I don't want him hovering around the table, begging.'

One by one, knives and forks were clattered onto empty plates. Rowan insisted that everyone stayed seated in order for her to gather her thoughts in the kitchen. She piled the plates in the sink and lifted the casserole dish out of the oven. She'd been slow cooking a joint of braised beef in a bottle of red wine for several hours. Alongside the beef were glistening shallots, golden carrots and floating bay leaves. Having pinched the bay leaves out with her fingertips, Rowan tasted the sweet succulent juices. It was a triumph.

She dished up meat with crispy roast potatoes, sweetheart cabbage and Yorkshire puddings. A plentiful supply of creamy horseradish sauce was already sitting in a jug on the table. Libby appeared, insisting on helping to carry the plates through to the lounge. Glasses were topped up and everyone started to loosen up as the alcohol flowed.

James was sitting opposite Rowan. 'This is delicious.'

'Thank you. I'm glad you like it.'

A little squeak sprang from the baby monitor. Everyone fell silent. All eyes looked at the little white plastic box sitting on the edge of the table. Silence.

'Phew,' said Nora. 'It's as if she's telepathic and knows when I'm eating.'

'How do you manage?' asked Libby. 'On your own, I mean.'

Nora shrugged and stabbed a piece of potato. 'It can be a bit lonely, but now I've moved in with Rowan and the boys, I get to talk to people.'

Libby persisted. 'It's just that children need stability.'

Nora looked up at Libby. 'She has stability. She has me.'

'Do you ever see Primrose's father?'

When Nora answered, her voice was strident. 'I'd rather not talk about Primrose's father, if that's okay.'

An atmosphere hung above the table like a dirty chandelier.

'Sorry, I didn't mean to pry. I just ...'

'It's okay,' said Nora. 'Let's just change the subject.'

After a little silence, Ace spoke up. 'Has James told you about the job I found for him?'

'No, I haven't and I'm not going to. I haven't decided whether I'm doing it or not, yet,' said James.

'Come on, spill the beans,' David urged.

James laughed. 'Believe me, now's not the time.'

'There seems to be a lot of subjects we're not allowed to discuss tonight,' said Libby.

Everyone fell silent.

Rowan excused herself and went to the en suite bathroom. She sat on the toilet lid with her face in her palms. What was wrong with everyone? She'd gone to all this effort so they could get to know each other, but it seemed as if everyone had brought their own demons to the table with them. To add to the atmosphere around the table this evening, she'd also received another anonymous note that was nagging away at the back of her mind. She took a few minutes to gather her thoughts before returning to the lounge where David and James were clearing the table. She joined them in the kitchen.

'Thank you. That's really kind. Would you mind taking this bottle to the table with you? I think we're out of white wine in there.'

'Of course.' David took the bottle from her and left the kitchen.

'You okay?' asked James.

'Me? Oh, I'm fine, thanks. Would you mind asking who'd like raspberry and chocolate cheesecake and who'd like cheese and biscuits, please?'

James paused and made eye contact with a raised eyebrow as if to say, 'You don't fool me.' Rowan ignored his questioning look and turned to lift dessert dishes out of the cupboard. She rinsed a bunch of grapes under the cold tap and shook them gently before draping them across the cheese board. James reappeared.

'Two cheese and biscuits, three raspberry cheesecakes and whatever you're having.'

Rowan turned her head and thanked him while she rinsed celery stems under the tap.

'You're welcome. Where's your bathroom?'

'Just go through the bedroom door and you'll see the en suite.'

James walked past the dining table and into Rowan's bedroom. It smelt of perfume and clean washing. Jet lifted his sleepy head from the duvet on the bed, gave a half-hearted wag of his tail and lowered his head to doze again. James had been in her room once before when he and Ace carried her worktop upstairs, but he hadn't been able to be a little nosey while Rowan had been present. His eyes scanned the pale pink and grey bedroom that was decorated with feminine pieces, but not overly cluttered. He walked to her bedside table and lifted a photo frame for a closer look. The smiling face of a man looked back. He appeared roughly the same age as himself, wore glasses and was holding Jet as a puppy. This must be her late husband, he thought. Feeling uncomfortable for prying, James replaced the frame and noticed Jet had one eye half open, looking at him.

'I won't tell you're lying on the bed, if you don't tell your mum that I've been nosey,' whispered James. He ruffled the fur on Jet's head and received a lick in return. 'Great, that's a deal then.'

While he was washing his hands a few minutes later, James noticed a screwed up piece of paper lying in a little wicker waste bin beside the sink. He'd never retrieved anything from a neighbour's bin in his life, but this paper appeared to have cut out letters stuck to it, spelling out a message. The kind of note he'd seen in detective programmes on the television. Curiosity got the better of him and he unscrewed the sheet of paper and read it.

YOU haVe a NOT mEMORY!
FOCUS On THE factS!

He frowned. Should he ask Rowan about it?

James rubbed a finger over the unevenly stuck letters on the paper, threw it in the bin again and re-joined the dinner party. The conversation appeared to have lightened. Ace was regaling everyone with the story of how he'd met Rowan.

'So there I was, freewheeling down the hill trying to catch the eye of a gorgeous man, who had an impressively large baguette by the way, and the next thing I know a car door opens and I go arse over whatsit onto the floor.'

Everyone was laughing and James was pleased to see that

Rowan was now giggling behind her hands. She'd looked pale when he'd first arrived, but thankfully she had a pink flush on each cheek now.

'But look on the bright side,' said Rowan, 'we wouldn't all be sitting here now if I hadn't opened the car door at that moment.'

'Are you saying it was fate? That it was written in the stars that we should collide at that moment?' Ace shook his head and grimaced as he held his neck. 'I should sue you. I've never been the same since. My neck aches and my shoulder creaks.'

'That's called age,' said James.

'No it's not. It's called lugging a bloody great worktop upstairs.'

James looked at Rowan. 'I told you he hadn't stopped moaning about that.'

'I'm sorry,' said Rowan, 'it seems I keep causing you pain. What can I do to repay you for your injuries?'

'For starters, you can turn that dross off and put some Kylie or Adele on. It's making my ears bleed.'

'What's wrong with Coldplay?'

'It makes me want to end it all very slowly, with a cheese grater.'

James watched Rowan push her chair back and walk across to her CD player. He noticed that she looked thin and haunted despite the smile on her face. Within seconds, Adele's 'Set Fire To The Rain' filled the lounge with melodious strains, prompting everyone at the table to join in. Rowan stood beside the table.

'Can I get anyone another drink?'

James watched as orders were placed and Rowan disappeared into the kitchen. As David was deep in conversation with Ace, and Libby and Nora appeared to be whispering together, James followed her. He found her facing the fridge, her forehead leaning against the cold enamel.

'Hi.'

She jumped back and looked flustered. 'Oh.'

'Sorry, I didn't mean to creep up on you.'

'It's all right. Now, what was I doing? Two coffees, three wines and a JD.'

She turned to move but James gently stopped her by holding her forearms. 'Are you okay?'

Her grey eyes glistened as she looked back at him.

'I'm fine. Really. It's just … it's just that I wanted tonight to be perfect. You know, old friends meeting new friends for the first time and getting to know each other.'

'It's been a wonderful evening,' he said, gently rubbing his hands a few inches up and down her arms. 'Don't take it personally that some people have brought private issues to the table.'

'You noticed it too?'

'I think the three wise monkeys would notice that Libby and David are having a few problems.' He lowered his arms. 'The best thing is to not get involved. As soon as you get involved, you're accused of taking sides.'

'I know. I think I know what the problem is but there's nothing I can do to help.'

James leant against a worktop. 'You *are* helping, Rowan. You've got them out of the house together and they're communicating to some degree.'

Rowan nodded. 'You're right. All I can do is support them.' She turned and filled the kettle for the coffee requests.

'Where's your ground coffee?' asked James.

'It's in the fridge above the milk.'

James lifted it out, opened the packet and spooned several scoops into the coffee pot. 'Do you mind if I ask you something?'

Rowan turned, wiping her damp hands on a tea towel. 'Of course not.'

'I was in your bathroom and noticed some paper in the bin. I didn't mean to pry, but it was on show and looked strange, so I read it.'

Rowan shook her head. 'I don't know what that's about. It's the second one I've received. I don't know if someone's got a strange sense of humour or if I should be worried. They're not threatening, I suppose.'

'They might not be threatening, but they're not normal either. When did you get the first one and what did it say? If you don't mind me asking?'

'Of course not. It was about six weeks ago, I think. It said something about me being exposed. Libby and I just laughed it off as a prank.'

'Maybe. Will you let me know if you get another?'

'Do you think I should be worried?'

'No. Don't worry.' James felt compelled to touch her again. He rested his hand on her upper arm to give reassurance but was surprised by the emotional jolt he received from the contact. The touch of the soft material warmed by her skin sent a shock of something more than just friendship through his body. It wasn't entirely physical lust which he'd experienced many times when surrounded by scantily clad Californian girls; it felt deeper than that. He didn't want to just touch her shoulder and mumble platitudes. He wanted to pull her into his arms and protect her from everything and everyone. To kiss her eyelids that flickered over her wide questioning eyes and tell her that everything would be all right.

'You okay?' said Rowan.

'Sorry?'

'You seemed miles away all of a sudden.'

James smiled. 'A lot on my mind. Here, let me make the coffee now the kettle's boiled.'

Still reeling and confused by his unexpected feelings, James filled the coffee pot, its rich aroma acting like smelling salts. Don't let me fall for Rowan Forrester, he thought. There's too much emotional baggage and trauma involved in a relationship with a young widow.

As they drove home, Libby could sense David's disapproval by the silence that filled the car. His jaw was set firmly as if he was gritting his teeth. Why had she been so awkward? Even as she asked herself the question, she knew the answer. Jealousy. She had so much to be thankful for but all she could think about were the two things she didn't have: her brother and a baby. One minute she felt ungrateful and selfish because she should count her blessings, which were many. She had a good husband, a job, wonderful friends, a lovely house and her health. But from seemingly nowhere, a waterfall of emotions would drench her with the unfairness of her situation. All she really wanted was for David to wrap his arms around her and tell her it would all be okay. Instead, she eased the pain with her credit cards and sniping comments. Perhaps she should try to make amends.

'I'm sorry about this evening.'

Staring straight ahead, David mumbled, 'I think it's Rowan you should be apologising to.'

'I know. I will.'

'What's wrong? Why were you like that?' He still didn't look at her.

'I'm … I don't know.'

'Are you so miserable that we can't even hold a civil conversation any more?'

'Of course not. I know how lucky I am. It's just—'

He took his eyes off the road for the first time and looked at her. 'Just what? Tell me, Libby, because I'm not a bloody mind reader.'

Libby's chin quivered and her eyes fill with tears. 'You don't have to shout.'

'I'm not shouting. I'm trying to understand why we haven't made love in nearly three months and can't seem to be in the same room together without having an argument.'

Libby wiped the tears away from her cheeks, but didn't reply. She wanted to scream at her husband to bring her brother back and to give her the baby she longed for. If that wasn't enough, her growing debt was festering like an infected wound. If she didn't deal with it soon, it could spell the end of her marriage.

Chapter Nineteen

Rowan sat back in her chair and examined the pieces of jewellery she'd made over the past week. There were three pairs of earrings, a bracelet and two necklaces that were ready to take to Nick at The Blue Moon. She held an earring up against the window, delighted by how the light shone through the yellow glass beads like dazzling embers. Her summer collection now consisted of a dozen pieces of yellow, green and blue glass beaded jewellery, set in silver findings.

It was late June and the radio presenter was proudly announcing that it would be twenty-five degrees by midday. Rowan looked at her watch. It had just gone ten and she hadn't taken Jet for a walk yet. It sometimes felt as if she spent her whole day just walking her dog.

'Jeeettt! Come here, boy.'

Footsteps pattered on the lounge's oak flooring, suddenly silencing as Jet ran across the soft carpet in the bedroom. He sat in front of Rowan, chin raised as he gazed adoringly at his mistress. His tail swept the carpet behind him.

'Shall we go for a walk?'

Jet barked and ran back through the lounge. He skipped in a circle next to his harness, hanging by the front door. Rowan placed her jewellery into a velvet wrap and laid it on her worktop. Pulling her apartment door to, she ran downstairs with Jet following on his lead. In the hallway, she noticed that Ace and James' apartment door was ajar.

'Hello,' she called.

As there was no answer, Rowan walked towards the door, pulling Jet who was straining to go out of the front door. She poked her head inside the door where she saw James holding up a pair of gold, sparkly shorts, shaking his head.

'Hello,' repeated Rowan.

James swung round, the shorts flying behind his back and out of sight. 'You made me jump.'

'Sorry. The door was open. I did call out at the bottom of the stairs.'

'I didn't hear. I was just ... sorting some laundry. Is everything okay?'

'Yes, thanks. I'm taking Jet for a walk before I catch the tube to Covent Garden. I've got some jewellery to deliver to The Blue Moon later.'

James walked towards the door, his arms and the golden shorts still hidden behind his back. 'Ace went out twenty minutes ago to the common. His mate Kevin is covering for him in the shop. He said he needed some fresh air.'

'It's okay. I wasn't after him. I just saw that the door was open and wondered if one of you had forgotten to lock it. Right, I'll be off then. They say it's going to be a hot one.'

James lingered by the doorway looking self-conscious. 'Good luck with your jewellery.'

Jet pulled Rowan towards the door as she shouted her thanks. She walked beneath the verdant canopy of the magnolia tree and out into the street. James didn't seem to be the kind of man to prance about in sparkly clothing. Still, if he and Ace wanted to dance around in sequins in the privacy of their own apartment, she supposed it was no one else's business but theirs.

Rowan passed the cyan blue lido, already full of children paddling. Watchful parents hovered around its edges, chatting. Just past The Holy Trinity Church, Rowan bent to let Jet off the lead. She'd done this every day since James had encouraged her to let him have a run and he'd been an obedient dog every time.

The huge expanse of grass stretched out in front of her and a rumble of traffic encircled the common. Rowan set off in the direction of the bandstand. It had become their regular walk, a direction that Jet had grown accustomed to. She worried that he might get lost if she changed their route.

Rowan sidestepped two skateboarders as they rattled by on the tarmac path. She smiled at a woman who pushed a pram in the opposite direction and watched as a family tried unsuccessfully to launch a kite in the gentle breeze. Than she noticed that Jet was standing still and sniffing the air. His tail began to wag excitedly as he picked up a scent.

'What can you smell? Rabbits? Squirrels?' Rowan laughed, bending to stroke him. But before she could touch him, he sprinted off towards some mature trees.

'Come here. Jet. Jet!'

Jet had now become a bounding black shape in the distance. Fearful that she might lose him, Rowan set off after him. He was running towards two people standing beneath a horse chestnut tree. What could have possessed her little dog? He was now running excitedly in wide circles around the tree trunk where the startled couple were embracing. Rowan caught up with him.

Rowan was panting by now. 'I'm so sorry. I've no idea what's got into him. He doesn't usually run off and hassle people.'

The couple pulled apart and faced Rowan. Her jaw fell open in surprise. One of the men's red trousers and cropped dyed hair appeared very familiar.

'Ace?'

'It appears I've been hunted down.'

'I wasn't looking for you. Jet caught a scent and found you.'

'I'd say that dog has exquisite taste in smells if he tracked down my Givenchy aftershave.'

Rowan had now turned her attention to the other person. A blond young man in his late twenties who was looking slightly embarrassed, his back still pressed against the tree trunk. Realisation dawned. Ace was cheating on James.

'I've just spoken to James,' she said.

'He's tidying up, I hope.'

'He was doing the laundry.'

'Good. I'll give him another hour to hoover and empty the rubbish. He says I'm anal about my cleaning, but he's a nightmare to live with. Clothes dropped on the floor, glasses left on the table overnight ...'

'I'm not interested in the state of your apartment, Ace. What are you doing?'

Ace looked confused. 'Rowan, please,' he said, his sideways glance trying to flick towards his friend.

'What do you mean, *please*? James is at home waiting for you to get back and you're out here ... canoodling.'

Ace laughed loudly. 'Canoodling?'

'Well, whatever you were doing it's not fair on James. You're both my friends and I don't think it's right.'

'What's not right?'

'Don't make me spell it out, Ace. Just think about James.'

'James is big enough to think about himself.' He turned to his friend. 'I'm sorry about this, Alan.'

'Don't you dare apologise for me.' Rowan turned towards the other man who appeared to cower. 'Do you know he has a boyfriend who lives with him? He's there now doing their laundry while you two are ... oh, whatever it is you're doing.'

Rowan was expecting to see Ace looking contrite and

guilty, but he was bent double and shaking. He stood up, tears streaming down his cheeks. 'You don't think ... you haven't thought ... oh this is the most hilarious thing I've heard in years!'

Rowan stood looking at Ace, confused by his response. Jet was now lying down with his chin resting on his paws, his eyes moving from one to the other as they spoke.

'What's so funny?'

Ace took a few deep breaths and wiped his eyes. 'James is my brother.'

Rowan heard the words but couldn't quite grasp their meaning.

'What?'

'James is my younger brother, not my boyfriend. Did you seriously think that I'd date a longhaired, untidy layabout? I'm disappointed in you, Rowan. I believed you thought my standards were higher.' He winked at his handsome blond friend, who was now feeling braver and grinning. 'Besides, I thought James had told you that he went to California to recover from a broken heart after Helen left him.'

'He mentioned a broken heart, but he didn't say who.'

'I wish I had a camera to take a picture of your face.'

Rowan swallowed. 'James is your brother?'

'Yay! She's got it.'

'James is your brother.'

'You're worrying me now. You're repeating yourself.' Ace laid his hand on her shoulder. 'Are you all right? Seriously, I can't believe you thought James and I were an item. Wait until the next dinner party. I'm going to dine out on this story for a long time.' He turned to his friend. 'This is Alan. We met last month at The Pink Feather.'

Rowan gave a sheepish smile and retreated a few steps. 'Hi. Sorry. I'd better go.'

'Give James my love and say I won't be long.' Ace winked.

'Sorry again.' She turned and called to Jet.

Walking back through the common she felt a mixture of shame and embarrassment. Her heart beat faster, she felt confused and light-headed, yet despite this she felt some other sensation racing through her veins. It was fingers of excitement prodding her for the first time in almost a year because James wasn't gay.

Chapter Twenty

Libby sat behind the wheel of the Tea Rose van, muttering to herself. She'd slept badly last night despite having had the bed to herself. Or maybe that was why she hadn't been able to settle. She and David had argued again and he'd sulked, saying he was going to sleep in the spare room. It didn't help that she was suffering with the recurring pains in her stomach.

Waiting at a set of traffic lights while applying her lipstick, she tried to ignore her boss' frequent phone calls. Her mobile was lying on the passenger seat vibrating and chirping every few minutes. It was bad enough that she had to do her morning make-up every time she stopped at a set of lights, but surely she couldn't talk on the phone too? Besides, Libby knew what the persistent phone calls were about. She was late again, having slept in for the third time in a fortnight and she wasn't relishing the words of disappointment waiting for her when she arrived at work.

With her lipstick slightly askew, she stopped outside Tea Rose. She couldn't risk parking it in their official car park because it would add another five minutes to her delay. Placing a dog-eared card in the windscreen with the message, *Back in 5 minutes – loading*, she ran in through the door.

As usual, the aroma of freshly cut flowers and heady blooms greeted her. She never tired of the sensory punch of colours and perfumes, although this morning she didn't have time to indulge in any olfactory appreciation. Mrs Tempeston's sinewy frame appeared in the doorway of the back office. She often reminded Libby of a meerkat.

Straight-backed with dark round eyes darting left and right. On the surface she was an efficient, friendly woman who bustled her way through life. However, her employees knew another side to her. They saw how she often lived up to her name, her bad mood brewing slowly until it reached storm force. For such a thin woman, her voice was as deep and forceful as a PE teacher's.

'What time do you call this?'

'I know. I'm sorry. I slept through the alarm.'

'Again?'

'It must be the batteries. I'll buy some more today.'

'Not in my time, you won't.'

'No, of course not. I'll pick some up on the way home.'

'I can't be doing with this, Libby. I have a business to run. I'll be typing you a final written warning today.'

Libby wrung her hands together. 'I'm sorry. It won't happen again.'

'Well, you're here now. As I'm in the shop today, I'll make up the orders. I want you to deliver a number of displays that I've assembled for a conference being held at The Carlton Hotel. It's their first order, but they've hinted that they could become ongoing customers, so be polite and helpful. And don't be late. I've said that they'll be delivered before eleven o'clock.'

'Of course. I'll take them now.'

'I want you to empty the cut-offs' bin first. It's full and I must nip upstairs now that you're finally here.'

Libby pointed to the front of the store where she'd parked her car. 'But I've—'

'I can't waste any more time on this conversation. And remember, don't be late.'

Libby wondered whether to move the van into the shop car park first. Deciding that she didn't want to incur any further wrath from her employer, she hurried into the preparation room at the back of the shop. The cut-offs' bin was what they called a plastic dustbin, into which they threw unwanted leaves, stems and broken flowers. Libby dragged the bin through the back door and with great effort managed to empty it into a large wheelie bin used for garden waste. While picking up a handful of leaves that had fallen onto the floor, Libby jumped when she pricked her finger. Instinctively she sucked the puncture wound, tasting metallic blood as her finger throbbed. She cursed as drizzle began to tap on the plastic bin.

Dragging the bin back into the back room, she wished she could work for herself. She was capable of buying blooms from the early morning market, making up displays, driving and delivering orders, so why was she working for someone else? It wasn't as if Mrs Tempeston was a friend who she could share a joke with. What was stopping her from running her own flower shop business?

As she pushed the bin back underneath the worktable, its base scraping on the concrete floor, she knew exactly what was stopping her. Money.

Libby wrapped her arms around one of the containers of Calla lily displays that her boss had made up earlier. Carefully calculating the distance between the flowers and the walls, she edged her way to the front door. Using her little finger to pull the handle down an inch, she stuck her foot in the narrow gap and wedged the door open with her shoe. So far so good, she thought. Opening the boot was a little trickier, but resting the display on her knee while hanging on to it for dear life, seemed to work well. Ten minutes later, three displays were sitting safely inside the back of the work van.

Libby slammed the door and hurried to the driver's door to get out of the rain. Then she saw it. A rectangular envelope fixed to her windscreen like a dirty yellow plaster.

Libby groaned and rested her forehead on the steering wheel. She'd be working all day just to pay a parking fine.

At The Carlton Hotel, Libby carefully manoeuvred one of the displays through the swing doors. The sumptuous entrance was carpeted in burgundy and highlighted by golden arcs of light emanating from bronze coloured lamps. Tasteful landscape paintings decorated the walls, resembling open windows looking out over acres of farmland. Inhaling the aromas of beeswax and reed diffusers, Libby struggled towards the reception desk to ask directions from the receptionist.

'Could you tell me where the conference is taking place, please?' She positioned the container on the desk to relieve her of its weight.

'In the conference room.'

Libby looked at the girl behind the desk. She appeared to be in her late teens but also seemed to be wearing the entire contents of the nearby Mac shop.

'You don't say,' said Libby, in no mood to play games. 'And where exactly would the conference room be?'

'Second floor.'

Libby sighed. 'Could you trouble yourself to tell me where the lift is?'

'Over there.' The girl pointed.

'Thank you so much for your warm welcome this morning. Could you tell the manageress I'm here, please.' She gingerly picked up the floral display and turned towards the lifts.

'It's being serviced.'

Libby stopped and half turned. 'Sorry?'

'It's being serviced. You'll have to use the stairs.'

'You've got to be kidding. I've got three of these. I can't walk up two flights of stairs three times with these heels on. Is there anyone who can help me?'

'Trevor could.'

'And where will I find Trevor?'

'It's his day off.'

Grappling with the flower display, Libby cursed into the lilies. It took almost half an hour to carry three displays up to the conference room. Libby's feet ached and her head throbbed, added to which, her hair lay flat against her scalp due to walking backwards and forwards in the rain. She paced up and down the conference room, waiting for the manageress to appear. Catching sight of herself in a gilt mirror, she groaned out loud. She tried to smooth her highlighted frizzy ends flat, but it immediately sprang back out of shape again.

'No, no! Not on the table.'

Libby turned round to see a smart, middle-aged woman, running in patent stilettos towards the long polished table that stood in the centre of the room.

'You might scratch the surface. Quickly, help me get them off.'

Libby hurried towards the manageress and helped her lift the containers onto the floor.

'This table cost a fortune. You really shouldn't dump things on it without asking.'

Libby bristled. 'Excuse me, but I didn't *dump* anything. Because your lift isn't working, I've had to carry these up two flights of stairs ... in these!' She lifted a shoe to reveal her heel.

'The lift was serviced last night. We never service it in the middle of the day when visitors will need to use it.'

Libby fumed. 'That sour-faced madam behind the reception desk said it was being serviced. God knows where she gets her manners from or how she got her job.'

The manageress tensed. Her over plucked eyebrows rose until they were hidden beneath her fringe. 'If we're talking about manners, what makes you think you can talk to a client like that? These three displays are costing us two hundred pounds with the vases.' She bent down and touched a broken bud, the closed lily hanging like a sleeping bat. 'The quality of the flowers appears to be as poor as the quality of Tea Rose's staff. And as for the madam behind the reception desk, my daughter has been trained in hotel management to a high standard. I suggest you leave and take these displays with you. I'll make alternative arrangements. Good day.'

Libby stood looking at her front door from the bottom of her driveway. Half an hour earlier she'd returned to Tea Rose where she'd been met by her incandescent employer. The manageress at The Carlton Hotel had phoned ahead of Libby and informed Miss Tempeston of her behaviour. She'd demanded a reimbursement of her money and made it clear that she would be taking her business elsewhere.

A startled blackbird screeched from a privet hedge and flew over the roof continuing to cry its alarm call. Libby stared blankly down the street into the middle distance.

She'd been sacked.

No job meant no money. No money meant that nothing was credited into her personal bank account. She'd opened the account when she was eighteen and it had been a godsend in hiding the amount of money she used to pay the minimum amount off her credit cards each month. No wages meant she couldn't pay her bills in secret.

As if her body was mocking her, a dull pain dragged at her thighs. Her period had started the previous day, declaring another failed attempt at conceiving. Not that she was surprised. She vaguely remembered a half-hearted bid to make love earlier in the summer. It had been mechanical sex, lacking whispered endearments or laughter. No pillow talk lying in each other's arms afterwards. Perfunctory sex.

Libby felt physically as much a mess, as mentally. Her clothes were smeared with compost, her hair was lank and her make-up was smeared with tears. Thank goodness David was at work so she could lie in the bath and work out what on earth she could tell him.

Chapter Twenty-One

Rowan smeared Spiced Kisses across her lips before spraying perfume on her neck. She hadn't been out with a girlfriend for a long time and was surprised by how excited she felt to be dressing up for a night out.

'Hello, it's only me,' called Nora, from the front door.

'Won't be a tick. Help yourself to a drink.'

'I'm okay, thanks. I'll wait on the sofa.'

'I need to feed Jet,' said Rowan, tottering towards the kitchen. 'I've forgotten how to walk in heels. It's been so long since I dressed up.'

Nora looked up. 'You look great. That colour really suits you.'

Rowan looked down and smoothed her plum coloured dress over her hips, a habit she'd developed when someone remarked on her clothes. 'Thanks, I found it in the sales.' She disappeared into the kitchen to find the dog food.

'We'll have to go shopping one day when Primrose is in nursery,' called Nora.

Rowan measured dried dog food into a cup and tipped it into his bowl. 'I'd love that. Libby and I rarely get into town because she works shop hours.' She placed Jet's bowl on the floor and walked back into the lounge. 'I presume Ace agreed to look after Primrose.'

'Yep. I left the baby monitor with him before I came upstairs. I told him that she rarely wakes up during the night now, so he shouldn't be disturbed. She seems to be over her teething for the time being.'

'Thank goodness.'

Nora agreed. 'It's great to get a better night's sleep. Shall we go?'

'Just a minute.' Rowan sat down next to Nora on the sofa and grinned.

'What?' asked Nora.

'Do you want to hear something really funny?'

Nora turned her body to face her. 'Oh God, what have you done?'

'Ever since I first met James, I thought he was Ace's boyfriend.'

Nora's mouth fell open. 'Why? What made you think that?'

'He moved in with him, they don't look like brothers, I hear Kylie playing in their apartment and I caught James holding a pair of gold sequinned underpants the other day. And neither of them told me any different.'

'You mean you never asked?'

'I suppose I just assumed. How did you know that he isn't, anyway?'

Nora shook her head. 'I talk to them. Ask questions. You know, make polite conversation with my new neighbours.'

Rowan leant forwards and held her head in her hands. 'I suppose I just put two and two together and came up with five.'

'Who told you he wasn't?'

'I had a go at Ace last week on the common. I saw him with someone else. It was so embarrassing. I haven't spoken to either of them since. I know Ace will have told James and I feel so stupid.'

'I really wouldn't worry about it if I were you. They'd just think it was funny.' She paused. 'Have you got a bit of a thing for James?'

'No. I mean, I'm not sure. I feel shy when he's around and anyone can see he's an attractive man, but … it's too soon. I feel guilty that I feel better when I see him. Is there a decent amount of time following a bereavement when you're allowed to find somebody else attractive?'

'I suppose it depends on how close you were with your previous partner.'

'We were very close. We were deeply in love and I miss him terribly. That's why I'm confused about how James makes me feel. I wish there were written instructions on becoming a widow.'

'Don't be silly,' said Nora. 'You just need to relax and stop thinking you're being judged. You can't help how you feel about someone.'

'You're right,' said Rowan, standing up. 'A couple of glasses of wine and I'll stop being so paranoid about everything.'

After settling Jet into his basket, Rowan switched off the lights before leaving the apartment. Carefully negotiating the stairs in her heels, she didn't notice James standing in the hallway until she was near the bottom.

'Hello. Are you coming or going?' Nora asked him.

'Supposedly going, but it wouldn't take much to talk me out of it.' He looked behind Nora to Rowan. 'Hi.'

Rowan smiled.

'Why don't you walk with us for a bit?' said Nora.

'Where are you going?'

'The Windmill.'

James opened the door and stood aside for the girls to go out. Rowan couldn't meet his eyes and stepped outside with her eyes firmly fixed on her shoes. She heard him close the door and the crunch of his footsteps following them onto the pavement. The sun was a bright orange orb sitting low in the sky. It was nearing the end of July and the evening was mild and sweet smelling.

As they walked, James in between the two women, he stuck his elbows out and looked from one to the other, inviting them to link his arms. Rowan slid her arm through his, instantly feeling a frisson at their closeness. A confusion of desire and betrayal knotted in her stomach whenever she was close to him. Believing that he was gay had been a safety barrier against her feelings of guilt. She'd tried to tell herself that it was because he was tall, strong and kind. He was the fortification in the house that she'd been missing. The masculine presence that helped her to sleep more soundly in her bed knowing that he was on the ground floor should the need arise for protection.

But now she could feel the warmth of his skin through his shirt. She could feel the rigid muscles of his arms. Now she wanted him to wrap his arms around her. She wanted to be held and told that everything was going to be all right. And kissed. Yes. She wanted to feel his lips pressing against hers.

'You're quiet tonight.'

Rowan blinked and looked at James. He was smiling at her, his hair falling over one eye. He flicked his head to move it. She saw Nora lean forwards to look at her from the other side of James. Why had she shared the fact that she found James attractive? She hadn't even told Libby how she felt. Now she felt she was betraying both Tom and Libby, the two people who meant the most to her.

'I've just got a lot on my mind, that's all.'

Nora interrupted. 'Where were you off to when we came downstairs?'

Rowan was relieved that Nora had distracted James' attention.

He groaned in response. 'Ace has been on at me about finding some work. I suppose I've been too choosy wanting to work in carpentry, so he said he'd lined something up for me at The Pink Feather. I thought he meant bar work, so I agreed.'

'Isn't it?'

James slipped his arm away from Nora and felt inside his shirt. He pulled out the gold-sequinned shorts that Rowan had caught him inspecting and dangled them in front of them. 'No.'

Nora squealed as she buried her head in her hands. Rowan was acutely aware that she and James were now walking along Clapham High Street arm in arm. It felt wrong despite feeling more secure than she had for many months, so she slid her arm out of his. She pretended that she was getting chilly and wrapped her denim jacket a little tighter around her body.

'Are you supposed to serve behind the bar in those?' asked Nora.

'It isn't bar work he's arranged for me. I should be dancing on a podium to, 'I'm Too Sexy For My Shirt!' This is the job that Ace was going to tell you all about at your dinner party.'

Nora snorted and Rowan couldn't help but laugh.

'We're coming to watch,' said Nora. 'Forget the Windmill.'

'You'd be wasting your time because I'm not doing it.'

'Aw c'mon. It'd be a laugh.'

'Exactly,' said James. 'I was going to stay on the tube until Covent Garden instead of getting off at Soho, but the Windmill sounds like as good an escape as any.'

They reached the road that circled Clapham Common and crossed when a gap appeared between cars. The sun had sunk quickly leaving a tangerine sunset glowing across the huge expanse of common, highlighting the metalwork on the children's play apparatus.

'You're joining us, then?' asked Nora.

Rowan stared wide-eyed at her friend. She was feeling uncomfortable enough as it was just walking with him, let alone sitting down for a drink with him. The rules had changed since she'd had a coffee with him near the bandstand. It was different now.

James aimed the shorts at a nearby bin and threw them. They landed with a clink on top of several discarded cans.

'Yes,' he said.

Fairy lights hung on the trees outside the eighteenth century rambling building, flickering as the branches moved in the breeze. The Windmill's visitors spilled out of the courtyard and onto the common, a hum of conversation and laughter drifting into the purple-tinged dusk. James, Rowan and Nora weaved through the crowd and in through the front doors.

Golden arcs of light spilled from lamps dotted around the cream washed rooms. Gilt mirrors and thick-framed paintings hung on the walls, lit by chandeliers that twinkled amongst the rafters. Spotting an empty table next to two leather sofas in a corner, Nora made a beeline for it.

'My treat. What can I get you to drink? It's the least I can do to thank you for rescuing me from the podium.'

'A dry white wine, please.' Rowan still wasn't able to meet his gaze as she looked over his shoulder towards the bar.

'Make that two,' said Nora.

Rowan joined her friend on the sofa. 'Why did you invite him?'

'What d'you mean? He mentioned joining us first.'

'God, I feel so stupid. Ace is bound to have told him about the park incident.'

'He probably hasn't mentioned it.'

'I doubt it but I hope you're right.'

She looked at James. He was laughing with the barman. His white shirt was tucked inside his straight dark jeans, his thigh muscles noticeably pronounced beneath the denim. Rowan closed her eyes and looked away. 'I don't think I can do this.'

Nora frowned. 'Are you serious?'

'Yes. He was like a girlfriend before. I chatted to him like a mate because he was gay.'

'He's never been gay.'

'You know what I mean. I *thought* he was.'

'I don't get it. He hasn't changed as a person. He's exactly the same. The only thing that's changed is your impression of him.'

'Shhh, he's coming back.'

James had noticed that Rowan was quiet and wasn't making eye contact with him. He tried to think whether he'd said anything to upset her. He walked towards their table holding a glass of wine in each hand and a pint of lager held precariously between his fingertips. The girls thanked him as he carefully placed the glasses on the table.

Nora sipped her wine. 'What will Ace say when he finds out you didn't go to The Pink Feather?'

'He'll call me an ungrateful sod, have a little strop and then forget about it after half an hour. If I time it right, he and Alan will be watching the repeats of *How To Look Good Naked* when I get back and he'll be paying more attention to Gok.'

He glanced at Rowan. 'So how's the jewellery business these days?'

She raised her head a fraction, her grey eyes meeting his. He noticed a pink flush colour her cheeks before she lowered her gaze once again.

'It's fine, thanks.'

James waited, but she didn't elaborate.

'What are you working on at the moment?'

151

Rowan shifted in her seat. 'Nick says that earrings sell well at Christmas, so I'm making twenty sets for him.'

'Christmas! It's the middle of summer,' said Nora.

Rowan shrugged. 'Shops start preparing for Christmas early. Lots have displays ready in September.'

'I suppose.' Nora suddenly beamed, her face breaking into a wide grin. 'I'm going to take Primrose to see Father Christmas in town. Now she's walking and saying a few words, she'll be a lot more excited than last year.'

'You mean *you* will,' said James.

'Okay. Me too.'

'How are Libby and David?' he asked.

Nora looked at Rowan over the rim of her glass and sipped her wine. 'Yes, are they getting on any better?'

'To be honest, I haven't spoken to Libby for a week. I left her a voicemail but she hasn't got back to me. I really should try her again.'

James had been hoping that Nora would excuse herself and visit the ladies room so he could ask Rowan if everything was all right, so he was disappointed when it was Rowan who left to powder her nose. Such an old-fashioned excuse, he thought, but very endearing. Maybe Nora would know why she was being quiet. He leant forwards to ask her but was interrupted by her mobile phone ringing. He watched as she searched in her handbag.

'Hello. No, I'm not far away. Why? Are you sure? Okay, I'm coming straight back. I'll be ten minutes max. Bye.' Nora stood up and sidled between the gap between the table and sofa. She stood next to James pulling her cardigan back on.

'Got to dash. Primrose has woken up crying and Ace says she feels hot. I can't wait for Rowan and don't want to make you leave your drinks. Tell her I'll see her tomorrow.'

Nora didn't wait for a response but hurried towards the front door. James sat back in his chair and chewed his bottom lip thoughtfully. He hoped Primrose wasn't ill, but it would be good to be left alone with Rowan. Subconsciously he smoothed his hair behind his ears and wiped his mouth dry of beer froth. He saw Rowan walking across the room back towards the table.

'Nora's had to dash.'

Rowan sat down. 'Oh, where to?'

'Ace rang. Primrose has got a temperature.'

Rowan looked concerned, two lines furrowing between her eyes. 'I'd better go after her.'

'She said to finish our drinks and she'll see you tomorrow. Primrose's molars are probably playing up again. It can make little ones feel rotten.'

He was pleased when he saw Rowan smile.

'How do you know about teething?' she said.

'Mum fostered babies for five years before I left home. You'd be amazed at what a dab hand I am at winding them and changing nappies.'

'A man of many talents.'

James watched her blush again, lowering her eyes as she sipped her wine. He rubbed his stubble. 'Do you mind me asking if everything is okay?'

'What d'you mean?'

'Have I done anything to offend you?'

'No. Why? Of course not. What do you mean?'

He laughed. 'Now that's protesting too much if ever I heard a denial.'

'You haven't done anything, honestly.'

'I just wondered because ... I don't know ... you seem a little distant.'

James watched her candle-smoke grey eyes look at him for a fleeting moment.

'Am I? I don't mean to be. Do you think we ought to go back and see how Primrose is?'

'Rowan. You're doing it again.'

'What?'

'You're being distant again and changing the subject.' James watched as she leant against the back of the sofa opposite him and sighed.

'Oh, it's so embarrassing.'

'What is?'

'Ace must have said something about last week.'

'I have absolutely no idea what you're talking about.'

'You know, about shouting at him in the park.'

'Nope. You're still talking in riddles.'

Rowan leant forwards and folded her arms defensively on the table in front of her. James noticed a line of three small freckles decorating the pale skin on the back of her wrist, causing an overwhelming desire in him to run his finger over them.

'I took Jet for a walk last week,' said Rowan. 'I took his lead off like you suggested, and he ran off. I followed him. He'd found Ace and another man hugging beneath a tree.'

'A blond man?'

'Yes.'

'That would've been Alan, his new boyfriend.'

'I know that, *now*.'

'So?'

'Well, that's where the confusion lay.'

'Go on.' James leant forwards on the table, bringing their faces to within a couple of feet of each other.

'I told him off.'

James raised his eyebrows. 'Why?'

'I thought *you* were his boyfriend,' groaned Rowan, before dropping her forehead onto her folded arms that were still resting on the table.

'Did you just say that you thought I was Ace's boyfriend?'

'Yeeess.' Rowan's voice came from inside her folded arms.

He leant forwards and touched her shoulder. 'Stop hiding.' He laughed. 'Speak to me.'

He watched Rowan sit up, her face flushed with a lopsided smile on her lips.

'What made you think that Ace and I—?' He shuddered involuntarily.

'You just turned up one day and you don't look like brothers. Kylie's always singing and when I first met you, you were only wearing a towel in his apartment. And don't forget I saw you with sequinned shorts.'

James clapped his hands together loudly, threw his head backwards and bellowed with laughter. 'That's hilarious. You've got to tell me what you said to him.' James wiped the tears from his eyes, feeling very relieved that it was only embarrassment that was making Rowan quiet.

'I told him that you were at home doing the laundry while he was out gallivanting with another man. I told him that he should be ashamed.'

'Fantastic. I love it. I can't wait to get back and wind him up.'

'I thought he'd have told you already. I felt so stupid and to be honest I've been dodging you both for the past week.'

'I'm just relieved that I hadn't put my foot in it and you weren't upset with me. Now that's cleared up, are we speaking again?'

Rowan pulled a face. 'Of course. Let's never mention it again.'

'Okay. It's a deal,' said James. He held out his hand towards Rowan and left it hanging in the air between them. He waited until she raised her arm and shook his hand. Her fingers felt delicate, cool and soft to the touch. He wanted to enfold her tiny fist into his palms but instead he took the opportunity and ran a finger across the freckles on her wrist.

Chapter Twenty-Two

Libby lay in bed listening to her heartbeat pounding in her ears. A shaft of morning sunlight shone through the V-shape at the top of the windows where the curtains didn't quite meet. The beam fell across the quilt and highlighted millions of dust particles suspended in the air. She watched them swirl and glint as the sun's rays caught them.

David had left for work ten minutes ago. She'd heard him go into the kitchen half an hour earlier, having slept in the spare room again. With each clang of the pots, she'd felt more anxious; a knot of fear pulling tighter until her body felt physical pain. Her ears had strained to pick up every sound he'd made. Every sniff. Every shuffle. Every footstep. She'd focused only on his movements. He'd finally left without coming upstairs or shouting goodbye. The hollow slam of the front door had been his final noise that morning.

Libby hadn't told him that she'd lost her job. She had lain in the bath the previous night until the water had cooled and she started to feel uncomfortable. They ate dinner in silence then David worked on his computer in the spare bedroom.

Now she lay on her back staring at the constellation of twinkling dust, realising that her hands were clenched into tight fists. She forced herself to relax her body for a few moments, before curling into a foetal position and crying into her pillow.

Several miles away, Rowan also woke early to the sound of an unfamiliar male voice talking in the hallway. She slipped out of bed, pushed her feet into her slippers and pulled her dressing gown around her shoulders. Unlocking her apartment door, she peered down the stairs into the hall. When she couldn't see anything, she crept halfway down and leant over the banister. Ace was standing at the top of the cellar door that led to Nora's apartment.

'What's happening?' asked Rowan.

Ace looked up. 'Primrose has had a bad night. She's been sick and her temperature won't go down.'

Rowan ran down the rest of the stairs and faced him. 'Poor little thing. Who's here?'

'Nora called the emergency doctor when Primrose developed a rash.'

Rowan's eyes widened in horror. 'My God. Should I go down there?'

'Give them a few minutes.'

'You're right. I'll go and get dressed.'

Rowan ran back upstairs and took one of the quickest showers she'd ever had. Tying her hair into a ponytail, she shrugged the towel from her body and rummaged in her drawer for underwear. She pulled on a jumper and some jeans, her haste slowed by the fabric sticking to her damp body. Her mobile phone rang and she cursed. Libby's name lit up the screen so Rowan answered it breathlessly. 'Libbs, sorry can't talk. I've got to run downstairs to Nora's. I'll ring you back in an hour or so.'

Eight minutes after she'd run up the stairs, she was racing back down them again. The front door closed and Rowan saw the outline of the departing doctor through the stained glass window. Hurrying down the carpeted cellar stairs, she found Ace standing with Nora while James cradled Primrose in his arms.

'How is she?' asked Rowan, stroking Primrose's hot forehead.

'The doctor said it isn't meningitis,' said Nora. 'I'm so relieved. When I saw the rash I just panicked.'

157

'I bet you did.' Rowan rubbed the top of Nora's arm, reassuringly. 'That thought went through my mind too.'

Rowan brushed the wisps of hair away from Primrose's forehead, aware that her fingers were tantalisingly close to James' chest. 'What did the doctor say it might be?'

'He says the spots look like little blisters, so he's pretty sure it's chickenpox. I've got to give her fluids, Calpol and dab calamine on her spots when she starts scratching them. He said it's good that she's picked it up early at nursery because it can be nasty if you get it when you're older.'

Ace put his arm around Nora's shoulders. 'Well, you can relax now. She'll be immune when she goes to school. I had it when I was seven and even at that young age I remember feeling stupid with pink dots of calamine on my face.'

James laughed. 'And now it's your favourite colour. I was lucky. I never caught it off you.'

'But you had it at some stage, didn't you?' asked Rowan.

'Not that I can remember.'

Everyone looked at James.

'No. You're kidding me,' he said. 'Surely only children get chickenpox.' He quickly handed Primrose back to Nora and stood looking at his hands.

'I don't think looking at your hands will prove whether you've caught the virus, bro. Go and get a shower, change your clothes and take one of my vitamin C sachets.'

Nora grimaced. 'I don't think it works that way. Isn't it inhaled or ingested? I don't know. Sorry, James, but like you, I just presumed it was a childhood disease.'

With his hands held out in front of him, James walked towards the door. 'I think I'd better have a quick shower. You never know. Where are your vitamin sachets, Ace?'

'In the bathroom cabinet. Underneath the painkillers.'

Libby sat at the kitchen table, staring through the French

doors that led to the patio beyond. David would have been at work for an hour now. He'd be sitting behind his desk trying to conjure up a new ad campaign for some company. She wondered how the tension might be affecting his work. Surely it was difficult to use your imagination to create innovative new concepts if there was a bad atmosphere at home.

Libby noticed that the barbeque was rusting, an orange hue spreading like fungus around its rim. She couldn't think when it had last been used. Probably before her brother had died. Is that when everything had started to go wrong? She stood up wearily and crossed to the door. No. Her spending had been out of control for a while before that.

Turning the key, Libby stepped out onto the wooden decking. Summer should be filled with friends and barbeques, she thought. She stepped off the raised decking, raised her arm and unclipped a peg from the washing line. She played with it between her fingers, opening and closing it; pinching her fingertips between its serrated jaws.

She'd rung Rowan last night, but her sister-in-law hadn't answered. She'd left a message saying that she needed to talk. When she hadn't heard back after an hour, she'd rung Ace. He'd informed her that Rowan had gone out with Nora to the Windmill. She'd felt hurt not to have been invited. She'd known Rowan for many years. How long had Nora known her for? A few months?

Libby thought about the second phone call she'd made to Rowan while lying in bed an hour ago. She threw the peg in anger, hitting the privet hedge at the far end of the garden. A blue tit flew out and into the neighbouring garden. Rowan hadn't given her a chance to say anything. Not a bloody word. She'd just got rid of her as soon as she could and said she was going down to Nora's apartment and would ring back later. She needn't bother. She could go to hell, thought Libby. I really needed her this morning and all she could think about was going downstairs for a cosy breakfast with her new best friend.

Everyone could go to hell. David, Rowan and Nora.

Chapter Twenty-Three

August found Rowan in the unexpected position of playing both nanny and nursemaid. The former came in the shape of babysitting Primrose while Nora took part in a photo shoot for *Rapunzel* magazine. The little girl was feeling much better and her spots were now small blemishes freckling her face and body. They'd played for half an hour on the carpet after Nora dropped her off and then made Rice Krispies chocolate cakes. It had been a great success but also messy. Having washed the little girl's chocolaty hands and face, Rowan was now sitting cuddling her.

She rested her lips on the little girl's soft curls and inhaled the sweet aroma of baby shampoo. Gently rocking backwards and forwards, Rowan watched as Primrose's golden eyelashes flickered several times, before closing. She stroked the toddler's cheeks with her forefinger and wondered whether her lost baby would have been a girl or a boy. Primrose's body felt good in her arms. She watched the little girl's chest rise and fall more slowly as sleep relaxed her tiny body.

Eventually Rowan stood up and carried the sleeping child into her bedroom. She wedged Primrose between two pillows for safety and stood back. The child was breathing heavily, occasionally twitching in her sleep with a red curl draped across her forehead. Rowan whispered, 'There was a little girl who had a little curl, right in the middle of her forehead.' She pushed it to one side so it spiralled across her temple.

Playing nursemaid downstairs was a different matter. Late last night, Ace had telephoned her with the news that James' bad cold had developed into a fever and some blistered spots had appeared on his back and thighs. James had contracted chickenpox and had been offered the luxury of his brother's bed while he recovered. Ace hadn't asked if she would pop downstairs to check on James, but he'd made a great deal of informing her of the guilt he felt at having to go to work. She'd promised to call in during the day to check on his brother, much to Ace's relief. So, while Primrose was sleeping, Rowan hurried downstairs and tapped gently on Ace's front door in the hallway. There was no reply. Rowan unlocked the front door with her duplicate set of keys and poked her head inside the apartment.

'Hellooo.' She listened for an answer but all she could hear was the dishwasher churning in the kitchen.

'James?'

Rowan walked through the lounge and towards Ace's bedroom. She knocked softly. 'James, are you awake? It's Rowan. How are you?'

Rowan bit her bottom lip nervously before slowly pushing the door open. Ace's bedroom was patterned with stripes of shadow from sunshine spilling through the wooden slats of the blinds. The room was hot and smelt of coffee and deodorant. The outline of James' body lay curled beneath the duvet, a fan of dark hair splayed on a pillow. Rowan swallowed.

'James? How are you feeling? Can I fetch you anything?'

She stepped closer and pulled back the duvet a few inches, exposing James' clammy forehead. She pulled it further down until she could see his face. His eyelids were half open but his eyes were rolling from side to side. Beads of sweat decorated his face and his breath was rapid. Rowan felt his forehead.

'You're burning up.' She pulled the duvet down to his waist, hurried into the adjoining bathroom, soaked a hand towel underneath a stream of cold water and wrung it out.

Returning to him, she wiped his face and neck with the cool towelling then paused, wondering whether to wipe his chest and arms.

He groaned, making her jump. 'Hel—'

'It's okay. You've got a fever. You just need to cool down a bit. It might feel like hell now, but you'll—'

'Hel-en?'

Rowan paused.

'Is that you, Helen,' he whispered. 'Don't go.' His head turned from left to right on his pillow.

Rowan stood up and crossed to the window. She slid her fingers in between the slats and unlatched it. Pushing it open, she breathed deeply as a cool breeze blew through the opening and then returned to the bathroom to fill a glass with water. She hesitated, the stuffy atmosphere in the apartment making her feel nauseous. Or was it the resentment of this unknown woman called Helen that made her stomach churn?

Sitting beside James, she gently shook his shoulder.

'James? James it's Rowan. Wake up.'

With some effort, James opened his eyes again and blinked several times.

'Here, take a sip.' She slid one hand behind his neck and lifted his head an inch. Holding the glass to his lips, she saw him purse his lips and take a few sips of water. He relaxed his neck and lay back down, his head sinking into the pillow. The room was noticeably cooler as the breeze nudged the blinds until they tapped against the windowpane. He closed his eyes again and appeared to settle.

'I ... I dreamed—'

'Just rest. You need to relax and cool down.'

His eyes slowly opened. 'Rowan? What're you doing here?'

'I'm checking on you. Ace said you were ill.'

'Did he? Am I?'

He was still a little confused so Rowan held his neck and offered him more water. A trickle dribbled down his chin and rested in a hollow between his neck and his chest. She sat the glass on the bedside table and wiped his face again with the damp towel, moving to where the drops of water had spilt.

'Thank you.'

'I hear you caught chickenpox from Primrose.'

'So much for Ace's vitamins. I'm fine now. I'll get up in a bit.'

'Stay where you are. You're hot.'

She watched a smile spread slowly across his mouth. 'Why, thank you, nurse.'

Rowan shook her head, pleased that he seemed alert enough to flirt. 'Behave. I was worried about you.'

'Where's Ace?'

'He had to go to work. Some meeting he couldn't miss.'

James stretched his legs beneath the covers. 'How did you get in?'

'The landlady always has a spare set of keys.'

'I'll have to remember that. I can't have you letting yourself in and taking advantage of me whenever you like,' he said, looking down at the duvet which was draped around his hips. He laughed weakly, followed by a fit of coughing.

Rowan's eyes glanced at his naked torso where defined muscles stood out on his stomach each time he coughed. She knew he was flirting without conviction because she'd heard it for herself. He wanted someone called Helen. It must be the name of the girl who left him before he moved to California. Rowan felt guilt and embarrassment. What had she been thinking?

Rowan stood up. 'That's my duty done.' She straightened

the duvet and patted his hand in a matronly manner. 'I'll let Ace know that I've checked on you?'

'Oh. Did he ask you to check on me?'

'Not in so many words, but he sounded worried so I said I'd pop downstairs. I'm looking after Primrose so I must dash before she wakes up. Remember to drink plenty of water. Are you hungry at all?'

James shook his head. 'No, but thank you.'

'You're welcome. What are landladies for? I'll come back down in a few hours and heat you some soup.'

Chapter Twenty-Four

'Bye.'

'What time are you back?' called David.

'About five.'

'Bye.'

Judging by the lack of communication they'd shared over the last few weeks, Libby thought that had been quite a lengthy conversation. David was working from home today so she'd set her alarm in order to appear to be going to work as usual. She still hadn't told him that she'd been sacked. The time had just never seemed right and, to be honest, she was too frightened to tell him. What if it tipped the balance and he asked for a divorce?

It had been fairly easy to keep the secret from David on the days he'd left the house at seven in the morning to go to the office, but a couple of days a week he worked from home. On these days, Libby usually trudged aimlessly around the city of London for seven hours before returning home. Today was such a day. Things couldn't continue like this.

August drizzle dimpled puddles as Libby walked towards the tube station. She folded her arms in front of her and thought about the measly eight pounds in her purse that had to buy her an underground ticket and something to eat. She'd hoped to put some bread in the toaster before she'd left, but David had come into the kitchen and filled the coffee pot. It was difficult to believe that their relationship had become so strained that she didn't feel comfortable making breakfast alongside him.

The station was busy as she vied for a place on the platform. A rush of air preceded the train as it whooshed out of the tunnel and screeched to a halt. Passengers spilled from the train before she and the other commuters surged forwards towards the gaping doors.

With nowhere to sit, Libby hung onto the leather strap on the overhead rail for the next ten minutes as the train swayed and jolted from station to station. Pulling into Covent Garden, she made her way towards the doors and stepped out. Following a snake of passengers along the platform towards the lifts, Libby wondered what she going to do once she was outside.

She felt terrible. Her aching stomach and throbbing head, along with standing in that stuffy carriage, had made her feel faint. She rubbed her right temple with her fingers in a soothing circular movement while she waited by the lift doors. It didn't seem to help, in fact, the pain intensified causing her to close her eyes and frown.

Squashed against fellow commuters in the lift, Libby suddenly felt sick. As the intermittent alarm warned commuters that the lift doors were about to close, she felt a sharp pain in her chest. Her heart began to pound. Her ears buzzed and a wave of anxiety consumed her body. She began to shake. The doors closed and the lift shuddered as it began to ascend. The conversations in the lift didn't appear to make sense and everyone seemed to be staring at her. She gasped for breath. She clenched her fists as pins and needles prickled her lips and fingertips.

'Are you all right, dear?' enquired a voice.

Her legs gave way and she collapsed into a sitting position on the grimy lift floor. The alarm sounded again as the doors opened at ground level. She felt several hands grasp below her arms and lift her out into the ticket lobby. Someone called for a chair. She could hardly breathe and flailed in panic. So this was how she was going to die, she thought. She was going to die with the indignity of sitting in front of an audience while gasping for breath. Was she having a heart attack? Was her heart about to stop, like her brother's? Why couldn't she breathe?

A smart, middle-aged woman knelt down in front of her and asked the gathering crowd to give them some space.

'I'm a doctor. My name's Rosemary. I want you to take a few deep breaths into this paper bag for me.'

Libby's hands shook as she did as she was told. With Rosemary's help, they secured the opening of the paper bag around her lips and she breathed rapidly into it.

'Slow down. Deep breaths. Nice and steady. That's it. You're doing fine.'

Libby's eyes were wide with alarm as she scanned the crowd.

'Don't worry about anyone else. Close your eyes and take slow, deep breaths. That's the way. Nice and slow.'

It took a full ten minutes for her to feel a little more relaxed. She held the paper bag tightly between her fingers, relieved that the commuters had wandered away.

'Do you feel a bit better?' asked Rosemary.

'Yes. Thank you. I don't know what happened.'

'It looks like you had a panic attack.'

'A panic attack? I've never had one of those before.'

'They can come out of the blue. Are you worrying about anything?'

Despite her situation, Libby laughed. 'I think it'd be easier to tell you what I'm not worrying about.'

Rosemary stood up. 'Fancy a coffee? I've got half an hour before I have to be at work and I usually stop off at Starbucks at this time.'

Libby knew she had many hours to fill and the lady seemed friendly. 'I'd like that. Thank you.'

She stood up shakily and followed Rosemary to the ticket machines. Once outside, she breathed in deep lungfuls of fresh air. The rain had stopped and the ground shone like mirrors with a weak sunshine glistening on the wet cobbles. Street artists were setting up their positions for an hour of juggling, magic tricks or preparing to take up stationary positions on wooden plinths.

'Here we are,' said Rosemary.

They walked through the double doors of the coffee house. Inside was bathed in the welcoming aroma of fresh coffee, while the melodious strains of Neil Diamond sang 'Mr Bojangles' through the speakers.

'Find a table and I'll get the drinks in. What would you like?' asked Rosemary.

'A latte would be lovely, thanks,' said Libby. A milky drink should keep her hunger at bay for a few hours. She sat down on the worn leather sofa and sighed. It was comfortable and reassuring and the soft upholstery hugged her thighs. She looked over to where Rosemary was ordering their coffees. What a lovely lady, she thought. A quarter of an hour ago they'd never met. Now they were about to drink coffee together. If only the circumstances of their meeting had been different.

Rosemary placed two steaming mugs on the table and sat down. 'How're you feeling now? Better?'

'Much better, thank you. This is so kind of you.'

'You're very welcome.'

Libby took a sip of her coffee. 'Is there a hospital nearby?'

Rosemary frowned. 'Why? I thought you were feeling better.'

'I do, it's just that you said you were a doctor on the way to work.'

'No, I'm a private doctor and have rooms around the corner. I do miss the hospital environment though. I used to work on A and E which was very exciting.'

'I bet it was. I love watching those reality hospital programmes on television.'

'What about you? Do you work?'

'I'm a florist. That is … I was.'

'Were you made redundant? I know many friends who're out of work because of cutbacks. It's a pretty miserable time for lots of people.'

'It's not as simple as that, I'm afraid. It's all a bit of a nightmare, to be honest.'

Rosemary sat back and sipped her drink. Libby felt reassured by her calm presence but also by the fact that she was a stranger in a big city who had cared enough to stop and help. Rosemary wore a smart skirt and cardigan over a white blouse. Her hair was scraped casually up into a bun with a few grey streaks at the temple, but such was the thickness of her loose curls, her style had a professional air to its arrangement.

'I was sacked,' said Libby. 'I'd had a few bad days. No months.' Libby shook her head and gave a derisive chuckle. 'Who am I kidding? It's been a shit couple of years.'

Rosemary continued to sip her coffee but kept eye contact with Libby to let her know that she was listening.

'We … my husband David and I … well, we haven't been getting on recently. We've been trying for a baby for a few years now, although if I fell pregnant now it'd be an immaculate conception. We're not speaking much.' Libby took a deep breath and drank more coffee. 'Then my brother died last September. He was only thirty-two. They said it was his heart and he could have died at any time. He'd just moved to London with his wife, Rowan. She's my best friend. Well, she was. It seems as if she's found a new best friend now, but I don't blame her. Why would she want to hang around with me if I'm always miserable? See what I mean? Even I don't want to be with me.'

'Can't you tell your husband that you're feeling anxious and low?'

'I haven't even told him that I've lost my job. It's been a fortnight now and I have to keep out of his way when he's at home so he doesn't ask questions.'

Libby pressed her forefingers against her temples and closed her eyes. 'If that's not enough, I owe money to several credit cards which he also doesn't know about. Poor man. He really has no idea what a crazy woman he's married to. I just don't know what I'm going to do about any of it.'

'You know you can't keep running away for ever, don't you?'

'I know, but what can I do? It's such a mess.' Libby wiped away a tear that had rolled down her cheek. 'I don't know how I got into this predicament. It sort of crept up on me. I was managing to pay my cards when I had a job, but now I can't make the end of August's minimum payment. It's all I think about. I'm dreading the twenty-eighth when the payment is due. I'm frightened of answering the phone or opening the post.' Libby looked up at Rosemary and forced a laugh. 'You really didn't know what a fruit loop you were being a Good Samaritan to when you stopped this morning, did you?'

Rosemary smiled. 'You'd be surprised how many people have the same problems. Sorry, I don't even know your name.'

'Elizabeth, but everyone calls me Libby.'

'Most of my medical students are in debt. Okay, theirs is due to study but there aren't many people sitting in this busy café without a debt of some sort. Have you thought about talking to Citizens Advice? They'll put you in touch with reputable companies who can consolidate your debts and organise it so you pay a smaller amount each month. I know professional people who've had to do that, so don't feel embarrassed.'

'No, I hadn't thought of that.'

'Instead of waiting for this dreaded date, why don't you take the first step? Panic attacks are all about feeling out of control and straying from your comfort zone. Take control back. Ring them and tell them you're having financial difficulties. These companies are a lot more understanding if you communicate with them.'

'Have you ever thought about going into psychiatry?'

'Not really, but listening plays a large part of my job.'

'It's so nice to have a chat over a coffee,' said Libby. 'I used to do it a lot with my sister-in-law. I really miss her.'

'Why don't you call her?'

'I have. She's always hanging round with her tenants now. They've become her new friends. I feel like I've lost everyone. Tom's dead, Rowan seems distant and David—'

'Have you thought that it might be you who's pushing them away?'

Libby raised her chin, her brow fretted with questioning lines. 'Not really.'

'Perhaps, subconsciously, you don't feel worthy of their love so you make excuses to argue or not speak to them. You expect rejection, so you don't put yourself in that vulnerable position.'

Libby paused before answering. She'd left the house this morning without having breakfast because she didn't want to have a conversation with David. Conversation meant questions, and questions required answers. Yes, she'd left before he'd had a chance to speak to her. And Rowan? Rowan had called several times and left answerphone messages, but she hadn't replied because she'd felt hurt that her sister-in-law had found a new friend. Instead of being friends with both of them, she'd pushed away her closest friend.

'Do you think it's all my fault?' said Libby.

'Of course not, but it's easy to panic and push people away when you're struggling. All I can tell you is not to look at all your problems together like a giant ball of tangled string. Look at each knot individually. Untie one at a time and it won't seem so daunting.' She placed her mug on the table. 'Talk to Citizens Advice, ring your friend and speak to your husband. He married you because he loves you.' Rosemary looked at her watch. 'Right, I must dash or I'll be late. I'm glad you're feeling a little better.'

Libby stood up and leant across the table. She kissed Rosemary's cheek. 'Thank you.'

'You're welcome. It was nice to meet you.' Rosemary stood up and hooked her handbag on to her shoulder. 'Bye then. Oh, and make an appointment with your doctor.'

'I'll be fine. I don't need antidepressants.'

'I didn't mean that. I was thinking more about looking into the reasons why you're not conceiving and it won't hurt to mention bereavement counselling. If you didn't have any other problems except your brother dying, it'd still be a huge thing to get over. You need to look after yourself and stop worrying about what others think of you.' She raised a hand as a farewell gesture and began to walk towards the door before turning and saying, 'Remember a paper bag or cupped hands can come in very handy if you begin to feel anxious again.'

Libby nodded and waved before draining her mug of coffee. She was nervous – no she was terrified of talking to David, but she knew she had to do it. She missed him, but she could now see that it had been her that had pushed him away.

Chapter Twenty-Five

Nora had collected Primrose just after midday, leaving Rowan to put a full load of laundry in the washing machine and make some glass beads. Sitting at her workbench, Rowan turned off the small blue flame of the torch and straightened her glass canes. She looked at her watch, remembering that she had told James she'd return with some soup. First she'd put the washing on the line.

Rowan walked downstairs carrying a linen basket full of damp clothes. While Magnolia House was being transformed into three apartments, she'd organised a new back door so that everyone could have access to the small courtyard outside. Previously the exit would have been through the French doors in the kitchen, which was now part of Ace's apartment.

It was a dry and blustery day, and although it would have been easier to throw her clothes in the tumble dryer, Rowan loved the smell of line-dried washing. She pegged out blouses, pyjamas and a pair of jeans on the short line then stood back, amused by the way the clothes swayed like cut out paper dolls.

On her way back through the hallway, Rowan noticed that the post had been delivered and several letters were sitting in the wire basket behind the letterbox. She placed two letters for Ace on the hall shelf then stopped abruptly. The envelope in her hands had her name and address stuck on with squares. Some letters were colourful, perhaps cut out of a magazine, while others were from a newspaper. Someone was still playing games. This was the third letter in as many months. She placed it in the laundry basket and went back to her apartment.

Having opened a can of tomato soup, she poured the thick brick-red liquid into a saucepan. While it warmed, she looked at the note once again.

SAY cheESe bitch

Who disliked her enough to spend time cutting out and sticking letters onto paper? She felt a prickly sensation of anxiety creep down her spine.

The first note was laughed at. The second had left her bewildered. This third one made her uncomfortable. Placing the note on a tray alongside the soup, she carefully descended the stairs with the soup swaying from side to side in its bowl, leaving a semi-circular tomato stain close to the rim on either side.

She paused in front of Ace's apartment door. If only she hadn't promised to bring James some soup. She was still feeling silly for having believed that he might like her. She'd fantasised that he thought she was special and was giving her space to grieve for her late husband. Now she knew that it was all nonsense and that he still pined for his ex. Somehow it had spoiled the innocent flirty nature of their friendship.

Rowan knocked and waited. She was considering placing the tray on the floor so she could unlock the door, when the handle turned. Dressed in a pink dressing gown, patterned with white stars, James pulled the door towards him and stepped to one side.

'The sheets were damp from my fever, so I shoved them in the washer.'

'I'd have done that for you,' said Rowan, stepping inside. 'You should be resting. It was only a few hours ago you were delirious.'

'I feel fine. Fighting fit.' James bent his right arm, flexed his bicep beneath his dressing gown. He then flinched and scratched his thigh. 'Bloody spots are itchy, though.'

'Don't scratch them or they'll scar. I'll text Ace and ask him to bring some calamine lotion back.'

'It's okay. Nora gave me Primrose's leftover lotion.'

Rowan placed the tray on the kitchen worktop and pushed the letter into her jeans' waistband. She reached for a spoon and carried the bowl of soup into the lounge, placing it on the coffee table.

'Sit down. It's getting cool because it's been in the bowl for five minutes now.'

James saluted. 'Yes, nurse.'

She sat opposite him and watched as he sipped the soup. His dressing gown had fallen open when he'd sat down, revealing one of his thighs. Rowan was trying to look everywhere except his leg.

'Perfect temperature,' he said with a smile, spooning another mouthful. 'Aren't you having any?'

'I had some cheese sandwiches cut into star shapes with Primrose earlier.'

'I was just thinking how lucky I was to have soup made for me and now I feel short changed. Where are my star sandwiches?'

Rowan smirked. 'On your dressing gown.'

James looked down at the pink starry dressing gown. 'You do know it's not mine, don't you?'

'How would I know that?'

Grinning, he tied the belt tighter around his waist and covered his bare leg. 'It was the first thing I found when I heard a knock at the door. You never know what stranger might come knocking.'

Rowan closed her eyes momentarily and shivered.

'You okay?' asked James.

'Strangers and even stranger notes.'

James scraped the bowl and swallowed the last spoonful. 'Have you had another one?'

Rowan pulled the envelope out of her jeans and handed it to him. 'You said I should show you if I ever received another one.'

James looked at her while reaching for the envelope. He slid the paper out and unfolded it, grimacing as he ran a finger over the glued letters. 'Bizarre.' He shook his head and looked up, scratching his back subconsciously. 'And you've no idea who sent it to you?'

'None.'

'Remind me what the other two notes said?'

'Something about having a poor memory and being exposed.'

James pinched his chin in thought. 'A poor memory. Could there be someone you've unintentionally upset in the last year?'

'If it was unintentional, I wouldn't know that I'd upset them. Besides, I don't really know that many people in London.' Rowan leant forwards in her chair with her elbows on her knees and raked her fingers through her hair. She watched James scratch his thigh before coughing. 'I'm sorry,' she said. 'It's selfish of me to show you this today. I'll leave you in peace to rest.'

Rowan stood up to leave but James held out his hand. Rowan wasn't sure whether to take hold of it or not. His hand remained in mid-air between the two of them. She took hold of it. He gently pulled her towards him on the sofa and motioned for her to sit next to him. She sat down and he took her other hand. With her two fists held inside James' palms, she felt the warmth of his skin as they enfolded hers. He must have had a shower when he'd got out of bed, because he smelt of citrus.

'You're not being selfish. I feel a lot better this afternoon. Well, I would if this damn itching would stop. I'm going to help you get to the bottom of this. It's probably some nutcase who wouldn't dare turn up at your door, but still, it needs to stop.'

Rowan nodded, strangely lost for words. Her head was spinning. Here she was having her hands being held by a tenant who was wearing a pink dressing gown and making her heart beat faster. If only he'd let go of her hands. She didn't need to fall any deeper for him. For the second time that day, she withdrew her hands slowly from his.

'You're very kind, but I think you should get some rest. It's gone grey outside and I've put some washing on the line. I ought to fetch it in if it's going to rain.'

James didn't answer.

'James?'

'Sorry, I was just thinking. What did your husband do for a living? Did Ace say he had something to do with filming or photography?'

'Yes. He was a photographer.'

'That's the link.'

'It is?'

'Yes. Your notes all have a connection to photography. Memory, as in a memory card. Exposure, focus and what does everyone say before they take a photograph? Say cheese!'

'But, why?'

'I have no idea, but at least we have a connection that links all the notes. Do you mind if I discuss it with Ace when he gets back home? Believe it or not, underneath his feathers and sequins he's got a sharp mind. He beats me every time we watch *University Challenge*.'

'I don't mind. Do you think I should tell the police?'

'I'm not sure how seriously they'll take the notes if they're not actually threatening you. Let me speak with Ace. The front door's got a Yale lock, hasn't it? It locks automatically and only opens with a key?'

'Or the buzzer.' Rowan's eyes were wide. 'You don't think they'd try to break in, do you?'

James rubbed her upper arm reassuringly. 'No, of course not. I was just checking.'

Chapter Twenty-Six

By three o'clock, the slate-coloured sky had darkened the room sufficiently for Rowan to switch on a lamp. Her blouses had been unpegged from the washing line and were now draped over dining chairs and her jeans were thudding rhythmically inside the tumble dryer.

Rowan was sitting at her workbench in the bedroom, polishing earrings she'd made for The Blue Moon. Her summer collection had sold out and Nick had emailed her to ask if she could make several sets of necklaces with matching earrings as soon as possible. She really must stop being lazy and look for more outlets for her work, she thought. She couldn't just rely on one shop and two rental incomes.

Jet was snoring at her feet, his body curled into a perfect circle with his head and tail tucked into his fur. Her features softened as she used her toes to stroke his back. His dark eyes opened sleepily just as Rowan's mobile phone rang. The screen read *Libby*.

'Hi, Libby. I'm so glad you called.'

'Hello. I need to talk to you.'

Rowan pulled a face at hearing her friend's dejected voice. 'Are you all right? You didn't answer my texts or calls.'

'I know. I'm sorry. I've made such a mess of things.'

'What things? Where are you?'

'Standing on the bridge looking over the lake in St James's Park.'

'Why?'

'It's okay, I'm not thinking of jumping. I don't think it's much more than a metre deep anyway and it doesn't look too inviting.'

'Have you delivered some flowers nearby?'

'That's why I need to speak to you. I've had a chat with a doctor and I've made some decisions. The first one is to be honest with everyone.'

'What doctor? Are you ill? You're worrying me.'

'No, I'm not ill. I'm on my way home.'

'What do you mean about deciding to be honest?'

'Firstly, I'm sorry, Rowan. I've been stubborn. I've really missed you but I've been jealous about your new friendship with Nora. It sounds like a playground tantrum now I'm saying it out loud, but I've had a shit month and it was just one more thing that led me to make a wrong decision.'

'I've missed you too, but I don't understand. Tell me what's the matter?'

'I spoke to a lovely lady who helped me this morning. We had a chat over a coffee.'

'What do you mean by she helped you? You're talking in riddles, Libbs.'

'It seems I suffered a panic attack, in Covent Garden tube station of all places.'

'Oh no, poor you.' Rowan was shocked. 'I didn't know you suffered from panic attacks.'

'I don't. Well, I didn't. This doctor was called Rosemary and she was so nice. She really helped me understand that I need to face my problems or they're just going to get bigger and overwhelm me.'

'Problems? Do you mean about you and David not getting on well at the moment?'

'I'm a mess, Rowan. I owe lots of money on credit cards and I got the sack.'

Rowan's jaw fell open as she gaped at a pattern she'd doodled on some paper. 'When?'

'A fortnight ago.'

'Why didn't you tell me?'

'I haven't told anyone. Not even David. This doctor was the first person who listened.'

'I'm so sorry. I've been so busy with my jewellery and helping James and Nora. I'm sorry I didn't realise you were struggling.'

'It's okay. I wasn't having a dig. To be honest, we've met up many times and I haven't mentioned my debts. I think it helped that Rosemary was a stranger. And older. And being a doctor didn't make me feel so crazy because she must have seen and heard a few weird things in her time.'

'So David seriously doesn't know that you lost your job two weeks ago?'

'No. I stay at home when he's at work and on the odd days he works from home, I go into town.'

Rowan leant forwards on the workbench. 'And do what?'

'Window shop.' Libby gave a hollow laugh. 'My credit cards are maxed and I don't have a job to pay the minimum amount, so I have no option but to just look.'

'If I can help pay your cards for a month or two, I would happily help.'

'Thank you, but this is my mess. I need to start putting it right.'

'You know you must tell David, don't you? How are you two?'

Rowan heard Libby sigh.

'We're okay.' She paused. 'Who am I kidding? We stay out of each other's way and rarely speak. He's even been sleeping in the spare room.'

'That bad? Have you had a row?'

'No. We just stopped speaking. It's my fault. I started to blame him for me having no sign of becoming pregnant. I started buying baby clothes and storing them for the day it eventually happened. It made me feel in control and organised. I moved on to other things. Clothes, jewellery,

182

pretty things that made me forget the longing. Then the bills started mounting up. I thought that if I didn't get into conversation with him, he wouldn't ask about the bank balance. And then I got the sack.'

'What for?'

'Arguing with a client and being late too often.'

'That's not like you.'

'I know. I don't recognise myself at the moment. This doctor also thought that I should see a bereavement counsellor.'

'Yeh?'

'Yeh. She thinks that my compulsion to shop eases the pain of not falling pregnant and this comfort spending escalated when Tom died. She says it's a reaction to grief. Grief for not conceiving and grief over losing my brother.'

'I feel terrible. I had no idea.'

'That's the point. Rosemary said that compulsions are secretive which is why they're so difficult to overcome, and, to be honest, I've been too ashamed to bring it up. Apparently once the secret's out, it doesn't have the same hold over you any more, so that's why I've got to be honest and tell friends and family.'

'When are you going to tell David?'

Libby inhaled deeply. 'I'm going home to talk to him now. It's so strange. I'm actually nervous about speaking to my husband.'

'He'll probably be relieved to find out why you both haven't been getting on.'

'I've been blaming everyone else for my problems. I realise now that it's me. I'm the one who's spending. I'm the one who turned up late to work and argued with a client and it was my fault that I've been keeping out of David's way.'

'He adores you. He'll understand.'

'I hope you're right. Wish me luck.'

'Good luck, Libby.'

Libby stood across the road from her house looking at the white paintwork on the windows and neat borders lining the garden. All the other houses on the street looked as if they'd been cloned from the show house, with only the cars parked on their driveways differentiating them. But that wasn't the only difference, she thought. Behind each door, secretive diverse lives played out, day in and day out.

David's car was parked in their drive, but what was he doing? Maybe sitting at his computer. Perhaps lying on the settee watching the news or preparing dinner. What mood would he be in? Here she was standing in front of her house in the late afternoon, trying to second-guess what her husband might be doing inside. How had things come to this?

Her stomach churned both from nerves and not having eaten since a dry sandwich from a deli that morning. She crunched up the gravel path towards the front door and unlocked it. She closed it behind her and was relieved to smell onions frying. It somehow made the house feel more welcoming.

Libby took off her jacket and hung it on the stair post. Walking through the hall, she tucked her hair behind her ears and smoothed down her floral top. Taking a deep breath, she pushed the kitchen door open. David hadn't heard her come in and was browning some onions and mince, stirring a frying pan with his back turned to her. She smiled despite her nerves. His shirt was hanging out of his waistband as usual. She used to tease him that he looked like a schoolboy with his twisted tie and untucked shirt when he came home from work. She had an overwhelming desire to walk up behind him and wrap her arms around his waist. He began to whistle while he stirred the mince. He was in a good mood. It gave her the courage to step forwards and slide her arms around his body.

David was startled and dropped the wooden spoon, splattering browned mince and oil down his shirt. 'What the—'

Libby jumped back. 'Sorry!'

'Are you trying to give me a heart attack?' David glowered as he crossed to the sink, turning the tap and waiting a few seconds until it ran hot. He grabbed a tea towel, shoved it under the steaming stream of water and attempted to wipe the stains from his shirt. 'You certainly pick your moments.'

'I'm sorry. I saw you cooking and just wanted to give you a hug.'

David's features softened. 'Never say sorry for hugging me; just give me a bit of warning next time.' He smiled uncertainly. 'Want to try again?'

Libby stepped forwards, threw her arms around his waist and buried her head in his chest. She could feel the damp material he'd just wiped but, more importantly, she felt his warm skin beneath it. He smelt like her David; maybe infused with a little onion, but she didn't care. A hint of aftershave mixed with his body heat always evoked a feeling of security and comfort, especially when she could feel his arms wrapped around her shoulders.

'This is all very lovely,' he said, 'but why now? I feel as if you've been trying to keep out of my way for weeks.'

Libby could feel his hot breath as he spoke, his lips resting on her hair. She didn't want to move or speak because she knew that when she spoke, this lovely moment would end. She hugged him tighter, hearing the air escape from his lungs as she did so.

'Hey,' he chuckled. 'What's all this about?'

She knew she had to do it. She had to leave his warm body and tell him the truth. Slowly, she pulled back, dropped her arms and stood in front of him. 'I'm so sorry,' she said. 'I've been a bitch and I need to talk to you.'

He took a step back, suddenly looking pale. 'You're not going to tell me you've been having an affair, are you?'

'No, no. Of course not.'

She saw her husband's shoulders relax.

'Well, that's all right then. Anything else I can handle.'

Libby swallowed and repeated, 'I need to talk to you.'

'Hang on. Let me turn the mince off or the fire brigade will be interrupting us.' After turning the hob off, he faced her. 'I'm guessing it's not going to be good news by the look on your face. Will we need a drink?'

Libby nodded.

As David uncorked the bottle, Libby began to shake. Remembering what Rosemary had said to her earlier that morning, she cupped her hands over her mouth and breathed slowly into them. She managed four deep breaths before David handed her a glass of wine.

'Thank you.'

David sat at the kitchen table, looking up at her. 'I'm all ears.'

Libby gulped a large mouthful of wine and decided to just come out with it. 'David, I've lost my job.'

David's brow furrowed with concern. 'What? How?'

'I was sacked.'

David shook his head barely perceptibly. 'What for?'

'For being late.'

'Couldn't that grumpy woman have just given you a verbal warning?'

'I'd already had two. And a written one.'

'When did this happen?'

'Two weeks ago.'

'Two weeks?' He raked his fingers through his short fair hair and then held them out in front of him, palms upturned as if waiting to catch a ball. 'I don't get it. Why haven't you told me before now?'

'I didn't know how. Things have been a bit strained lately and … I don't know. I suppose I kept putting it off.'

'You didn't know how?' He looked incredulous. 'I'll tell you how you deal with a problem. You share it with me.' He took a gulp of wine. 'How do you think it makes me feel when my own wife can't come to me?'

'I'm sorry. I've been a mess. I had a panic attack this morning and a doctor told me that I should—'

'A panic attack? What doctor?'

'Just a nice lady who helped me this morning.'

'What were you doing this morning?'

'I went to Covent Garden to walk and think.'

'Oh my God. You were escaping from me because I was at home.'

Libby saw how pale he looked and that his eyes had a defeated look about them.

'No, it wasn't like that. Not really.'

'Sit down, Libby.' He pointed to an empty chair and not his knees. 'Why did you keep it a secret from me? Why didn't you feel that you could tell me?'

'I was cross with you,' she replied, taking a seat.

'What for?'

Libby shook her head. 'It doesn't matter now. I know you're not to blame.'

'Blame about what?'

'David really—'

'If we're going to sort this out, I need to know why you were cross with me.'

Libby swallowed audibly and inhaled shakily. 'For me not having a baby.'

Silence filled the kitchen. The tap dripped. A dog barked in a neighbour's garden.

'What?'

'I said I know you're not to blame. Everything just got to me and—'

'What do you mean, for *you* not having a baby? Wouldn't I be the father? Don't you think that I'm gutted every month that *we* don't make a baby? Do you just think I'm the chap that impregnates you – or not in this case. It kills me month after month to see you in tears? I dread seeing your disappointment. And now I find out that you blamed me?'

To Libby's horror, David's eyes glistened with tears.

'I'm so sorry, David. The doctor thinks I'm still grieving for Tom. She thinks I need counselling.'

David stood up and crossed the kitchen. He ripped a sheet of kitchen roll from its holder and wiped his eyes roughly before blowing his nose. 'I understand that you lost your brother and that's tragic. But I lost my best mate, too.' David wiped another tear away. 'I can't just stop working and feel sorry for myself. I need to continue working to pay the bills and God knows where the money's going. At the rate we get through our income, it'll be a miracle if we can afford to have a baby. Christ, and now you've lost your job.'

Libby thought she was going to be sick. She'd upset David. She'd only seen him cry once following the death of his mother and now that the subject of money had been brought up, Libby knew that this was the time to admit to her debts. If he found out in a few weeks or months' time, it would make matters worse.

'I owe money on some credit cards. I've been paying the minimum amount off a few cards each month. I'm so sorry. That's where the money's been going.'

David looked shattered. His eyes were red and his shoulders drooped, making him seem smaller than he really was. It was difficult to believe that she'd caused this to happen. She remembered hearing him whistling a quarter of an hour ago, totally oblivious to the storm that was about to erupt. He'd been cooking dinner for her despite the way she'd been treating him recently. How could he ever forgive her? Her own tears swelled until they balanced on her lower lashes. One by one they fell and rolled down her cheeks as she watched him walk to the fridge and fill up his glass again. He took several mouthfuls and asked flatly, 'How much?'

'About twenty.'

'TWENTY! Twenty thousand pounds?'

His eyes were so wide with disbelief, that Libby could see the white of his eyes around the whole of his iris.

'I'm so sorry, David. I—'

'Fucking hell, Libby. Twenty grand. What in Christ's name have you spent twenty thousand pounds on?'

'It's been over a couple of years.'

'On what?'

'Baby things.'

He sneered through his sarcasm. 'Oh, come off it. It can't be just on baby things. I don't think even the Beckhams could spend that much just on baby things.'

Libby had never felt so ashamed or full of self-loathing in all her life. She wiped the tears away from her cheeks and sniffed. 'Clothes, household things and a lot is interest which is being charged every month on each card.'

'On each card? How many have you got burning a hole in our bank account?'

Libby almost whispered, 'Six.'

David covered his mouth and nose with his fingers as if he were praying. He didn't answer but sat down slowly opposite her. Libby could see his shoulders rising and falling as he stared sightlessly into the middle distance, lost in thought. She wished he would say something. The silence was worse than his anger.

Chapter Twenty-Seven

Rowan was emotionally exhausted after the day's events. She'd gone to bed early and was asleep within five minutes of her head touching her pillow. She dreamed of Tom in their old Wilmslow apartment. He was holding a black cat that he stroked backwards from tail to head, making the cat's fur stand on end. Nothing seemed out of the ordinary in her dream. She'd looked up at Tom who was now stroking a baby. She stood up and the baby disappeared. Tom pulled her towards him and kissed her. They'd been kissing passionately but when they'd moved apart, it was James she'd been kissing.

She woke up, disturbed by a distant siren passing along Clapham Road. Its wail grew fainter and she reached for the alarm clock. The red numbers flashed 01.46. She hadn't even been asleep for two hours. She stared into the darkness recalling her dream, a confusing blend of emotions engulfing her. She'd *seen* Tom again. Funny how she hadn't remembered that he was dead or felt excited by his presence in her dreams. And that kiss. She closed her eyes and tried to remember the feeling. She'd felt nothing, until … no she mustn't think of James. She refused to.

Leaning over, she switched on the bedside lamp and picked up two framed photographs of Tom. The first was of Tom holding Jet as a puppy and the second was a picture taken while they'd been staying with her parents in France. The photograph had captured the moment he'd been sitting on the veranda, playing Scrabble and holding a glass of wine. She thought about letters that made up a word. Strange how they're amusing and sociable in the context of a game, but cut them out of paper and stick letters on a sheet of paper and they become intimidating.

She laid the photograph on the duvet and swung her legs out of bed. Reaching for her dressing gown, she slid her arms into the sleeves. In the lounge she retrieved the anonymous notes from a set of drawers and studied them again. James had found the link and it seemed ridiculous now that she hadn't noticed it before.

Jet trotted over to her wagging his tail excitedly.

'Sorry, boy, it's not morning yet.' She bent to stroke him. 'I think I've got a bit of salmon left in the fridge. Do you want a midnight snack?'

Jet followed Rowan into the kitchen and watched her open the fridge. As she pulled the door open, a jar of marmalade fell from the top shelf. She made a grab for it but it fell with a loud crash on the hardwood floor. She shooed Jet out of the kitchen and stood looking down at the broken glass, while thick marmalade oozed over the shards like molten lava. Rowan reached for a cloth but before she'd even had a chance to wet it, she heard a knock on her apartment door. She opened it to find Ace and James standing side by side. Ace was wearing his pink dressing gown and James was wearing baggy joggers and an old T-shirt.

'Is this a private pyjama party or can we all join in?' said Ace.

'Are you okay?' asked James.

'Yes, I'm fine. Sorry, did the crash wake you? A jar of marmalade fell out of the fridge. It's just a bit messy but I'll soon have it cleared up.'

'We'll help.' Ace marched past her and into the kitchen.

James stood in the doorway. 'We weren't asleep. I couldn't get into the sofa bed until his bloody film had finished. At least I'll be able to get some shut-eye now.'

Rowan felt self-conscious standing in her pyjamas. 'Come in a minute. I'd better rescue Ace.'

Rowan realised that her dressing gown was open revealing her cream shorts and T-shirt pyjama set. She wrapped her gown around her waist as James stepped through the door. He was greeted by Jet who bounced around his feet.

'What did Ace have you watching?'

'*Mamma Mia*. Again!'

'Did I hear someone taking Sam's name in vain?' said Ace, looking up from the floor where he was gingerly gathering the broken shards of glass.

Rowan frowned. 'Who?'

'Pierce Brosnan,' said James. 'He's his latest crush.'

Rowan fetched an old newspaper to wrap the broken glass in. When the last of the sticky residue had been cleared up, Ace stood up, arched backwards and groaned. 'Why on earth were you eating marmalade at one in the morning?'

'I wasn't. I was getting a treat out of the fridge for Jet. I've been asleep once but I had a bad dream. When I woke up, I started thinking about the stupid notes I've been getting.'

Ace looked concerned. 'James told me about them. Complete weirdo, I'd say.'

Rowan smiled at her two tenants. 'I feel really safe with you two downstairs. I only have to drop a jar and you're here helping me.'

'Oakland brothers at your service, ma'am,' said Ace, bowing.

They walked back into the lounge where Ace draped himself on the arm of an armchair. 'If I was a detective, I could tell you what newspaper they'd been cut out of. I'd also ask you if Tom had any enemies.'

Rowan looked at him. 'Enemies? Have you been watching the re-runs of *Columbo*?'

'No, but I do have a dodgy rain mac.'

James joined them. 'Listen, this isn't a joke if it's disturbing Rowan's sleep. Some nutter out there has actually gone to the trouble of making these notes. If not enemies, do you know if Tom had fallen out with anyone?'

Rowan liked to hear him say her name. 'Not that I know of. Occasionally people refused to pay until Tom had sent their photographs but Tom refused to send them until he'd been paid. It occasionally led to some choice words being typed into emails from both parties. But surely that's something that any businessman comes across occasionally?'

'It certainly doesn't sound like it would lead to sending cryptic messages a year later. I might call in at the local paper and ask a few questions about typography and print styles. I know someone who works there. You never know.'

Chapter Twenty-Eight

Summer slipped into early autumn, causing leaves to curl and fade. Rowan had just returned from The Blue Moon having delivered three bracelets and half a dozen pairs of earrings. She was delighted to have been told by Nick that her stock was his bestseller. It was nearing midday by the time Rowan arrived back home and her head was so full of new design ideas that she nearly bumped into a lady who was looking up at Magnolia House.

'Sorry. I was miles away,' said Rowan.

'That's okay.'

Rowan looked at the tall, slim woman and saw an ethereal beauty about her as the sun highlighted her from behind. Her blonde hair was pulled back into a ponytail, leaving her large turquoise eyes to peer from beneath a long fringe. Her small nose looked as if it had been chiselled to perfection by a love-struck sculptor.

'Are you looking for someone?' asked Rowan.

'I've been told an old friend of mine lives here at Magnolia House. I was just wondering whether I should disturb them or not.'

The woman was so beautiful that Rowan guessed she must be one of Nora's modelling friends. 'Actually, I live here too. Come on in.' She inclined her head and smiled an invitation for the lady to follow her up the path. 'Oh, I've just remembered,' said Rowan, stopping at the gate having recalled that Nora had taken Primrose to Hamleys. 'They've gone out until one o'clock, but you're welcome to wait in my apartment until they get back.'

'Are you sure? That's very kind.'

'Of course, come in.'

Rowan turned the key and pushed the door open, a warm hallway greeting them. 'I live upstairs. My husband and I used to live here alone but since he died, I've turned it into three apartments.'

'Oh, I'm sorry.'

'It's okay.' Rowan felt as if she was being disloyal to Tom's memory by glossing over his death in a fleeting sentence. It wasn't intentional; she just didn't want to talk about the whys and wherefores.

The lady followed her upstairs. Unlocking her front door, Rowan walked into the apartment. 'Would you like a cuppa?'

'Actually, do you have something a little stronger?'

Rowan was facing away from the kitchen door and surreptitiously looked at her watch. It was just after midday. Even during the early days following Tom's death, she hadn't been tempted to drink this early in the day.

'I've only got beer that a friend brought round.'

'Great. I just need something to calm my nerves.'

Rowan poured a glass of beer. 'What're you nervous about?'

'I haven't seen my friend for a couple of years. We didn't part on the best of terms. I've got some apologising to do.'

'I think you'll see that things have changed a bit in the last couple of years. There are two of them now.'

'Two?'

'A gorgeous little girl, called Primrose. She's walking now.' Rowan watched the woman's jaw fall open.

'There's a child?' The woman tipped her head back and drank the glass of beer. She wiped her lips with her fingertips. 'Perhaps I should leave. I'm beginning to wonder if this was such a good idea. May I use your bathroom first?'

'Of course. It's through the bedroom off the lounge.'

The woman placed her glass on the work surface, leaving

Rowan looking perplexed in the kitchen. She's come all this way and wants to leave when she finds out that Nora has a child? A knock on the front door disturbed her thoughts. She opened it to find James standing in the doorway.

'You're back,' he said and grinned at her.

'I'm back. Come in.'

James stepped inside. 'Have Tiffany been in touch yet about your jewellery?'

'Less of your sarcasm.'

James laughed. 'The Blue Moon today, De Beers tomorrow.'

Rowan lowered her voice. 'Talking of beer, one of Nora's friends has just nipped into the loo after drinking a glass of beer, in one go.'

The smile fell from James' face. 'What's he doing here? You really shouldn't be letting strangers into your flat, especially when you've been receiving dodgy notes in the post. Are you sure he's one of Nora's friends?'

'He's a she. I invited her in while she waits for them to get back.'

'Okay.' His shoulders relaxed.

They glanced towards the bedroom door when they heard the toilet flush, but James continued.

'That mate I was going to have a word with at the local paper has moved on and no one has his forwarding address. They didn't seem to be much help when I asked them about fonts and printing. Said it wasn't their department.'

'It was kind of you to ask, but don't worry. If I get another one I'm going to take them all to the police and see what they say about them. Anyway, did you come upstairs for something?'

'Oh, yeh, nearly forgot. I need to borrow you for two minutes?'

'What have you done now?' she asked, hands on her hips and a wry grin showing her delight at being asked.

James feigned a hurt expression. 'What makes you think I've done something wrong?'

'Let's just call it a woman's intuition.'

'It wasn't my fault. It was the bloody cotton's fault.'

Rowan laughed. 'Go on.'

'I was sitting on the bed sewing a button on a shirt—'

'And?'

'And it looks great. It's really sturdy and won't be falling off again.'

'So what's the problem?'

'When I picked up the shirt, the duvet cover came with it.'

Rowan laughed. 'You've sewn your shirt to the bed.'

James tried not to smile. 'The thing is, it's Ace's bed and he's superstitious about sewing on the bed. Apparently it's bad luck. He says it means that someone will be stuck in bed with an illness. Are you okay to pop down after she's gone?' He inclined his head towards the bathroom.

They both heard the lock to Rowan's en suite slide open.

'Of course.' Rowan looked over her shoulder towards the bathroom before whispering behind her hand. 'This woman's nervous about something. Apparently they last saw each other a couple of years ago after some sort of a fallout.'

James didn't answer. He was gazing past her shoulder as if she didn't exist. She turned to find the woman looking back at James with the same expression etched on her face.

James spoke, his words almost a whisper. 'Helen? What are you doing here?'

Rowan stood to one side so she could see them both. She turned her head from one to the other.

'I heard through a friend where you'd moved to. I thought I'd come and see how you are.'

'Why?'

Helen smiled weakly. 'I've missed you.'

A feeling of iced water rushed through Rowan's veins. Helen was the name he'd spoken when he was ill with a fever. She'd obviously misread this situation very badly.

James pinched his lips with his thumb and forefinger, as if his fingers were subconsciously telling him not to speak. He slowly shook his head. 'I don't understand. What are you doing up here?'

'This lady ...' Helen looked at Rowan. 'I'm sorry, I don't know your name.'

'Rowan,' said Rowan, her voice sounding as if it belonged to someone else.

'Rowan invited me in for a drink because you were out at Hamleys.'

'No I wasn't. I was downstairs. Nora's gone to Hamleys with her daughter.'

'Who's Nora?' asked Helen.

Rowan interrupted. 'Sorry, I assumed you'd come to visit Nora.'

Helen looked at James. 'Is Nora your girlfriend?'

'No.'

'So you don't have a child?'

James shook his head. 'No, I don't have a child.'

Helen appeared relieved as they continued to stare at each other, making Rowan feel as if she was intruding in her own home. Then Helen held out her arms, so that they hung limply between her and James. 'Can I have a hug?'

No you bloody well can't screamed a voice inside Rowan's head.

James stepped forwards and held her in his arms. Rowan could see Helen's face on his shoulder, her eyes were closed, her cheek pressed against his neck and a satisfied smile stretching her perfect lips.

'Can we talk?' asked Helen as James pulled away.

James nodded and gestured for her to follow him. He looked over towards Rowan.

'I'll sort the bed thing out.'

They left the apartment. As the door closed, all that was left was the lingering scent of Chanel Nº5.

James held Ace's apartment door open for Helen to walk through. He inhaled the same intoxicating perfume that she used to wear as she glided past him into the lounge.

'Can I get you something?' James asked, rubbing his palms together nervously.

'No, thanks. Rowena got me a drink.'

'Rowan.'

'Oh, yes.'

They hesitated just inside the door.

'Take a seat. Make yourself comfortable.' James noticed *Stud* magazine and last month's *Vogue* on the sofa. He hurried to move them.

Helen smiled and sat down, crossing one slim leg over the other until her thigh was exposed. 'Changed your reading habits, then? It used to be *The Times* you could never take your nose out of.'

'They're Ace's. This is his place.' He shoved the magazines underneath the coffee table and sat on the opposite sofa. 'I'm just staying for a while.'

'Did you sell your flat?'

'No. I made a mistake with the paperwork. I'm essentially homeless until next July.'

'And Mason? What's he doing these days?'

'He's still into his vintage clothing but he's moved to a bigger shop.'

Helen pursed her lips, distracting James for a second as his eyes were drawn to her glistening mouth.

'So, you don't get your own place back for another eight

months. Pity.' Helen looked up from beneath her fringe. 'We had some good times there, didn't we?'

James didn't know how to answer. He didn't know how he felt. Helen had broken his heart but he'd truly believed that he was over her. It all felt very different with her sitting opposite him reminding him of the good times.

'Why are you here, Helen?'

She studied her long red nails. 'Like I said, I've missed you.'

James leant his head back and looked at the ceiling. He inhaled before breathing out a long controlled breath. 'What about your new boyfriend? The one you left me for without so much as a goodbye?'

'I did say goodbye, James.'

James leant forwards. 'You sent me a text, for God's sake.'

She looked up. 'I was young. I was only twenty.'

'Can someone mature in less than three years?'

'I think so. I've travelled and experienced heartbreak for myself. I understand how awful I was to end things the way I did. I was young and looking for adventure, not marriage. Michael's a footballer in Germany. He's rich and I was introduced to famous people he knew. We travelled every other month. I was just star-struck, I suppose. After a few months I began to think I'd made a terrible mistake. He had other women fawning all over him wherever he went and he didn't always refuse them. I heard you'd left for America. I know money's not important now, but back then ... I was naive.'

James had winced at Michael's name. He hadn't known the name of the man who Helen had left him for, and had been glad of it. 'What makes you think I don't have a girlfriend? How do you know that I haven't moved on?'

'I don't, but I had to come and find out. When Rowan

invited me inside, I thought that she must be your girlfriend if she lived here with you. A friend said he knew where you were living, but he didn't say Magnolia House was split into apartments?'

For a moment James envisaged Rowan being his girlfriend. 'Rowan owns the house. She was widowed last year and had it converted.'

'Haven't you got a girlfriend, then?'

He bristled because she hadn't acknowledged Rowan's loss. 'Why do you care? What do you want from me?'

'I want to say that I'm sorry, that I miss you and maybe we could try again.'

James slowly shook his head. 'You can't be serious. You can't walk back into my life after nearly three years and expect us to carry on where we left off.'

'Is that because you have a girlfriend?'

'No.'

'I'm surprised. You're still gorgeous.'

'Stop it, Helen. It's nice to see you but it's all in the past now.'

'It doesn't have to be.'

Helen uncrossed her legs, sliding one from the other before standing up. She walked around the coffee table and sat down beside him. Once again the provocative aroma of amber and vanilla infused the air. He turned to face her, remembering her exquisite turquoise eyes and how he'd loved to wake up and look into their penetrating gaze each morning. It had been like drowning in a tropical lagoon. She smiled, showing even white teeth.

'I've moved back in with Mum and Dad for a few months until I get organised.'

'How are they?'

'They're having a great time now they're retired. They're going on two cruises a year and have joined a bridge club.

Dad still does a bit of private medical work but only for a few days a month to pay for their cruises.'

James felt her soft fingers tracing the length of a blue vein on his forearm. Her gentle touch aroused memories of their lovemaking. He remembered her pert breasts and pictured the curve of her back that led to her small, round bottom.

'Stop it, Helen. This isn't a good idea.'

'Why not? We're both single. I hope we're still friends.'

'Friends don't come on to each other.'

'They do if they're friends with benefits.' She slid her calf over his shin and rested it on his knee. 'What's the harm?'

He heard Jet bark upstairs. A vision of Rowan trespassed on his thoughts. He'd left her standing at the doorway. Had he even said goodbye?

James stood up. 'It's good to see you again, Helen, but we can't just pick up where we left off. Too much has happened since then.'

'Can I see you again? I promise not to rush things. We could get to know each other again.'

James needed time to think. 'Another time. Give me a call next week.'

Chapter Twenty-Nine

Several weeks passed. Late autumn announced its arrival by whitewashing Clapham Common with a hoar frost. Rowan had noticed the ice-frosted beauty of the trees earlier while she'd crunched on the frozen grass during Jet's morning walk. Even the tarmacked paths sparkled like spilt glitter.

Back at home Rowan was sitting at her workbench listening to a group of boys playing football in the street. Her lampwork torch smelt of burnt toast as she tried to fashion spherical beads from thin glass rods. Several misshapen attempts lay like distorted eggs on the worktop, waiting to be thrown away.

Once again Rowan found herself wondering if Helen had slept the night with James. Were they spending passionate nights together just a few feet below her? She'd seen them together once or twice over the past few weeks as they'd come or gone from Magnolia House, but James no longer shared a pot of coffee or walked Jet with her. She felt sick with jealousy but also guilt for caring so much.

She clattered the torch onto its stand and switched it off at the mains with her foot. Jet licked the bare inch of skin between her jeans and her socks as she did so.

'Now you're just taking advantage, aren't you? Just like a boy.'

Jet stood up and wagged his tail, thumping it against the table leg to a steady rhythm. Rowan scratched behind his ears and he buried his head in her lap.

'What was I thinking? Trust me to have a crush on a man who thinks I'm just the landlady.' She stood up and walked to her full-length mirror. 'Pathetic,' she said to her reflection, before turning and falling onto her bed. She lay on her stomach, her arms above her head as if she was about to swallow dive into a pool. Of course he only thought of her as a friend. How could he possibly have feelings for a miserable widow? If she wasn't complaining about her lack of motivation for making jewellery, she was signing the receipt book after receiving his and Ace's rent. She knew she scrubbed up quite well when she made an effort, but James usually saw her with no make-up on and her hair tied in a ponytail. Jet jumped up onto the bed and sat watching her, occasionally nudging her leg. She rolled onto her back and reached for him.

'It's okay, Jet.' She stroked his forelegs. 'You're the only boy for me now.' He settled down beside her and snuggled against her waist, but not even her spaniel's unconditional loyalty could stop the stabbing jealousy Rowan felt inside.

Five minutes later, just as Rowan's eyes were growing heavy, someone knocked at her front door. She sat up immediately, her head swimming from a rush of blood. Groping for her hairbrush, she raked it through her hair several times. She found a compact on the bedside table and wiped away a greasy sheen that had appeared on her face. Perhaps it was James. Perhaps it hadn't worked out with Helen.

Rowan hurried to the front door and opened it with a smile set on her lips.

'Thank God you're in,' said Nora. Primrose was perched on her hip as she walked past Rowan into her apartment. 'I hate to impose but I've been asked to stand in for a model who's suffering from tonsillitis and the nursery's full. It's for a Sunday supplement that could lead to bigger and better things. Please say you can look after Primrose for a couple of hours.'

Rowan looked at the little girl clinging to her mother. Her tousled hair fell across her eyes. She wasn't in the mood for making glass beads so perhaps cuddling a warm little body would help her take her mind off James. She smiled at Primrose.

'Do you want to make some chocolate crispy cakes with Ro-Ro, just like last time?'

Primrose's thumb remained in her mouth and her head still leant on her mother's shoulder, but the little girl nodded.

'Good girl,' said Nora. 'You love chocolate, don't you?' She looked up at Rowan. 'Thank you. You're a lifesaver. I shouldn't be more than a few hours.'

'It's okay. We'll have fun together, won't we, darling?' Rowan held out her arms towards Primrose.

The little girl's thumb popped out of her mouth and dribble trickled down her chin. She leant forwards with her arms extended towards Rowan.

'Ro-Ro, choc-choc,' said Primrose.

Rowan smiled as she took the little girl's weight.

'Thanks. I must dash.' Nora kissed her daughter's cheek and turned to leave before stopping suddenly and facing Rowan once more.

'I just passed Helen in the hallway.'

Rowan bit her lip and readjusted Primrose in her arms. 'Did you?'

'Yeh. She always seems to have that cat-who's-got-the-cream expression on her face, if you know what I mean. Then again, so would I if I slept in James' bed.'

Rowan gave a tight-lipped smile.

'Must dash. Bye, darling,' she said, kissing her daughter's cheek once more. Nora waved and hurried through the open door.

Rowan closed the door and groaned. 'Why does Mummy have to rub it in, eh?'

'Choc-choc.'

'Of course, chocolate makes everything better, doesn't it? Let's get our priorities right and find the Rice Krispies.'

Rowan and Primrose spent a peaceful afternoon making cakes and reading stories. By two in the afternoon, Primrose's thumb had been firmly reattached to her mouth while she lay against Rowan on the settee. *The Very Hungry Caterpillar* and *The Gruffalo* lay on the cushion next to them and Rowan yawned. Primrose smelt like a bag of Dolly Mixtures and felt soft and warm.

As often happened when she was looking after the little girl, Rowan's mind drifted as she wondered how old her own baby would be now if she hadn't fallen downstairs. Would she have chosen the ground floor to live in if she'd needed to use a pushchair? Would she have visited her mother in France and met Ace? And if she hadn't met Ace, she wouldn't have ever known James. She closed her eyes and rested her lips on Primrose's curls. The child's breathing had become deep and slow and although Rowan couldn't see her face, she knew that the little girl was sleeping. Maybe if she'd told Tom about the baby before he'd gone to play football, he would have cancelled and stayed at home. If he'd stayed at home, then maybe she could have saved him.

It all seemed such a long time ago now. So much had changed in the fourteen months since she'd been widowed. She now had new friends who Tom had never met. She was selling her jewellery to a gift shop *and* she was a landlady. What would Tom think of that? She smiled into Primrose's titian hair, knowing that he'd have been proud of her.

The peaceful moment was interrupted by the telephone. Rowan gently laid the sleeping child on the settee and answered it.

'Hello.'

'Hello, is that Mrs Forrester?'

'Yes, it is.'

'Hello, my name's Henry and I work at Aubergine

Advertising. I understand your husband was a photographer.'

'Yes.' Rowan looked out of the window, leaning her forehead against the cool pane of glass. Strange how she'd been thinking of Tom and now someone was calling about him.

'We've been approached by the Sports Council who've asked us if they could have permission to use some of your husband's photographs. They've initiated a project about improving facilities in the inner city areas and have asked us to work alongside them. I know ... I mean ... I understand your husband passed away last year and I was very sorry to hear that. But the company thought it was only polite to ask your permission, under the circumstances.'

Rowan looked around at Primrose who was curled like a comma on the settee. 'Um, yes. I don't see why not. What pictures are you talking about?' She leant against the window once more and watched the neighbours unpacking their supermarket shopping.

'It's a set of athletics photographs he took two years ago in London. The shots were taken in the part of the city they're interested in. They say that paying you for using them is a lot easier than hiring a photographer and setting up a whole new photo shoot. Plus the light is poor now that the nights are drawing in and your husband's photographs were taken in the month of June.'

'That's fine. Use them. I'm sure he'd have been delighted to have been asked.'

'Thank you, Mrs Forrester. That's very kind and of course we'll pay royalties.'

'Thank you, that'll be welcome.'

'Just one more thing, if you don't mind. Your husband has the contacts of the athletes he used and we need to ask their permission too. Would it be possible for you to forward them on to us? I know it's a nuisance and we're sorry to ask, but we can't use the images unless we have their permission.'

Rowan frowned. 'I'm not sure where I put his mobile phone, but I'll have a look. Hang on a sec while I get a pen and take your number and the names of the athletes.' She found a biro next to the crossword she'd attempted that morning and jotted down the information.

Rowan replaced the receiver and rubbed the cold pink circle on her forehead made from the pressure of leaning against the glass. The neighbours opposite disappeared through their front door and closed it.

Checking once more that Primrose was sleeping, Rowan walked through into her bedroom. She knelt down in front of the wardrobe and pulled out an old box her slow cooker had come in when it was new. The tattered corners and dented sides still held firm and contained papers, camera accessories, electrical instruction manuals and, hopefully, Tom's old mobile phone. It was lying at the bottom of the box. She held the oblong of plastic between her fingers, running her thumbs up and down the screen. She smelt it then held it against her cheek. So many times she'd seen Tom pacing the hallway holding this phone against his ear. He'd told her he loved her on this phone. They'd discussed menus, nights out, meetings with friends, dentist's appointments and had the occasional disagreement on it.

She pressed the button despite already knowing that it wouldn't work. The screen remained blank. Digging deeper inside the box she unearthed photographs of herself, newspaper cuttings where journalists had used Tom's photographs, old unused 35mm films and some wiring. Rowan pulled at the wires that slithered through the contents of the box. It was the charger. She attached it to his mobile, plugged it into a nearby socket and sat back on her heels waiting for it to spring into life. After a few minutes, a light flickered as the battery began to recharge. Rowan watched the green light winking on the screen. By plugging in Tom's phone, she felt as if she was awakening something that shouldn't be disturbed, rousing something that belonged in the past. It contained a history of their texts, a lexicon of his friends' and colleagues' names and numbers that he'd punched out countless times.

Rowan heard shuffling coming from the lounge. Jumping to her feet, she went to the bedroom door thinking that Primrose had woken up, but the noise was Jet lying on his back wriggling on the carpet with his legs in the air. Rowan smiled to herself as she watched him blissfully twist and squirm from left to right. He stopped, stood up and shook himself.

'Do you feel better after that little wriggle?'

He followed her back to Tom's phone. The screen was now bright and Rowan picked it up. She scrolled through his contact list, reading many names she'd never heard of. He'd met so many people through his line of work and she felt wistful that she'd rarely enquired about his days. She'd just greeted him whenever he'd returned from photographic shoots and glibly asked if he'd had a good day. Why hadn't she shown more interest? After all, she'd moved to London because of his job yet she'd never paid that much attention to his chosen career.

Rowan clicked out of contacts and went into his messages. A list of texts were stacked one on top of the other in date order. The last sent text had a date of August 17th. It simply read, *Hi beautiful, back around 7 after footy. x*

She closed her eyes, trying to block out the thought that he never had returned from that game of football. Pulling herself together, she scrolled through many texts noticing that one letter in particular occupied a large part of his inbox. The contact was called E. She clicked on one message and immediately saw two kisses at the end of the text. A sudden rush of blood surged through her veins as she read, *Hey, why didn't you call last night? Miss you. E xx*

She frantically opened and read earlier messages, wondering why this old phone didn't record the date and time.

Shame you couldn't stay over. Is she giving you a hard time? Perhaps we should tell her. Love E xx

Rowan clicked on another, her heart crashing against her ribs as the phone bristled with unspoken secrets.

Can still taste you on my lips. Can't wait for the weekend. When can you escape? E xx

Her fingers stumbled on the buttons as she frantically searched for the sent messages. Why would Tom need to escape her and the house? And to whom was he escaping?

As Rowan began to read the texts that Tom had sent to E, she thought she would be sick there and then sitting on the bedroom floor.

Don't call when R is at home. Will speak later.

She scrolled down.

Need to see you. Ring me after 9.

Rowan shrieked and threw the phone across the room. The wire it was attached to yanked it back, crashing it into the wardrobe door with a loud bang. Jet sidled off with his tail between his legs while she wiped angry tears from her eyes. She held her head in her hands, shaking and hyperventilating.

'Bastard! Unfaithful bastard.' He'd relegated her name to the letter R. Rowan's head was spinning with confusion. She leant against the bed trying to absorb this new information. A wave of nausea swept up to her throat making her gag. She ran to her bathroom and retched into the toilet bowl before grabbing a towel and holding it to her face. How can your impression of the man you've loved, change in an instant? It was as if she was viewing him through a distorted fairground mirror, where his image had changed beyond all recognition.

'Mummy?'

Rowan quickly wiped her eyes. She'd momentarily forgotten about Primrose and her shouting must have woken her. She had to find the strength from somewhere to look after the little girl until Nora came back. Standing up and scraping her hair behind her ears, she set a smile on her lips and walked in to comfort Primrose.

Chapter Thirty

The last radiant colours of autumn had faded. It was a dank and bitterly cold November morning that greeted the two friends when they met. Rowan waved, having spotted Libby outside Notting Hill tube station. They'd agreed to meet up for a hot chocolate in one of the cafés on Portobello Road and to browse through the market stalls for Christmas presents. However, the main reason Rowan had arranged to see her sister-in-law, was that she'd been mulling something over in her mind and needed to ask Libby's opinion about it. And, of course, she needed to finally tell her about Tom's affair. She'd kept it to herself for a few weeks while trying to come to terms with the shock.

'Hi. It's bloody freezing,' said Libby, shivering. She linked arms with Rowan and they hurried across the road through a gap in the traffic. 'You can keep this British weather. Give me the Californian sunshine any day.'

Rowan didn't answer immediately. The mention of California had brought James to mind after she'd spent the last few weeks trying to dodge him and Helen. She'd heard them coming in through the front door of Magnolia House a couple of times when she'd been about to leave her apartment. She'd hovered out of view on both those occasions. The first time she'd dodged them, the hall was left with a lingering bouquet of Helen's floral perfume and the echo of her laughter. On the second occasion, a mouth-watering aroma of sweet and sour Chinese takeaway was left behind as Rowan had tiptoed across the Minton tiles to leave the house. The irony that she was creeping out of her own house hadn't escaped her. It had been as if she was a teenager again, escaping for an hour to meet friends while her parents had been asleep. To add to her jealousy, Ace was away for two weeks in Cancun with Alan. This meant that James and Helen had the apartment to themselves for ten days – and nights. What better way to reignite the old flame again?

But as Rowan walked arm in arm with her sister-in-law down Portobello Road, it wasn't James she wanted to talk about. She chewed her bottom lip, wondering how to phrase her next statement. She decided that there was no easy way of leading up to such an emotive subject. 'Tom was having an affair.'

Libby stopped walking. 'What?'

'I'm sorry, Libbs, but Tom was having an affair.'

Libby shook her head in disbelief. 'What makes you think that?'

'I had a phone call a couple of weeks ago asking for a contact number that Tom had. I charged his mobile to look for the number and came across some texts.'

'What did they say? You must have been reading more into them, surely?'

'Let's go in here.' Rowan pulled her inside a small café. 'I'll show you.'

Finding an empty table next to the bay window, they ordered two hot chocolates. While the waitress disappeared into the back kitchen, Rowan rummaged in her handbag for Tom's mobile phone. Having pressed a few buttons, she passed it to Libby. She watched as Libby scrolled through numerous messages, noticing how her eyebrows rose and her mouth opened wider as the seconds passed by.

'Shit! Do you know anyone with a name beginning with E?'

Rowan shook her head.

Libby was rereading the texts. 'I can't believe it. Tom?'

'He calls me R. There's something deeply insulting about

calling me by my initial. It's impersonal and dismissive. It's almost as bad as knowing he was having sex with someone else. It feels as disloyal and offensive as the act itself.'

'It was probably guilt. I know he loved you very much. Perhaps by not texting your full name he felt like he was keeping you out of their seedy affair.'

'Are you defending him?'

'Of course not. I'm horrified he's done this and so sorry. I'm just trying to say that, I don't know, that by not writing your name it was somehow protecting you.'

'We'll never know now, will we? Not that it matters. He was still screwing her.'

Libby winced. 'Don't hate him. I couldn't bear it if you hated him.'

Rowan didn't answer as she gazed out of the bay window at the shop fronts opposite displaying their wares. Clothes and Union Jacks danced in the breeze as they hung from hooks above folded sun canopies.

After a pause, Rowan said, 'I don't hate him. I've had a few weeks since finding out, to try and make sense of things. All I've come up with is that it changes nothing and yet it changes everything. How do you rage against a dead man? Sorry. I know that sounds awful, but how will I ever find out who E is if I can't ask Tom any questions? At the same time, I feel as though the man I was married to was a completely different person to the man in these texts. Like most relationships we had our difficulties but was our marriage only a success in my imagination?'

They waited while the waitress returned with two sweet-smelling hot chocolates. When she'd placed them on the table and left, Libby tried to reassure her friend.

'He loved you. It was probably a meaningless affair.'

'How can you say that? No affair is meaningless. It means you're bored, or fallen out of love, or that the life you're living isn't enough. No one cheats unless something is missing.'

'I don't know what to say.'

Rowan sat with her fingers entwined round her mug of hot chocolate and idly blew the steam away from her face. 'I feel shocked. Used. Stupid. At first I wondered what I'd done wrong. How had I created such a void in Tom's life that he felt he needed to fill it with another woman? But now that I've had a couple of weeks to think about it, I feel bloody furious, not guilty. I left Wilmslow for him. Gave up a good job to support his career. Happily invested my inheritance from Grandma into that house. Why do women do that, eh? Their husbands have an affair or leave the family, and it's the women who wonder what they've done wrong. It's crazy! I'm just left feeling bloody furious. But who can I direct my anger at? A memory? A photograph?'

'At E.'

'She'll have moved on and be destroying another marriage. E for bloody evil.'

'You could ring her number.'

'I did. There was a continuous out of service tone.'

'There aren't any dates on these texts.'

Rowan sipped her chocolate. 'I know. He'd had the phone for about three years so it's anyone's guess when it happened. It could have still been going on until ... you know.' She raised her eyes to the ceiling and groaned. 'It's as though I've been thumped in the stomach by a ghost. There's nothing to fight back against.'

'I'm so sorry. I feel partly responsible.'

'Why?'

'He was my brother. Should I have sensed it? I could ask David if he had any clues or if Tom ever hinted at anything.'

Rowan nibbled the skin around her thumbnail. 'How's David? How are things at home now?'

'Not great but we're talking, of a fashion. He's still really angry about the debt and secrets but he wants us to work it out. I'm job hunting and busy uploading lots of the things I'd bought on to eBay. I had the receipts for quite a few things, so I've made several trips to return stuff. We're okay. It's you I'm worried about.'

'Don't be. This has helped in a bizarre sort of way. I'll always love Tom, but this has freed me a little from the guilt I felt at moving on with my life. I can't keep selling bits of jewellery to a local shop and taking rent to pay the bills for years to come. James seems to be back with his ex, Ace is now in a steady relationship and Nora won't want to live in a basement when Primrose is going to school. I really don't want another group of strangers coming to live with me when they decide to move on. Also, I know those cryptic notes seemed to have stopped now, but I don't like the idea of some crazed stalker knowing where I live.'

'You're thinking of moving again, aren't you?'

'I think so. The house doesn't feel the same.'

'Please don't say you're moving back up North again. I've loved having you so close.'

Rowan smiled. 'I don't know how I'd have got through this last year without you. I'm not going back to Wilmslow. I was thinking of France.'

'France!' Heads turned in their direction. She said more quietly, 'France?'

'Mum and Dad live there and I sort of speak the language. I could live on a quarter of the money I spend in London and sell my jewellery to tourists and gift shops. Property is so much cheaper and I could earn more cash by doing a little bed and breakfast as a sideline.'

'My God, you've really thought about this.'

'I've had nothing else to do but make jewellery and think for the last few weeks.'

'What about James?'

Rowan felt herself blushing. 'What do you mean?'

'I thought you really liked him. I thought something might happen between you two.'

'Why? What makes you think that?'

'C'mon, Rowan. We've known each other for a long time. I've seen the way you both try hard not to look at each other while stealing furtive glances. I've listened to you tell me about him with a silly smile on your face. I've seen him fidget and be tongue-tied with you. It's okay to be attracted to someone else, you know?'

'I've felt guilty for liking him. Not that anything will happen now that Cruella de Vil is back on the scene.'

'Is she horrid?'

Rowan rested her chin on her fists and groaned. 'No, she seems lovely as well as being gorgeous. Even Helen's name conjures up mythological powers and beauty, being the name of Zeus's daughter. As for me, a Rowan is a short, hardy tree, with small leaves.

'Stop moaning. People pay to have your colour hair.'

'Okay, okay. I'll stop feeling sorry for myself, but Helen has got her man back so any possible future relationship with James stopped before it even started.'

'Is that the real reason you're running away?'

'Libby!'

'I'm sorry, but you can't seriously want to live in the depth of the French countryside twiddling away with metal and beads while cooking breakfast for overweight American tourists.'

'Excuse me, but I don't twiddle. I create.'

They both laughed.

'I don't know what I'm laughing at,' said Libby. 'My marriage is clinging on by a thread and my best mate is planning to cross the Channel.'

'The plane journey is just over an hour, so I could reach London faster than I could when I lived in Wilmslow. *And* you can visit me.'

'When are you thinking of doing this?'

'Maybe spring. I need to give everyone plenty of notice to find somewhere else to live and Christmas is just around the corner. I might spend it with Mum and Dad and have a little mooch about the estate agents out there.'

'What if Magnolia House takes a while to sell?'

'I'll extend the tenancy contracts a few months at a time while I stay with Mum and Dad. I've only been thinking about it for a short while, but I feel like it's the right move to make.'

The waitress brought the bill and slid it onto the table.

Rowan thanked her and reached for her handbag. She picked up Tom's mobile phone and dropped it inside. 'I'll get these. You bought the soup last time we went to town.' They stood up, re-fastened their coats and gathered their scarves and bags. Rowan placed a five-pound note on the table before they braced themselves against the late November chill.

Chapter Thirty-One

Libby sat on the top deck of a double-decker London bus, looking out at the passing landmarks. She'd left Rowan in Notting Hill because her sister-in-law wanted to call in at a jewellery shop to enquire about selling some of her work for Christmas gifts.

Libby had thought that her life was slowly getting back on track, but now two more worries were making her feel anxious. Her best friend was making plans to emigrate and her brother had been having an affair. She twisted her wedding ring around her finger. Both she and her brother had kept secrets from their partners. They'd both been deceitful.

As the bus crossed over Battersea Bridge, Libby looked out at the slate-grey Thames and tried to imagine her life without Rowan in it. Okay, she could have the odd weekend in France, but with all the debts she had to repay she couldn't imagine seeing her regularly.

Realising that she was still twisting her wedding ring, she rested her hands on her lap. It made a change to be going home from the shops without any carrier bags. David had made it clear that if they were going to get through this problem, she had to promise to try and find a new job and she had to stop buying things that weren't necessary. He hadn't treated her like a child and confiscated her bankcard, he'd trusted her to keep to her side of the bargain, and she was determined to prove him right.

Libby got off the bus on Balham High Street but instead of going straight home, she decided to call in at Mason's Closet, Ace's vintage clothing store. He and Alan had returned from their holiday in Cancun and Ace could always make her smile. Turning the corner, she saw outfits hanging on metal clothes racks outside his shop. Before going inside she flicked through the nearest rail of clothes. Original second-hand Levi jackets and a selection of leather bomber jackets took up half the rail. There were maxi skirts, cable-knit jumpers and T-shirts with screen icons pictured on the front. Hanging at each end were different coloured feather boas that looked as if they might take flight in the breeze.

'Look who we have here.' Ace sashayed out of the shop looking tanned and happy. 'You're looking a bit peaky, honey. What's the matter?' He air kissed Libby an inch away from each cheek. 'Mwah. Mwah.'

'I'm okay. Did you have a good holiday?'

'Sun, sea and sex. What's not to love.'

Libby chuckled. 'You're incorrigible.'

'And you're pasty. Come in and tell Uncle Mason all about it.'

He walked back inside his shop. As Libby entered, an over-powering smell of body odour and mothballs filled her nostrils. The shop usually smelt of patchouli joss sticks, not as if something had died. Ace saw her wrinkling her nose.

'I know, don't say a word,' he said, holding up the palm of his hand to her face. 'I asked Kevin to stand in for me while I was away and what does he do? Only accepted and hung up dirty clothes. I now have to go through all my stock, sniffing each item to throw out anything unsavoury. I've been sneezing all morning. I know it's cold today but I'll leave the door open a bit if it helps you.' He wedged it open with a second-hand pair of burgundy Doc Martens.

'Park your derriere. I'm all ears.'

Ace stood in front of Libby with arms folded, looking at her intently.

'I'm not sure you'd make a very good counsellor. I don't think it's a good technique to stand over your victim ... I mean patient, giving them the death stare.'

'This is my *paying attention* look,' said Ace.

'Would you mind continuing to sniff clothes while I have a moan? I think it'll help.'

'Women. No wonder I'm gay. I just don't understand you. I'm paying you one hundred per cent attention and it's still not good enough.' He turned to a nearby rack of shoes and stuck his nose inside the first one to test for hints of stagnation.

'You know about my ... my ...' said Libby.

'Your obsession for spending money you haven't got and being sacked for slagging off a client,' he said, picking up another pair of shoes.

Libby blinked. 'Okay. Don't hold back, will you?'

'Just telling it how it is.'

'Well, on top of that, I now find out that Tom was unfaithful to Rowan and she's leaving to live in France.'

Ace stood up with a leather moccasin still pressed against his nose, making his voice sound muffled. 'Isn't that an overreaction, especially as the poor guy passed away over a year ago?'

'She's not leaving because he was unfaithful. It's because she has a thing for somebody and that somebody has got back with his ex.'

'Poor girl. How did she find out?'

'She's seen them together over the past month or so.'

'No. I mean how did she find out about the affair?'

'She recharged Tom's mobile for a telephone number and all their texts were unashamedly there for all to see.'

'Careless.'

'Ace!'

'Sorry, but it is. The first rule of adultery is to cover your tracks.'

'Are you an expert in the field?'

'Cheeky. I'm a film buff who watches a lot of chick flicks.'

Ace picked up another leather shoe, held it to his nose and sniffed loudly. He slowly lowered the moccasin and looked at her. 'My brother has just got back with his ex and he lives in the same house as Rowan. Is there a connection?'

'No. Yes. Damn it! You can't say anything. She'll kill me.'

'Well, well. Rowan has a soft spot for James Gregory Oakland.'

'Gregory?'

'Mum had a thing for aging actors. Hence James and Mason.'

Libby looked blank.

'James Mason – the late British actor.'

'Yes, I know. I was wondering where the Gregory came in.'

'Gregory Peck was another actor from years ago.'

Libby giggled.

'What?' asked Ace.

'Does that mean your middle name is Peck?'

'Hilarious, I *don't* think. If you must know, it's Clint.'

Libby buried her head in a woolly hat that was lying on the counter and snorted. When she looked up, Mason was stood looking at her with pursed lips and raised eyebrows, which set her off again into hiccoughing laughter.

'I just knew I'd feel better if I came here,' said Libby.

'Laughing at someone else's expense isn't a very nice quality to possess,' said Ace, his lip twitching with amusement. 'Anyway, tell me more about Rowan and my brother.'

'There isn't anything to tell. That's why she feels it's okay to up and leave Magnolia House.'

'Do you mean she's selling it?'

'Listen, I shouldn't be telling you this. She'd be furious if I'd let on she had a thing for James and that she was moving. Can you keep it a secret until she tells you about it herself?'

'I'll do my best, but I'm not making any promises. James might need a little nudge in the right direction. I never did like that Helen much. Likes to put her oar in but can't row the boat.'

'Eh?'

'Opinionated and fickle.'

'You don't think it'll last then?'

'From what James says, they're seeing each other but not dating. Sort of, getting to know each other again. Whatever that means. In my opinion they're just not suited. James is laid-back, loves to teach, works with natural materials and is a genuinely nice guy. Helen is a high maintenance diva who doesn't have much natural about her: false nails, false tits, false eyelashes and false hair extensions. I could go on.'

'I've set you off on a mission, haven't I? God, I'm in so much trouble.' Libby sunk her head into her arms again. 'I wish I'd never said anything.'

Two students walked in through the open shop door. They hadn't even started to sort through the clothing before they wrinkled their noses and left again.

'That's it. Get sniffing, will you?' said Ace. 'Two noses are better than one. I've got to find the offending articles or I'll have to get environmental health in.'

An idea sprang to Libby's mind. 'Are you offering me a job, Mason Clint?'

'I'd call it a temporary olfactory workout.'

'You can dress it up however you like. It's still working

for you. What do you say? If I work a couple of days a week, I'll sort the stock into sizes, tidy out the store room and clean this mess,' she said, running her finger along the grimy worktop.

'Vintage clothes have vintage dust. It comes with the territory.'

'Is that a no?'

Ace thought for a moment. 'I suppose I could help Alan out a bit. He's been pestering me to help him with a plumbing job in Brighton for weeks.' He pinched his lips with his fingers in thought. 'Okay. Can you work tomorrow and see how things go?'

'You mean I've got a job?'

'I can't pay much.'

'How much is not much?'

'Let's see what you manage to sell first.'

The following day, buoyed by the excitement of having something positive to do with her day, Libby arrived before eight o'clock at Mason's Closet. The shop usually opened at ten, but she'd come laden with cleaning materials and a colourful plant. David had dropped her off before he'd set off to the office for an early meeting, before spending the rest of the day working from home.

Ace had found the pungent piece of clothing the previous afternoon. The malodourous article had been a parker coat that smelt as if someone had been living in it for several years. It was now rotting away in the local tip.

Libby switched on the shop radio and set about disinfecting the sales counter, shelves and racks. She mopped the floors and polished the shop window. Then it took half an hour to hang the jackets and coats together, fold jeans and tidy the shoe rack. Just before ten o'clock, she placed the pillar-box-red poinsettia plant next to the till and stood back to admire it. Finally, she unwrapped the outfit that she'd spent an hour hunting for last evening. After a little tussle with the ancient mannequin, it stood proudly in the shop window wearing an old Father Christmas outfit. The shop looked tidy and smelt fresh. The storeroom could wait for another day.

Chapter Thirty-Two

'How did you get on yesterday? Did they want to buy some of your jewellery?'

Rowan balanced her lampwork torch on its stand and readjusted her mobile phone so she could hear Libby more clearly.

'Yes, it was worth calling in. They've commissioned two necklace and earring sets for starters and said they'd see how much interest they got in them.'

'That's great. I'm really pleased for you.'

'Thanks. How are you?'

'I'm fine. Guess where I am?'

'At home? In town? At my front door?'

'Nope, nope and nope. I'm behind a cash desk at work.'

'You went back to Tea Rose?'

'Of course not. I'm working a couple of days a week at Mason's Closet.'

'Ace's shop?'

'How many Mason's Closets do you know?'

'I didn't know he was looking for staff.'

'He wasn't really. I sort of made him an offer he couldn't refuse.'

'I'm guessing it wasn't a sexual favour or you wouldn't have got very far.'

Libby laughed. 'It was a disinfecting favour with a bit of expert clothes folding thrown in for good measure.'

'Well done. What does David think?'

'He was a bit iffy to start with. He thought it was a case of friends being charitable and feeling sorry for me, but I explained that I'd be working for my money, not just receiving a handout. I know it'll only be pocket money of sorts, but every little helps until I can find something more permanent. It sounds as if the more I sell, the more money I'll earn, so I've got my sleeves metaphorically and physically rolled up and ready to sell some paraphernalia.'

'That's really good news. Hey, perhaps Ace could have a little counter with some jewellery in it?'

'Hmm, not sure your stuff would sell here. People are looking for a vintage bargain not contemporary quality pieces.'

'I like that. Can I quote you?'

'Of course. Contemporary quality pieces as described by junk shop assistant, Elizabeth Jenkins.'

'Don't let Ace hear you call it junk. You'll get the sack on day one.' Rowan grimaced into her mobile. 'Sorry, words were out before my brain was in gear.'

'It's fine. I'm glad I got sacked. I hated working there.'

'I'll call in and see you later.'

'That'd be great. Come and tell me what you think of the changes I've made. Oh, someone's come in. I'd better dash.'

'See you later then.'

'Bye.'

Rowan fastened Jet's harness before leaving her apartment with him. She was wrapped up in her padded jacket, scarf and gloves, looking forward to a brisk walk on the common having worked on her jewellery for three hours. At six o'clock that morning she'd lain in bed tossing and turning from side to side, stressed over her new order and wondering whether she could deliver the pieces before the deadline of the weekend. Since getting up early, Rowan had completed another necklace and only had two earrings sets left to make. She'd proudly laid them out on her workbench to admire; pleased with her choice of beads and the way the colours complemented each piece.

On reaching the hallway, Ace's front door opened. Realising that she was likely to bump into James and Helen, Rowan fumbled with the door handle trying to hurriedly leave the house before they saw her. As the front door opened, a gust of wind blew a flurry of brown crinkled leaves into the hallway where they spiralled on the Minton tiles. Jet made a playful lunge for them causing the lead to tangle around Rowan's legs, essentially immobilising her.

'Hang on. I've got it.'

Rowan turned to see James hurrying towards her. He crouched and untangled Jet's lead, touching her thighs with his arms as he unwound it.

'That was a close one,' he said. 'He nearly had you over.'

'He's desperate to get out. I should've taken him when I woke up at six, but it was dark so I put in a few hours of work. I picked up a new commission in Notting Hill. I went with Libby to do a little Christmas shopping.' She felt silly, aware that she was prattling on.

'That's great. Ace tells me Libby's in employment again, too.'

'Yes. Good news. Right. I'll take Jet then.'

James laid a hand on Rowan's wrist. 'How are you? I haven't seen you for ages.'

'I'm fine. I haven't popped downstairs because, well, I haven't wanted to disturb you and Helen.' She flicked a hand into the air as if it was of no consequence. 'I'm sure you have a lot to catch up on and don't need any interruptions.' Rowan held his gaze for a few seconds.

'It's not like that,' said James. 'We're just hanging out a bit.'

Is that what they call a relationship nowadays, thought Rowan.

'It's nice to see you,' he continued.

Nice, thought Rowan. What a bland word. He could

have used it to describe seeing his distant cousin twice removed. She noticed that his hair had been cut into a new style, shorter at the back but still longer at the front. Several strands hung sexily in his eyes. It suited him. To complete the alluring look, he wore loose-fitting jeans with a work belt slung low around his hips, tools hanging from its loops. His jeans were tucked casually into chunky boots that gave him a sexy Oliver Mellors type appearance; not that she looked anything like Lady Chatterley in her quilted coat and unwashed hair.

'You look tired,' said James.

'That'll be the lack of make-up. You look ...' *don't say gorgeous* '... like you've got a busy day ahead.'

'Yep. I got talked into making some garden furniture for Helen's parents while they're away. Apparently the patio set has seen better days and they want some raised beds making out of old railway sleepers. I'm just off to measure up and look at the layout of the garden. Wrong time of the year, if you ask me, but I'm not complaining about the money and neither is Ace.'

Rowan looked over James' shoulder. 'Isn't Helen with you?'

'No. She's lent me a bike that used to be her brother's. I'm quite looking forward to cycling there. I could do with getting fit again.' He patted his stomach.

It looked taut to Rowan and for a moment she was lost for words. A lacklustre 'Good,' was all she could muster.

James pulled on a thick reefer jacket. 'I don't suppose we're going to get much done if we both stand about chatting. Enjoy your walk.' He bent down and rubbed Jet's head. 'Don't pull for your mum.' He stood up smiling. 'See you.'

'Bye.'

She watched him walk past the skeletal magnolia tree,

a hammer and screwdriver hanging from his belt and chinking together with each step he took. He unlocked the bike that he'd fastened to the drainpipe and pushed it onto the pavement. Swinging one leg over the seat, he raised a hand to wave as he pedalled down the road.

It didn't seem that long ago that they'd gone together on a dog walk with Jet, she thought. They'd strolled through the common, stopping at the little café near the bandstand and talked much more easily than they'd just done now. What had happened to change things so drastically?

Five minutes later as she crossed the main road leading to Clapham Common, it occurred to Rowan that there were two main reasons for her sudden inability to converse with him light-heartedly. The first was Helen. Rowan felt sidelined, jealous and angry. *She* had been James' confidante and friend and now Helen had usurped her. She was cross with her for turning up out of the blue and angry with James for dropping their friendship so swiftly. The sooner she left for France, the better, because the second reason she felt unable to relax when she was with him was because she'd fallen in love with James Gregory Oakland.

Forty-five minutes later, following a contemplative walk past the lido to the bandstand and back, Rowan stopped just inside her garden gate and stared at the front door. It was ajar. She thought back to her earlier conversation with James and had to admit to herself that she couldn't recall closing it.

She hurried in through the front door and shut it behind her. Everything was quiet as she stood and listened. Jet began to pull towards the stairs so Rowan let him lead the way up to her apartment. A few steps from the top, she caught her breath. Her apartment door was open. A rush of adrenalin made her heart beat faster. Surely she had closed it? Her ears strained for any sound.

'Hello,' she called. 'Who's there?'

Rowan looked at Jet. He was panting from his walk but not showing any sign that an intruder was in their home. She bent to unfasten his harness, leaving him free to run through the open door. She heard him pad into the kitchen and start lapping from his water bowl just as he did after every walk. Feeling a little more reassured, Rowan walked hesitantly through the door and looked around. Everything was just as she'd left it. She knew she'd been stressed that morning, but could she really have left for Jet's walk without shutting her door? She must have done. After all, she'd left the front door to Magnolia House unlocked, too.

She breathed a sigh of relief, pushed the door closed and followed Jet into the kitchen. Filling a glass with tap water, she took several gulps before taking her coat off. She really must get her act together, she thought. What if those notes *were* from a psychotic stalker? She may as well have written him an invitation to come and get her.

'I'll feed you in a minute, boy,' she said, walking towards her bedroom. She lifted down a coat hanger, slipped her coat onto it and hung it up. Glancing across at her workbench, she noticed that the necklace she'd made earlier wasn't on her workbench.

'I'm sure I left it there,' she said, aloud. A shiver ran up her spine. She *had* left it there. She'd been admiring the colours, pleased with her efforts and had laid it out flat.

Someone had been in her apartment. Someone had taken it.

Rowan ran back out of her apartment and downstairs, closely followed by Jet. She hammered on Ace's door, knowing that James was out, but hoping that Ace might be at home. No one answered. She turned and knocked on Nora's door that led down to the basement. Again, the door remained unanswered. Rowan hurried back upstairs and dialled Libby's mobile number.

'Hello.'

'Libby, someone's been in my apartment and stolen some jewellery I made this morning. No one's in and I don't know what to do.' Rowan could hear the tremor in her own voice as she spoke.

'Did you see them?'

'No. I've just come back from walking Jet. Should I call the police?'

'Of course. If someone's broken in you must call them straight away.'

'But they didn't break in. I left the door open. I left both the bloody doors open.'

'Why?'

'What do you mean, why? I didn't do it purposefully. I just forgot.'

'Okay, but you must still call the police if you're sure something's gone missing.'

'I definitely left the jewellery laid out on my workbench before I took Jet, and it's not there now.'

'Okay. Ring them and I'll phone David because he's working at home today. He'll be with you very soon. Ring them now and tell them about the anonymous notes, too. Make sure your door is shut until they arrive.'

Libby turned off her mobile, having told David about her phone conversation with Rowan. She leant back in the chair that was next to the till. What a day it was turning out to be. Just before Rowan had phoned, she'd been counting the cash she'd made during her first morning's work. It was only midday and she'd sold clothes and shoes to the value of £97. Ace often moaned that he'd only taken half that amount in a whole day. She couldn't wait to tell him of her success. It had been quite simple. A fresh smelling shop with organised clothing and a warm greeting accompanied by a friendly smile. It had been nothing more than putting in a little effort and customer service. But now, all she could think about was David rushing to her sister-in-law's side before the police arrived. She'd give it half an hour and then give him a call to see what was happening.

After twenty minutes and having just sewn a button on a pair of trousers, Libby was leafing through a magazine when laughter made her look up. Three students were browsing through the rail outside. If only she could make one more sale, she'd phone Ace and tell him that she'd sold over £100 worth of stock during her first morning.

One of the youths was tying a feather boa around his friend's neck. Libby listened to their bantering while she moved the electric heater to an angle that blew warm air onto her legs. She'd turned cold since she'd stopped rushing around and the door was wedged open.

Ace's radio was tuned in to the local station. The DJ announced that it was eleven forty-five as the teenagers came into the shop. Libby was listening to a weather warning. Snow had fallen over the country north of Nottingham and was making its way south. Roads were blocked and schools had been closed for safety reasons.

She looked up at the lads. 'Snow's forecast,' she said with a smile and raised her eyebrows. 'That's all we need, isn't it?'

One of them came towards the desk. He leant forwards, his face stopping a few inches from her face. His breath smelt of tobacco and alcohol. 'Wrong, actually. All we need is the money from the till.'

'Sorry?'

'No need to be sorry, lady. Just give us the money from the till and be quick.'

This had to be a joke, thought Libby. The police had only just been called to Magnolia House. This was just too much of a coincidence. As the newsreader calmly informed listeners that local house prices had risen over the last quarter, Libby realised that two of the youths had scarves over their noses and mouths and the third one, who seemed to be waiting close to the doorway, had the feather boa over the lower part of his face.

Libby's thoughts of proudly telling Ace she'd made £100 suddenly disintegrated. She'd have to tell him that she'd lost stock and money. It was the last thing she wanted to do. Anger rose inside her and adrenalin coursed through her veins making her heart race. 'Leave now,' she shouted. 'Leave now and I won't call the police.' Inane thoughts of *Crimewatch* on television entered her thoughts for a split second.

The man at the door signalled with a thumbs-up sign. Perhaps it meant that no one was nearby.

'There won't be no fuckin' trouble 'cause you're gonna hand over the cash, ain't that right?'

When she didn't move, more from fear than bravery, one of the teenagers hurried around to her side of the counter. Libby instinctively put up her arms to protect herself but she was pushed into the counter. The sharp corner jabbed into her abdomen, making her cry out in agony. This seemed to panic the group.

'What the hell did you do?' yelled the lad at the door.

'Just fuckin' pushed her.'

Libby was doubled-up and wailing loudly.

'Two old biddies are coming. Hurry!'

Libby was aware of the scuffling of feet, leaflets being

scattered to the floor and footsteps running away. Her stomach was on fire with hot stabbing pains as she sat crouched on her heels leaning against the cash desk.

Chapter Thirty-Three

Nora was sitting at the pine dining table with Primrose in the basement of Magnolia House, spending precious time with her daughter, painting and sticking pictures together. The sky was darkening with low charcoal-coloured clouds. Nora glanced up at the sound of soft tapping on the casement windows.

'Look, darling, it's started to snow.'

Lamps were lit in the apartment and the warm radiators occasionally clicked. Disney's *Beauty and the Beast* played on the television in the background with Nora occasionally bursting into song along with Belle. She showed her daughter how to squeeze a little glue onto golden stars and silver hearts, before guiding her fingers to stick the shapes onto some sugar paper and sprinkle with glitter.

'That's it. Just a little squeeze because we don't want to spoil the pretty picture, do we?'

'Doowee,' said Primrose.

'Good girl. What a clever helper you are?'

She kissed the top of her daughter's curly hair. 'Oh, that's Mummy's phone ringing.' Nora pushed her dining table chair back and went to fetch her mobile phone from the bedside table.

'Hello.'

'Hello. Is that Nora Adams?'

'Yes.'

'Do you know someone called Elizabeth?'

'Who are you?'

'My name's Ken. I'm a paramedic and we've been called to a shop in Balham where a young lady has been assaulted.'

'How have you got my number?'

'I have the young lady's mobile and she mentioned her husband's name but he's not picking up. Your name is the first female name on her contact list.'

'But I don't know anyone called Elizabeth. Where are you exactly?'

Nora heard the paramedic call to a colleague to shout him the name of the shop.

'It's called Mason's Closet.'

'Libby. Yes I know her. It's her first day today. Is she all right?'

'We're taking her to the Chelsea and Westminster Hospital now. Would you be able to contact her next of kin?'

'Of course. Her sister-in-law lives upstairs. I'll go and let her know.'

Nora hurried into her bedroom again and grabbed her handbag. She threw her mobile phone into it and unhooked her and Primrose's coats from the back of the bedroom door. Within three minutes, Nora was carrying her daughter up the stairs to Rowan's apartment. She knocked loudly on the front door.

Nora heard Jet bark and Rowan shushing him before the door opened.

'Libby's been hurt at Ace's shop. We've got to let David know and go and see if she's all right.'

'Hurt? What do you mean?'

Nora saw the panic in Rowan's eyes. 'The paramedic said she'd been assaulted. He rang from her mobile and said they were taking her to hospital.'

'I'll grab my coat.' Rowan disappeared back into her lounge.

Nora yelled after her, 'Do you know if James is in?'

Rowan reappeared wearing her padded jacket. 'He went

out this morning to measure up for some garden furniture. I don't know if he's back. Why?'

'I wondered if he'd watch Primrose for an hour.'

'You could knock. Have you called David?'

'The paramedic said he tried but got no answer. I don't have his number in my phone.'

'He came round here an hour ago to check on things. Long story. I'll try him again but he's probably got his phone on silent.'

They hurried downstairs where Nora hammered on Ace's front door and Rowan tried to contact David. James opened the door, holding a newspaper in his hands.

'I need to ask a huge favour,' said Nora.

'What's the matter?'

'Libby's been assaulted and we've got to go to A and E. Would you mind if Primrose sat and watched television with you for an hour?'

'Is she okay?'

'We don't know. We haven't been told much.'

'Of course I'll have Primrose, but you'd better come in for a minute and settle her.'

Five minutes later, Rowan and Nora were running towards the station amidst a ticker tape of snowflakes. They hurried wordlessly towards the station where they bought tickets and walked down the escalator, oblivious to the myriad of adverts enticing the public to visit shows at nearby theatres. A train arrived with a rush of air, the doors hissed open and a stream of passengers got off.

'I need to get fit,' said Nora, taking a seat. 'You'd think running around after a toddler all day wouldn't leave me so breathless after a short run.'

'Me too.' Rowan rested her head against the window and sighed.

'Try not to worry. I'm sure she'll be okay,' said Nora.

'I hope so. But it's not just Libby. I've had a dreadful morning.'

Nora sat forwards. 'Why? You said David had called round to check on things.'

'I went out without closing the doors this morning. I took Jet for a walk and when I got back and went upstairs, my jewellery wasn't where I'd left it. Libby said to call the police.'

Nora looked shocked. 'This morning? How come I missed all this? I only spent an hour with Primrose at the local playgroup.'

'The police were only there for ten minutes. It was so embarrassing. I had just explained to one policeman that I'd left both doors open, when the other officer came out of my bedroom holding the missing jewellery.'

'Where had you put it?'

'Apparently it was on top of the wardrobe. It doesn't make sense. Then I had to sit through a patronising lecture about locking doors and always placing valuables out of sight before I leave the house. I've got absolutely no recollection of putting them up there. I never put things on top of the wardrobe. I can't find a set of earrings I made this morning either, but I'm not calling them back. And now Libby's in hospital. What a crazy day.'

'Perhaps you're stressed. When people have too much going on, their mind plays tricks with them and they forget things.'

'Maybe, but surely the memory should come back once you've been reminded. I'm sure I'd pass a lie detector test to say that I didn't put my jewellery on top of my wardrobe.'

'But you didn't remember the doors, did you?'

Rowan shook her head and nibbled a thumbnail.

The journey seemed to take an age, so it was with great

relief when the train pulled in at the station and they made their way to the exit. Before long, Rowan and Nora were hurrying down several corridors of the hospital, looking for A and E.

'This way,' said Rowan, pointing to a sign next to a lift.

Having turned left, the corridor opened up into a lobby. They walked to the reception desk where a young woman with an uneven conker-brown spray tan was sitting at her computer.

'Can I help you?' she asked, without looking up.

'We're looking for Elizabeth Jenkins.'

The woman glanced up. 'One minute and I'll check for you.'

'Mrs Elizabeth Jenkins has been transferred to Nightingale Ward, second floor.'

'Thank you.'

They turned back the way they'd just come. Once upstairs, they were disappointed not to be allowed onto the ward.

'I'm sorry, but visiting hours don't start until four o'clock,' said a nurse. 'Mrs Jenkins is about to have a laparoscopy, so I'd come back after six if I were you.'

'What's a laparoscopy?' asked Nora.

'I'm sorry. I can't discuss this with you. We've contacted Mr Jenkins and he's on his way. Perhaps you should speak with him later.'

Back at Magnolia House, James was having a terrible time. Primrose had been crying for the last twenty minutes and he hadn't a clue what to do to stop her. He'd carried her, jiggled her, pointed out objects around the flat, played peep-bo from behind his hands and had made her a glass of orange juice. The juice had temporarily stopped the tears, but they soon began again in earnest when he tipped the glass too steeply and cold sticky juice trickled down the front of her clothing.

'Sorry, little one. I'm useless at this, aren't I?'

James undid her wet cardigan and took it off. With a small child wailing in the middle of the kitchen floor, James felt helpless and out of his depth. He stood looking at her little body with an orange stain soaked through each layer of clothing and her face smeared with tears and mucous. His raised his hands to his head and raked his fingers through his hair. What Primrose needed was clean dry clothes and perhaps her favourite soft toy.

He bent down and lifted the little girl up into his arms. Patting her back gently, he walked towards the apartment door. 'I think we'd better check if Mummy's left the door unlocked so we can find some clean clothes, don't you?'

'Mummy,' said Primrose, between wails.

'She won't be long, honey. Mummy won't be long.'

James walked along the hall towards the basement door. He tried the handle and could have kissed its paintwork when it opened. Thank goodness Nora had been in such a rush.

Once downstairs, he pushed open another door that led into the lounge. He'd only been down here a couple of times before, once when Primrose had been poorly with chickenpox and once to help Nora carry the pushchair downstairs. It was warm and homely, with crescents of light spilling from several lamps. He could see that Nora had been entertaining her daughter with paints and felt a new respect for his neighbour. She was a good mother. Primrose had stopped crying and was relaxed in his arms for the first time since Nora had left. He wandered into the bedroom and saw a child-sized bed next to a larger double bed. A rag doll was lying on the smaller bed.

'Who's this?' asked James, picking it up.

'Lou-Lou.'

'Pleased to meet you, Lou-Lou.'

James handed her the rag doll. Primrose tucked it under one arm and started to twiddle its long hair. She wrapped the wool hair around her fingers and then slowly unwound it so the wool tickled her hand.

'Ah, so that's the magic that keeps you happy.'

James sat her in the middle of Nora's bed so that she wouldn't fall off and then searched for a clean vest and top. 'Now then, where does Mummy keep your clothes?'

'Mummy,' said Primrose, but continued twiddling the woollen hair, without tears.

James opened a few drawers but could only find Nora's clothes. He felt very uncomfortable searching through someone else's personal things and wondered whether to leave Primrose in her damp clothes after all. As he was about to leave, he noticed that the little girl's bed had divan drawers beneath it. He slid one open and was relieved to find piles of neatly folded clothes inside. He chose a white vest and soft blue jumper.

'Won't Mummy be impressed with Uncle James?' He gently pulled the little girl's T-shirt and vest off. 'He found your Lou-Lou *and* clean clothes.'

With Primrose clean, dry and comforted, James threw the wet clothes into a linen basket in the corner of the bedroom before lifting the little girl into his arms again.

'Shall we try again with a drink of juice, but use your beaker this time?'

Back in the kitchen he saw a pink plastic beaker on the pine table. 'Here it is and it's still got some juice in it.'

Primrose took the proffered beaker and with elbows raised, drained it with satisfied gulps. While she drank, James stared at the paperwork on the table, his heart racing. Readjusting the little girl on his hip, he moved a sheet of sugar paper covered in hearts and stars, to reveal a half-hidden sheet beneath. He shuffled the cuttings from the newspaper around with his fingers. Nora had been cutting letters out of them and sticking them onto paper to form words. The words spelt out on the paper read,

lOOK at The WiDe n picTU7e!

James' mouth hung open in shock. He breathed deeply. He looked at the angelic face of the innocent little girl in his arms. It was unbelievable. He touched the cuttings as if just looking at the evidence wasn't enough. Nora had sent Rowan the messages. But why? And how was he going to tell Rowan? She'd never believe him.

Thinking a little more clearly for a moment, James pulled out his mobile phone while precariously holding Primrose on his hip. He took a photograph of the note and debris of cuttings on the table before slipping his phone back into his pocket. It would be difficult enough persuading Rowan to believe that her close friend was sending her the cryptic messages, without Nora vehemently denying it having cleaned the table of the evidence. He placed Primrose's picture on top of the cryptic message.

Half an hour later and back upstairs, Primrose had fallen asleep on his sofa bed while James paced the lounge floor. Should he face Nora and insist she stop this bizarre letter campaign or should he speak to Rowan? He could really do with a beer right now, but knew it wouldn't go down well to smell of alcohol if there was to be some sort of a showdown.

He flinched at the sound of the main front door opening and voices becoming louder in the hallway. He recognised them as Rowan and Nora. There was a knock. Primrose moved her head before settling again. James closed his eyes, inhaled deeply and walked towards the apartment door. He'd play it by ear; see how the conversation panned out.

He opened the door to see Nora standing in front of him while Rowan lingered in the background near the stair post.

'Has she been good?' asked Nora, stepping into the room.

'She had a few tears at first. She's on the sofa.' James could hear that his voice sounded strained. He watched Nora walk towards the settee and crouch down to stroke her daughter's hair.

James turned to Rowan, who was leaning against the bannister in the hallway. 'How's Libby?'

'They wouldn't let us see her. Next of kin only because it wasn't visiting time. A nurse said she was waiting for a laparoscopy. I'm really worried.'

James heard her voice break and saw tears fill her eyes. Without thinking, he stepped forwards into the hall and folded his arms around her shoulders, pulling her towards him. 'I'm sure she'll be okay. She's in the best place and you can visit her later. I'll come with you, if you like.' He felt her sink closer against his body and could feel her breath on his collarbone, surprised at the heat it sent through his body. Helen didn't make him feel so protective or give him such a corporeal longing like this. Rowan's hair smelt of peaches, probably her shampoo, and it was damp from melted snowflakes. He closed his eyes and inhaled deeply. This was where he wanted to be. This is where hc felt he belonged.

James heard a noise and looked up. The front door had been left half open and he saw Helen glaring at him. He didn't let go of Rowan despite Helen's presence. They weren't officially a couple and all he was doing was comforting a friend. A friend he wished was more.

'Hi, Helen. Rowan's had a shock. Her sister-in-law's been attacked and is in hospital.'

Rowan pulled away on hearing his explanation. She gave

a thin-lipped smile to Helen. 'Hello.' She turned back to James. 'Thank you. I'd best be off.'

Nora joined them, cradling a sleeping Primrose. 'Thank you for looking after her, James. You're a star. See you all later.' She walked to the basement door and went down the stairs.

James watched Rowan walk towards the stairs before Helen strode past him and closed the apartment door, blocking his view. She smelt like a perfume shop and with overtones of tobacco smoke. He hadn't had a chance to speak to Rowan about his discovery downstairs and Nora hadn't seemed to notice her daughter's change of clothing.

'I've bought lots. Let me show you. Nail varnish, a pair of boots and a gorgeous little skirt.'

James felt his mood puncture and followed her into the flat. He was going to have to end this ... whatever *this* was. What did you call the odd meal, occasional kiss and infrequent trips out? He hadn't even felt the desire to sleep with Helen, despite her repeated attempts to coerce him into bed.

Chapter Thirty-Four

The aroma of a roast dinner along with antiseptic spray, lingered in the four-bed bay on Nightingale Ward. Libby was leafing through an old magazine she'd found in the day room. The cloying smell of vegetables from her untouched dinner plate was making her feel queasy. She'd never eaten a roast dinner as early as noon before and certainly couldn't face it today with the familiar dull pain in her abdomen. She closed the out of date magazine with a frustrated sigh and looked around the ward at the three other patients. Two women were dozing after their dinners and the third was walking, hunched like a Lowry figure, towards the bathroom while dragging a drip stand behind her. The bare cupboards were devoid of flowers due to the hospital's fear of spreading infection, so the only colours in the room were from the gaudy dressing gowns belonging to the patients.

Poor David had arrived yesterday afternoon as soon as he'd heard about her accident. He'd looked so pale and concerned, making her feel relieved to know that he obviously still loved her. It had felt so good to have his arms around her again.

With a sudden swish, the curtains around her bed were swiftly pulled closed by a figure in navy blue. Libby jumped in surprise. Once the curtains were shielding them from prying eyes, Ace sat on her bed and winked.

'Missed you.' Ace had tears in his eyes. 'I stayed at Alan's and had forgotten my mobile charger. It wasn't until I called in at the shop and saw police tape ... I was so worried.'

'I'm fine,' said Libby. 'Stop worrying and give me a hug.'

Ace squeezed her gently and stood up. 'God, you look

awful in that hospital gown. It hasn't got any shape and whoever designed it deserves a long prison sentence.'

Libby smiled. 'They weren't designed for catwalks. They were designed for comfort and easy access. Anyway, how on earth did you get past Nurse-Visiting-Times-Only? Even David couldn't get in yesterday until four o'clock on the dot.'

Ace stood up and gave a twirl in his navy blue boiler suit. 'Alan lent me this while I helped him out with a plumbing job. I followed the housekeeper through the ward door and no one batted an eyelid.'

'You mean you broke into the women's ward?'

'You know fluffy slippers and negligees don't press my buttons.'

Libby saw Ace's face soften.

'How are you feeling, Libbs? I feel so guilty?'

'Why do you feel guilty? It wasn't your fault. Did you know I made nearly a hundred pounds yesterday morning?'

'Seriously?'

'Yes, I was really enjoying myself until they came in. But it hasn't put me off. I loved chatting to customers and rearranging the stock.'

'You haven't told me what the doctors have said about your pain. I heard you'd had stomach ache and were having a lobotomy.'

Libby giggled. 'A laparoscopy. I had it yesterday evening under a general anaesthetic. That's why I had to stay in overnight. They wanted to keep an eye on me. The ward round is scheduled shortly and they'll give me the results then. They suggested it was just deep bruising. It's only a dull ache now, not as painful as yesterday.'

'Well, that's a relief.'

'How was Brighton and working with Alan?'

Ace beamed. 'I loved it. You wouldn't imagine it could

be so much fun lying on a bathroom floor fiddling with a U-bend. But working with Alan was such a laugh. I just drank coffee, passed him tools, drank more coffee, chatted with old dears and presented him with a length of hose occasionally. Wink, wink.'

'You dirty old man.'

'The innuendos were ridiculous and the old dears had no idea.'

'Like what?' asked Libby, sitting forward.

'Alan was seriously telling a woman that her plastic nipple had become wedged and he needed to fetch a nipple extractor from the van. Seriously, I nearly damaged my own plumbing trying not to laugh.'

Libby wiped the tears of laughter from her eyes. 'What's a plastic nipple?'

'It's a short piece of tubing that connects two pipes. But you know how it is when you know you shouldn't laugh and you have to be professional. I really don't think I've had so much fun in years. We talked about us working together.'

'What? Full-time?'

'Yeh. Alan and Ace. *AA Plumbers do it with knobs on.*'

Libby snorted behind her cupped hands and Ace cackled loudly. This caused them both to laugh even louder. As they were both rolling around, the curtains were drawn back. Light flooded the bed and a group of eight doctors stood looking at them both. The ward round had begun.

Rowan lay on her bed, her arm draped around Jet's warm body. Occasionally he nudged her with his wet nose to encourage her to stroke him again, which she did. Her thoughts were crowding her head and squabbling with each other.

I'm nearly thirty-three, she thought. In seven years I'll be forty. Isn't that middle-aged? And what have I achieved?

I'm a widow with a stupid crush on a tenant downstairs. My husband was shagging someone else. I pretend I have a jewellery business when really I'm selling odd bits to two measly shops. I'm planning to run away before I'm forced to sell up and I'm the shameful owner of a criminal record, albeit earned innocently.

But what about James? How could she compete with a beautiful, leggy blonde who was ten years younger than her? Not only that, but now she had to add the missing earrings and the mystery of the moved jewellery to her list of anxieties along with the anonymous notes. She was even beginning to doubt herself. Perhaps she'd absentmindedly put the jewellery on top of the wardrobe?

A distant siren made her think of Libby and put an end to her self-pitying musings. Libby was still in hospital, struggling with infertility, the loss of her brother *and* trying to keep her marriage together. Her tenant, Nora, didn't have it easy either. She'd struggled by herself to bring up Primrose and never seemed to moan. Rowan sat up. 'This is ridiculous,' she said, out loud. 'This isn't me. I don't sit about feeling sorry for myself. I need to get on.'

Jet wagged his tail in response.

'I've got you, good friends and my health,' she said, ruffling the soft fur beneath his ears. 'It stops here.' She patted his belly, making a hollow sound.

Swinging her legs over the side of the bed she silently rebuked herself for such maudlin, self-indulgent thoughts. She pulled the chair out from her work desk, determined to move on. Reaching for a pen and notepad, she began scribbling down ideas. It was time to make plans to live abroad. To move on to a beautiful part of the world that she'd always loved. She'd widen her list of jewellery by designing anklets and toe rings for the sun-kissed holidaymakers. She'd set up a website and sell her jewellery online and could set up a market stall in the local square. There's no way she could rely on her tenants for an income forever. Ace would probably move in with Alan and James would be moving back to his own flat next summer, if he hadn't moved in with Helen beforehand. And poor Nora couldn't be expected to continue to live in a cramped one-bedroom basement with a growing child. They would all leave and with them would go the steady income. Yes she could advertise for new tenants, but now she craved peace and being able to close her front door and having her own private space. And who knows? The future might include a handsome Frenchman who could teach her vocabulary and grammar while they sipped wine as the sun slowly sank in the Charente skyline. A year ago she hadn't known James and she'd coped. She'd cope again.

Jet jumped off the bed and curled in a ball beneath Rowan's feet underneath the workbench. Meanwhile Rowan continued to scribble down ideas with a strange feeling growing inside her. It was excitement for the future.

Ace had been politely asked to leave the ward and had been invited to return at visiting time. Libby was sure she'd seen a twist of a smile on the consultant's lips when Ace had replied, 'I'm sorry, dah-ling, I mean, m'lord,' before bowing and shimmying along the corridor.

The team of doctors assembled around her bed and the curtains were closed once again.

'Good morning, Mrs Jenkins. I'm Mr Sherbourne. I performed your laparoscopy yesterday. How are you feeling today?'

Libby looked at Mr Sherbourne. He was a tall, grey-haired man, dressed in a white shirt and burgundy tie. She felt a little overwhelmed with ten pairs of eyes and ears waiting for her to respond.

'Not too bad, thank you. I still have a dull ache but it's not as bad as yesterday.'

'I think I can explain that. The camera picked up moderate endometriosis.' Mr Sherbourne turned to a red-haired junior doctor. 'Can you explain to Mrs Jenkins what endometriosis is, Dr Powell?'

Dr Powell blushed like a ripe tomato and fiddled with the stethoscope around his neck. 'Erm, it's from the Greek endon which means "within" and metra which means "womb".'

'I'm sure our patient isn't interested in the meaning of the word. I'm pretty certain that Mrs Jenkins would be more interested in the mechanics and how it affects her body.'

Dr Powell slid a finger around the inside of his tight collar. 'It's a medical condition in which cells from the lining of the uterus appear outside the uterine cavity, most commonly on the ovaries.'

'Quite right, Dr Powell. What causes this, Dr Symmonds?'

A short doctor pushed her glasses further up her nose and answered confidently, 'Hormones, Mr Sherbourne.'

'Indeed. Hormones,' he replied. 'The uterine cavity is lined with endometrial cells, which are under the influence of female hormones. If these cells grow in the wrong place, they cause pain and occasionally bleeding. What makes the symptoms worsen, Dr Kennedy?'

Dr Kennedy was tall and handsome and must have recently holidayed somewhere hot. His tan glowed as he pushed aside a stray length of hair. A thought fleetingly passed through Libby's mind that she wished she'd put a little make-up on this morning.

'Pain usually increases during the menstrual cycle.'

Great, thought Libby. Dr Handsome was looking at her bare face and talking about her menstrual cycle. It was toe-curlingly embarrassing.

'Correct. Endometriosis is typically seen during the reproductive years with symptoms worsening during menstruation. Its main, but not universal symptom, is pelvic pain in various manifestations. Endometriosis is a common finding in women with infertility problems.'

Libby's attention suddenly sprang from atttractive Dr Kennedy, to Mr Sherbourne's last remark.

'Infertility?'

'Most definitely. Have you been trying for a baby?'

'Yes, for a few years.'

'Have you sought any help yet? I presume you haven't had any investigations or else you'd know that you suffered from this disease.'

'Disease?'

'It's a term we use for the more severe growth, as in this instance. Did you say you'd sought any help yet?'

'No. We discussed researching IVF last year, but we can't afford it at the moment.' God, thought Libby. Could this be any more excruciatingly personal? They'd want to know her bra size and how many partners she'd slept with next.

'That could be one option for the future. Dr Patel. How do we treat this problem?'

Dr Patel stroked his black moustache calmly, taking his time to answer. 'There are several ways. If the symptoms are mild or even non-existent, no treatment is required. If the lesions cause pain and infertility, hormone replacement or surgery can help.'

'Quite right. Treatment for endometriosis associated with infertility needs to be individualised for each woman. There are no easy answers and treatment decisions depend on factors such as the severity of the disease, its location in the pelvis, the age of the woman, length of infertility and the presence of pain or other symptoms. As we have now established with Mrs Jenkins, she suffers from both pain and infertility.'

Libby was now feeling like an exhibit in a museum. This was her life they were discussing. This was personal. Her fertility had led to obsessive behaviours and brought stress to her marriage. It was being debated over like a subject on *Question Time*.

'Are you saying that this disease is stopping me from getting pregnant and that something can be done to put this right?' she asked.

'I can't give you a definitive answer. We can certainly help in several ways. In your case, we may suggest surgery to remove as many of the lesions as we can. Drug therapy may also reduce the symptoms from recurring for a year or so. As the drug therapy will stop your periods, you won't fall pregnant during this time. However, you stand a reasonable chance of recovering your fertility when you stop the hormone drug therapy and before the lesions grow back; if indeed they do.'

'And what if I don't become pregnant during this time?'

'Then we can look at inter-uterine or in-vitro fertilisation. But let's not get too ahead of ourselves. I'll write you up a prescription for some painkillers and reassess your results. I'll write to you and your GP in the next week or two, explaining what we intend to do next. Any more questions?'

'Just so I can be clear, you're saying that you've found a physical reason for my pain and the fact that I can't get pregnant. Are you also saying that there's a good chance it can be cured?'

'Maybe not cured, but improved and managed so you stand a better chance of conception.'

'Thank you. Thank you so much.'

Chapter Thirty-Five

December brought gifts of gales and snow flurries. It had been three days since Libby had been hurt and Rowan had decided to buy a Christmas tree early in an attempt to cheer herself up and keep busy by decorating the whole apartment.

She pressed her nose against her lounge window and gazed outside at the white-dusted rooftops opposite. The street below was quiet with a silence that only snow can bring. Lights illuminated a neighbour's windows as a car crunched slowly down the centre of the road, sounding as if it was grinding cinder toffee beneath its wheels. She turned away from the window, leaving a circle of condensation where she'd breathed on the glass.

Libby had come out of hospital the day before and was now back at home recovering. Despite being worried that the doctors had found a problem, Rowan was relieved that it could be operated on safely and would give her sister-in-law a better chance of conceiving in the future. She'd sounded so happy and optimistic on the telephone that Rowan couldn't help but share her elation. It also eased her guilt about leaving for France. Now she just had to broach the subject with Ace, James and Nora. But that could wait until the New Year.

The gentle strains of Bing Crosby's 'White Christmas' was playing in the background and a batch of mince pies baking in the oven were filling the apartment with a sweet spicy aroma.

Rowan turned and surveyed her lounge, wondering where she could stand the Christmas tree. It was still wrapped in green netting and stood in a bucket of water in the kitchen.

Ace had helped her collect it from B&Q the day before in the old van he used for collecting old pieces of furniture and vintage clothing. They'd had such a laugh trying to carry its bulk up the stairs yesterday, that they'd been too exhausted to unwrap it.

She walked around the coffee table, imagining it in different places. Last year she'd only put up a Christmas tree because it was part of the festive ritual. She hadn't been excited and had decorated the small tree as if it was a chore. It seemed incredible that a year had passed since David and Libby had come round to visit her on Christmas Day. Her house hadn't even been divided into three apartments back then. This year, she felt different. She felt more confident for having not only survived the past year on her own, but also for achieving quite a lot. She'd organised the redevelopment of Magnolia House, she'd set up a small jewellery business and had made new friends. She shouldn't underestimate her accomplishments during such a difficult year.

Rowan viewed her lounge from the front door and decided that the tree would look perfect next to the large window overlooking the street. She set about cutting the netting off the Christmas tree. It was nearly three o'clock and the purple luminosity of dusk had started to dim the natural light of the day. The apartment lamps were shedding a golden glow across the lounge and the aroma of a cinnamon-scented candle filled the room. She felt content.

Rowan stopped cutting when she heard footsteps walking up to her front door. She hesitated, waiting for a knock that didn't come. Then she heard a creak on the floorboards outside the door. Curious to know who it was, she stood up, her hand hovering close to the door handle with her scissors in her hand. She held her breath so that she could hear more clearly. What if it was the anonymous sender of the notes who'd broken into the house? What if that person was about to slide another unpleasant message under her door? Indignant at being made to feel nervous inside her home, Rowan swung the door open.

James stumbled backwards, holding his chest as if he'd been shot. 'Shit! You scared the life out of me.'

'I scared you? Why didn't you knock? I heard someone outside the door and thought it might be the stalker.'

James let out a deep breath through pursed lips and rubbed his face nervously. 'Can I come in? I want to talk to you about something.'

Rowan stood back and watched James walk into her lounge. He was wearing a chunky black jumper that made him appear even broader than usual.

'What's the matter?' asked Rowan 'Why didn't you knock?'

'I was debating whether to go back downstairs. This is the third time I've attempted to come upstairs in two days.'

Rowan frowned. 'Why? Have you broken something downstairs? It doesn't matter, you know. The house is insured and I don't bite.'

'No, nothing's broken.' James spotted the Christmas tree lying on the floor. 'Need a hand?'

Rowan was sure that whatever the problem was, it could wait a minute or two. He'd actually arrived at an opportune moment.

'Thanks. I was just wondering how I was going to struggle with the tree and not get spiked with hundreds of pine needles.'

'Where do you want it?'

'I was thinking over there,' she said, pointing. 'Just to the side of the window, so it doesn't block the daylight. I've put the tree stand over there already.'

'Okay.' James groaned, hauling the tree to a standing position. 'It's not too heavy, just a bit awkward now the netting's off. Might have been a better idea to have kept it on until it was in position.'

'Too late now,' she panted, helping him to shuffle the tree across the room. Rowan kept the Christmas tree upright while James knelt and fastened the water-soaked trunk into its stand. He twisted several screws until they gripped the trunk and held it rigid. Rowan tentatively let go of the tree. They stood back and admired its shape.

'Good choice.'

'Thanks.'

Rowan watched James inhale the pine and earthy scents coming from the needles.

'Smells great, too,' he said. 'You can't beat the real thing.'

She ran her fingers along a sprig, feeling its soft waxy texture. 'I think so too. Thanks for helping, but I'm curious why you tried three times to come upstairs to talk to me.'

James rubbed his palm across his mouth several times, making a rasping sound caused by friction on his two-day growth of beard. 'I discovered something a couple of days ago while I was in Nora's apartment, with Primrose.'

'Oh?'

'I was babysitting. You and Nora were visiting Libby. Primrose had spilt juice down her clothes and I had to change her because she wouldn't stop crying. But I saw something.'

Rowan was standing a few feet away from him, hugging her upper arms. 'You're worrying me now. She hasn't set up an illegal distillery or converted the old dark room into some dodgy plant nursery, has she?'

James was looking worried and wasn't smiling. She watched him take out his phone, click a few buttons and held it out to her. Rowan took it from him and looked at the photograph on the screen.

'I don't understand. Has Nora had a weird note, too?'

James closed his eyes momentarily. 'She *created* the notes, Rowan. A newspaper and magazines were cut up on the kitchen table alongside scissors and glue. If you look at the paper, it's the same creamy colour as the others you've received.'

Rowan's mind reeled.

'I'm really sorry,' he continued. 'I didn't know what to do because you're friends with Nora and I know you've been worrying about Libby too. But then I figured that Nora's not the friend you think she is if she's doing this and I know Libby would agree with me that you need to know. I suppose there was no good time to tell you.'

Rowan walked towards the settee and sat down on the edge of the cushion, all the while staring at the photograph. 'But why?'

She sensed James follow her. He sat down beside her. She felt him gently take the phone from her hand and unexpectedly took her hand in his. His fingers felt warm and safe as they enclosed hers. Feeling numb, she leaned sideways and rested her head on his shoulder. His woollen jumper felt soft to her cheek and smelt of fresh air as if it had been line-dried. She sat still and silent for a few moments, a dichotomy of emotions tumbling over each other. She was leaning on James' shoulder with her hand in his. She could smell him; feel the gentle rise and fall of his breathing and the warmth of his skin through his clothes. But at the same time, she was trying to understand why her friend had gone to the trouble of cutting out and pasting letters onto paper in order to send her unpleasant messages.

'What should I do?' asked Rowan. The shock was quickly replaced with anger and before waiting for an answer she sat upright. 'She called me a bitch in one of them. I told her about the notes and how worried I was and she said she'd keep an eye out for whoever might be posting them.' She stood up and walked to the window.

'I can talk to her, if you like,' said James. 'I was going to speak to her yesterday, but she was with Primrose all day and I didn't want to risk an argument in front of a toddler and frighten her.'

'No. I've got to do it. But thanks,' she said, still gazing out of the window. 'Look at the wider picture.' She turned to James who was still sitting down. 'What does that mean? Why can't she just ask me? Why is she doing it?'

'I don't have any answers, but can I suggest you sleep on it and maybe wait a day or two to see if the message arrives? That way you have proof that it was her who sent the others. I'm really sorry to have brought you bad news, but I thought you should know.'

'Of course. Don't worry. Of course I needed to know.'

'Can I do anything? Do you want help to decorate the tree?'

Rowan paused before shaking her head. 'I don't think I'll decorate it today. I'm not in the mood now. But thanks for offering.'

James stood up. 'I'll be going, then. Are you okay?' He touched her arm. 'I feel bad leaving you like this.'

Rowan forced a smile. 'I just need a little time to let it sink in. I'll be fine, honestly.'

'You know where I am. Knock three times on the floorboards if you need me.' He laughed weakly, walking towards the door. 'Seriously though, let me know, won't you?'

Rowan nodded.

Chapter Thirty-Six

The winter sun streaked across the living room floor, shining through a cut glass vase of chrysanthemums and creating a sunburst pattern on the opposite wall.

'There you go,' said David, handing a mug of tea to Libby. 'How're you feeling?'

'Just a little sore, but I'm fine. Don't worry.'

'I'll just fetch my drink.'

Libby sat propped up on the settee as she watched her husband walk back towards the kitchen. His tall, slim frame disappeared behind the kitchen door and she smiled to herself. She'd been home from hospital for a couple of days and David had been very sweet and attentive. When he returned he sat opposite her, sipped his tea, then leaned back into his chair. He closed his eyes and sighed contentedly. After a few moments, Libby turned to face him.

'I'm sorry.'

He opened his eyes. 'What for?'

'Everything. My behaviour, my distance and especially for blaming you every month I didn't conceive. I feel as if I went mad for a while. I'm really sorry.'

David leaned forwards, placed his mug on the coffee table and knelt on the floor beside her. 'It's okay. You don't need to apologise. I should be apologising for being so grumpy. God knows you had a lot on your mind with Tom, worrying about money and your nagging pain. I know I appeared angry when you first told me, but I was hurt more than anything. I was gutted that you'd kept your problems and worries from me. I love you and anything that affects you, affects me.'

Libby felt tears prick at her eyes. One fell and David wiped it away with a finger.

'It doesn't matter that you blamed me, but it does matter that you don't share how you're feeling with me. Do you know how impotent that makes me feel? And I choose that word very carefully.' He grinned.

'I'm sorry.'

He laughed, shaking his head. He leant forwards and kissed her lips. 'Stop saying you're sorry. We've got through it and we're looking forwards now, okay?'

'Okay.'

'Good. I'm going upstairs to the office for half an hour to send a few emails. Can I get you anything before I go?'

'No, I'm fine thanks. I might just have a little nap. I feel a bit sleepy.'

'I'll make us some supper in a bit. Close your eyes and rest.' David kissed her forehead, picked up his tea and left the room.

Libby closed her eyes and listened to his footsteps walking up the stairs to the box room they grandly called the office. There was a time when his footfall had sounded oppressive, almost frightening. She'd resented him for what she'd perceived to be his indifference, when all he was doing was working hard and trying to stay positive. How could she have been so selfish to the man she loved? But now that all her secrets were out in the open, she'd been prescribed a low dose of antidepressants and there was new hope for conceiving in the future, life seemed a nicer place to be. She thought about how lucky she was to have fresh optimism.

Then Libby thought of Rowan and cringed inwardly, remembering how jealous she'd been about her sister-in-law's friendship with Nora. Why couldn't she have just been pleased that Rowan had found a new friendship to help fill her lonely days? She'd make it up to everyone. With renewed confidence growing, her eyelids began to close.

Libby heard what she thought was her alarm going off. Her arm flailed about waving in the air as she tried to turn it off in her stupor. After a few seconds, she sleepily opened her eyes and remembered that it wasn't morning and she was lying on the settee. Her mobile phone continued to ring while Libby slowly came to her senses.

'Yehz, hello.'

'Are you drunk?'

Libby yawned. 'Yaaahhhh! Hi, Ace. I've just had a doze.'

'A dose of what? Vodka?'

'A *doze*.'

'I believe you. Millions wouldn't. How're you feeling?'

'Apart from sleepy, I'm happy, thanks.'

'Right, that's Dozey, Sleepy and bloody Happy out of the way, what about the other four dwarves?'

'Idiot. What have you been doing today? Have you been to the shop?' She yawned again.

'No, I've been with Alan at The Rose and Crown for a few hours.'

'How long have I been asleep for?' Libby strained to focus on her watch. 'It was midday when I fell asleep and now you're out drinking.'

'It's twenty-five to one. What makes you jump to the conclusion that I've been drinking?'

'The Rose and Crown sort of gave it away.'

'Working, dah-ling. I was working.'

'Honestly, Ace, I can't keep up with you. First it's the shop, then it's plumbing and now it's pulling pints.'

'Listen, Kevin's looking after the shop and I'm working with Alan at The Rose and Crown putting in new customer bathrooms. I've got my swanky overalls on again.'

'D'you know what? For someone who's so fussy about what he wears, you seem to have an unhealthy penchant for ugly boiler suits.'

'I think it's the all-in-one thing that does it for me. If you want a pee you have to undress to get to the necessary bits. A bit kinky, don't you think?'

'It just sounds time consuming to me.'

'Anyway, apart from finding out how my new shop assistant is, I have a proposition for you.'

'Should I be worried?'

'No. You should be excited. As you know, I've taken to this plumbing lark, like a ... well, like a plumber to water.' He laughed. 'Alan and I have had a long talk and he's asked me to become his work partner. I've spoken to the owner of the shop premises and he says I can either give three months' notice to move out of Mason's Closet, or find someone to take over the lease.'

There was a pause.

'Well?' he prompted.

'Well, what?'

'Are you interested or not?'

'In taking over your shop?'

'Not the stock, just the shop. I'll clear it out. I thought you'd like to set up a flower shop.'

Libby stopped breathing for a few seconds as the words sank in. 'I *love* that idea!'

'I knew you would. There isn't a flower shop about for miles, if you don't count the supermarket nearby.'

'Will I be allowed to decorate it? David could do the advertising. I could set up a website and have a little car with Libby's Flowers painted on the side. I can choose my own blooms from the early morning flower market. It's such a romantic place before anyone else is up. I can make window displays for Christmas, Easter, Mother's Day and Valentine's Day. Oh, it'd be fantastic. Do you really mean it?'

Ace was laughing down the phone. 'Slow down.'

'I can't. I'm so excited. You won't change your mind, will you?'

'Don't worry about that. I've been bored of smelly old clothing for a while. Thought I'd make a change and work with smelly old bathrooms instead.'

'Are things pretty serious with you two then? What happens if you decide it's not working as boyfriends but you're stuck as partners in AA Plumbers?'

'I think he's the one. I'm going to ask him to marry me.'

She squealed. 'That's wonderful news. When? Where? I must buy a new outfit. Oh no, I'd better not. I'm trying to save money. I'm sure I've got some lovely dresses upstairs—'

'LIBBS! You're ranting again. What have they done to you in that hospital?'

'Sorry. I'm just so relieved. They've found out what was causing my pain and the reason why I can't get pregnant.'

'I'd heard. It's fantastic news. It looks as if life is finally sorting itself out for us both, doesn't it?'

'I hope so, Ace. I really hope so.'

Chapter Thirty-Seven

Rowan felt as if life was getting more complicated by the week. James had left her apartment an hour earlier, having told her about what he'd seen on Nora's kitchen table. She was curled up in her armchair with her feet tucked up under her legs, looking at the bare Christmas tree. For the first ten minutes after he'd left she imagined she could still smell the fresh scent from his clothes lingering in the air. She had breathed deeply as if to draw him closer.

Her thoughts returned to Nora and she groaned out loud, waking Jet who was curled on the carpet in front of her. Leaning forwards she patted him while thinking about her tenant two floors below her. Perhaps she should confront her now. Did it really matter if the note arrived or not? James had taken a photograph and it was definitely Nora's kitchen table in the picture with the evidence on it. And anyway, how could she possibly sleep tonight without knowing why Nora had done it?

'I'm doing it now.' She stood up and walked to her bedroom, mumbling to herself. 'I've babysat for her. I've lowered the rent when she hasn't had any work booked. We've shopped and gone for a drink together. I've even shared my most personal thoughts about Tom with her.' Rowan felt her rage rising. She strode around her bedroom then pushed open the en suite door and checked her reflection. She looked tired and drawn. She splashed her face with cold water, reached for a towel then marched purposefully towards the kitchen. Throwing the towel on the worktop, she pulled open the fridge, poured half a glass of white wine and took three large gulps. She grimaced, took a deep breath and left her apartment.

In the hallway she could hear music coming from inside Ace and James' door. Were the brothers inside or was Helen in James' arms? No time for jealousy now. She opened the door in the hall that led to the basement and walked downstairs. She steadied herself, then knocked on Nora's apartment door. After a few seconds, she came to the door.

'Oh, hi,' said Nora.

'I need to talk to you.'

She appeared flustered. 'I've just put Primrose to bed. Is everything all right?'

'Not really. I need to sort a few things out.'

Nora stepped to one side. Without thinking, Rowan automatically scanned the kitchen table for cut up newspapers. There was only a half empty mug and a vase of wilting red carnations on it. Rowan stood hugging her arms for comfort then turned to face Nora.

'I thought we were friends.'

'We are. What's the matter?'

'Did James tell you that he came down here with Primrose to change her clothes?'

'When?'

'While we hurried across town to see Libby in hospital.'

'No. Why?'

'Because you'd been cutting and pasting at the kitchen table earlier in the day and you hadn't cleared up.'

Rowan watched Nora trying to remember and saw the moment her tenant's expression changed from confusion to realisation. Rowan waited, expecting Nora to deny it or cry and beg forgiveness, but her friend's reaction shocked her.

'I don't have to explain anything to you. I'd like you to leave.'

'What?'

'You heard.'

'You don't think I deserve an explanation?'

'You don't deserve anything, especially—' Nora bit her lip.

'Especially what? Don't stop now because I'm not going anywhere until I understand this madness.'

Nora pushed past her and closed the bedroom door. 'This isn't the time,' she said, turning to face Rowan with folded arms.

Rowan gasped. 'Well, perhaps you could tell me when the ideal time will be for explaining why you've been sending me unpleasant messages? Why, Nora? What have I ever done to you?'

Nora spluttered out a forced laugh. 'You've no idea, have you? You live up there completely oblivious to what's really happening around you.'

'You'd better tell me, because I've no idea what you're talking about.'

Nora pointed a finger at Rowan. 'It's not been easy pretending to be friends with you, you know. Have you any idea what it's like, knowing that—'

Rowan's lips were set in a tight straight line, her heart pounding as adrenalin coursed through her veins. Why was Nora so angry, when it was *her* who'd come downstairs feeling enraged?

'Carry on. Knowing what? Knowing that I've thought of us as friends. Knowing that I happily looked after Primrose for you. Knowing that we've socialised and shared confidences. I even told you about the notes and you said you'd keep an eye open for whoever was posting them. I need you to explain, because I don't understand why you'd do this. Am I going to wake up in the morning to another one? "Look at the wider picture."' Rowan held her upturned palms in front of her. 'What the hell does that mean?'

'It means you need to open your eyes. Haven't the

notes made you think? Have you just put them to one side without trying to look at their meaning?'

Rowan groaned in exasperation. 'Are you seriously having a go at *me*? You've actually got the gall to berate me for not understanding your pathetic cryptic messages?'

'Yes, I am. It's your fault. You're just getting on with your life as if—'

'Just bloody well spit it out, Nora, because I'm sick of guessing what this is all about.'

'You're just carrying on as if Tom hadn't existed.'

Rowan blinked. Neither of them spoke. His name had shocked her into silence. Then she remembered. The notes included photographic terms. Tom must be the link; not his business. Rowan broke the silence quietly and calmly although her heart was beating frantically.

'What does Tom have to do with this?'

Rowan watched Nora looking at the floor and shaking her head. When she looked up to speak, her mouth was twisted into a sneer.

'Libby told me about Tom's texts you'd found. She asked me to be gentle and not to mention Tom because you'd found out he'd been unfaithful. She wanted me to keep a close eye on you in case you were struggling. But you're not, are you? That's the point. You're not struggling, but *I am*.'

Rowan watched as Nora roughly brushed away tears from her cheeks.

'If you're talking about struggling with the rent, you know that I charge less when—'

'It's not about money. It's about Tom. I'm called Nora for short, but my name's Eleanor.'

Rowan frowned, trying to make sense of why this information might be important. Then Nora's concern over Tom, the mention of her struggling and the tears all became clear.

'You! You're E.' Rowan leant one hand on a kitchen chair for support.

'I'm sorry,' said Nora, sounding matter-of-fact. 'But Tom and I loved each other. It's as simple as that. It just happened.'

Rowan swayed before meeting Nora's narrowed eyes. 'It. Just. Happened,' she repeated. 'Tell me, how does it just happen that you decide to sleep with another woman's husband? And how sick is it to not only make friends with his wife, but to bloody well move in with her too? Just how twisted … oh my God …' Rowan looked around at the whitewashed brick walls. 'You wanted to move into the basement because it's where Tom worked, didn't you? DIDN'T YOU!'

Nora's hands were clutched in front of her. 'I wanted to be closer to him. I wanted to live where he'd breathed. Where he'd thought. Where he'd created.'

'How dare you. This is *my* husband you're talking about. Tell me, how did this so-called love affair start?'

'I think we've said all that needs to be said.'

'You don't call the shots over when this conversation ends. You owe me. I think I deserve to know how you got your claws into my husband. I could always call the police and see what they have to say about sending anonymous offensive messages.'

Nora chewed her bottom lip before meeting Rowan's gaze. 'Tom was the photographer on a fashion shoot I was hired to do. It lasted several days in London and we became friends and had a couple of meals. He sent me texts and asked to meet up when he was next in London.'

'You think you had this all-encompassing passion because of a bit of fooling around with a gullible man? Grow up, Nora. I want you to leave this house.'

'I will. I knew it'd come to this one day. But I'll leave

knowing that I still grieve for him. I still miss him. I still love him.'

Rowan shook her head slowly. 'You have two days to pack up and leave and I only give you that long because I'm thinking of Primrose. I don't want you to come upstairs again. I never want to see you again.' She glared at Nora. 'What you had was a sordid affair. Don't pretend it was something romantic, because it was nothing of the sort. Tom and I loved each other deeply and were trying for a baby, so don't think you had something special, because you didn't.'

Rowan turned and walked out of the basement apartment. She climbed the basement stairs, amazed at how steep and tiring they'd suddenly become. She passed Ace and James' apartment door and could hear Helen's laughter and smell the aroma of Asian spices. A noise escaped Rowan's throat. A low groan. She clasped her hands to her mouth to keep it in, but another escaped her lips as she ran upstairs. She flung open her apartment door and slammed it behind her. There she stood for a few seconds, shaking and unsure what to do. She groaned again, a deep primordial sound of grief and loss, frightening herself with the intensity of it. Then she ran, through the lounge and into her bedroom. She fell onto her bed. Her and Tom's bed. A bed where they'd laughed and loved. Deep racking sobs shook her body as she pressed her face into her duvet. Each time she gasped for breath, her mouth would suck in damp material until she wailed once more into its softness. Her body heaved time and time again, the feather and cotton of her bedding stifling the sound of her anguish.

It took five minutes for Rowan to become still and silent. Occasionally she gave a shuddering breath. She felt a warm body press against her and a cold wet nose prod her arm. Rolling onto her side, she pulled Jet closer and pressed

271

her face into his velvety fur. He smelt like the inside of her grandmother's jewellery box, both comforting and musty.

'How did I get into this mess, boy?' Rowan rolled onto her back and stared at the shadows on the ceiling. She felt as if she'd been deserted for a third time. First by Tom's sudden death, then by the fact that he'd been unfaithful and now she'd lost Nora who it turned out had never been a real friend in the first place. She hated that Nora had spoiled the past. She'd rewritten history for her.

She patted Jet and stood up. In the en suite she wiped her eyes and blew her nose, deciding that she'd finish the bottle of wine in the fridge. Jet followed her into the kitchen where the mince pies were sitting on a cooling rack. She poured a glass of white wine and took a large mouthful, realising that cheerful Christmas songs were still playing on repeat. They seemed incongruous given the last dreadful twenty minutes.

Someone knocked on the door. Her heart leapt. James had come back to check on her. She hurried across the living room and turned the latch before opening the door. Nora stood in front of her.

'I've got nothing more to say to you,' said Rowan, and began to push the door to.

Nora pressed her palm flat against the glossed paintwork. 'There's something you need to know.'

'You've got a nerve,' said Rowan. She pointed at Nora's face. 'I'll tell you why you're doing this. Because you can't bear the fact that you were just a meaningless fling.' She gripped the door handle for support. 'You couldn't face the reality that he was married and not interested in a future with you. Don't think for a minute that you were anything special. You were a prop to be dressed, photographed and used once or twice.'

Rowan felt sick to her stomach, not only because she hated confrontation, but because she'd described Tom in such derogatory terms. But how else could she make this woman believe that she hadn't been important to him? Bizarrely, as she was pondering this she noticed that her poinsettia on the landing was wilting over the side of its pot. Inanely, she made a mental note to water it.

Nora stared impassively back at her. 'I can prove he cared.'

Forcing herself to remain calm, Rowan remembered that her mother always said that you'd lost an argument as soon as you lost your temper. 'I'm not interested in hearing any more. You have two days to leave.' She'd started to close the door but momentarily turned her head when the telephone rang.

In that second Nora pushed past her into the lounge, knocking the wine glass from her hand. It dropped to the floor and smashed. Shards of glass littered the doorway and wine seeped in between the gaps in the floorboards.

'What the hell are you doing?' asked Rowan.

The telephone continued to ring as Nora walked towards a framed photograph of Tom. She picked it up, tracing her forefinger around his profile.

Rowan pointed towards the door and almost growled. 'Get out!' She rotated her hand so that her palm was facing upwards, gesturing that Nora should hand her the picture frame. Her hand shook visibly as she held it in the empty space between them.

The phone stopped and for a few seconds the room was quiet.

'How can you just move on?' asked Nora. 'What's the point of having pictures sitting around the place if you intend to exchange him like faulty goods?' She replaced the photograph and walked towards the window, her breath clouding the glass. 'I could have made him happy, you know?' she said quietly, almost to herself.

Standing with her arms folded, Rowan watched Nora peer into the street below and wondered if she was capable of physically removing her from the apartment. She doubted it. It was taking all her self-control not to run to the bathroom and retch. And how dare she suggest that Tom wasn't happily married?

'Spending a few nights with my husband doesn't add up to a relationship.'

Nora spun round. 'If I'd been Tom's wife, I wouldn't be running round after another man. I don't know why you don't just ask James to move in, instead of all that ridiculous flirting that goes on. It's sickening to watch.'

'James is in a relationship. He's a supportive friend.'

'Friend? Come off it. It wasn't long ago I had to listen to you giggling over what James had done or what he'd said. It made me sick to hear how quickly you'd moved on. And don't insult me by using the old cliché that you and James are just good friends. The only reason you're not an item is because he doesn't feel the same way about you.'

Rowan was shocked by how deeply those words affected her. The notion that James didn't think that they had a close friendship made her feel as if she'd lost something special. It hurt.

Chapter Thirty-Eight

James emptied a pan of basmati rice into a colander, leaning backwards away from a cloud of steam. While it drained, he reached for a wooden spoon, stirring the homemade chicken balti before tasting it. Curry and Adele singing in the background; it should be the recipe for a wonderful evening, but James felt as if something was missing.

He called to Helen. 'Dinner's ready. Can you grab some cutlery?'

He began to dish out rice onto large oval plates, creating a hole in the middle of the fluffy grains with the spoon, ready to ladle the sauce.

'Sorry,' said Helen, 'but I've glued some nails on and now I'm painting them. They might smudge.'

James rested the spoon on the side of saucepan, feeling resentment building. This was typical of Helen. She knew he was cooking, so why choose now to paint her nails and make the lounge smell of acrid varnish? He finished dishing out the curry and removed two naan breads from the toaster. He sliced them in half and placed them on each plate before taking two knives and forks from the drawer and carrying the meals through into the lounge.

He saw that Helen had strewn her manicure set across the table where they were to eat and was painting her nails purple. He waited next to her holding the plates.

'James? You don't half choose your moments.' She rolled her eyes and moved her files, spare nails and glue to one side with her wrist. 'You start. I just have three more fingers to paint.'

The pungent smell of nail varnish mixed with the aroma of spices to create an unpleasant artificial odour.

'Do you have to do that now? You knew I was cooking dinner.'

'I know,' she said, concentrating on her nails. 'But you were taking so long and you know I like to look nice.'

James bit into some bread then took a sip of wine. 'To be honest, I prefer the natural look on a woman. I don't like those long false nails and that weird purple colour.'

'Weird purple colour! It's Chanel's Ballerina and it's a mauvey-pink.'

James screwed his nose up to make his point. 'I prefer short natural nails.'

'Liar. Men always say they prefer natural until they see some fake boobs in a magazine and suddenly artificial seems very alluring. It's called double standards.'

James stabbed a piece of chicken. 'So you think I've got double standards?'

'Men in general. Don't be so touchy.'

'I just thought it'd be nice for us to eat together, seeing as I've gone to the trouble of buying it and cooking it.'

'I'll eat it. Look.' She lifted one unpainted nail. 'One more to go.'

James had now been seeing Helen on and off for a couple of months and he'd hoped the same powerful emotions of their previous relationship would return, but this time round their friendship seemed hollow, on his part at least. A new Helen had emerged. A Helen who liked to get her own way. A Helen who was happy to do nothing but be adored. Why hadn't he noticed these negative traits two years earlier? Back then he'd have forgiven her anything. Two years ago their relationship was intoxicating. He'd found her stimulating, strong and exciting. Now he saw the same girl as selfish, spoilt and high maintenance. He was going to let her know he didn't want to take their relationship to the next stage and he was going to do it now.

'We need to talk,' he said. 'About us.'

He watched her gingerly pick up her fork, taking care not to smudge her nails.

'Good. This *wait til Christmas and see how it goes* idea is ridiculous.' She picked at a piece of onion and pushed it to the side of her plate before spearing a piece of chicken and sliding it off the fork with her teeth, so as not to smear her lipstick.

'Well at least that's something we both agree on.'

Helen looked up, predatorily. 'Does this mean I can stay over tonight?'

'I don't think you understand. What I mean is that we're not—'

They both stopped eating. Voices were arguing upstairs.

'Oops! Someone's not happy,' said Helen.

James felt a sense of foreboding. He'd felt terrible leaving Rowan alone after informing her about Nora, and that was probably why he was in such an unforgiving mood with Helen. He felt guilty that he'd delivered bad news and then run away from the fallout. Not that he'd wanted to leave so quickly, but he was afraid of what he'd do next. Rowan had seemed so small and vulnerable in his arms. She'd looked at him with her pale grey eyes, her tousled brown hair falling out of a ponytail and into her eyes. She was make-up free and her slim body seemed lost inside loose jeans and baggy jumper. He'd wanted to keep her in his arms and protect her from everything. He needed to check on her.

'Have you seen my mobile?'

'It needs charging,' said Helen. 'I was catching up with *EastEnders* and it died on me.'

James sighed but refrained from suggesting she use her own phone. He found Rowan's number on Ace's telephone pad and silently thanked his brother for being so fastidious. He picked up the landline and punched in the number. He could hear it ringing but no one was answering. Then he heard the sound of glass breaking. If Rowan wasn't up there, then who was? He put the phone down and hurried to the door.

'Where are you going?' asked Helen.

'Upstairs to check everything's okay.'

'Oh, so suddenly dinner's not that important?'

James ignored her comment. Pulling the apartment door open, he hurried up the staircase two at a time, where he was surprised to see Rowan's front door open and Nora standing in the lounge. Judging from the look on Rowan's face, it was obvious that her ex-tenant's visit was unwanted. 'The Little Drummer Boy' rum-pum-pum-pummed from her speakers.

'I just phoned you. I heard something smash.' He took a step forwards and crunched on broken glass sitting in a residue of wine. 'What's going on?' James looked from one woman to the other.

'Well, talk of the devil. Were your ears burning?'

He ignored Nora and looked at Rowan. 'Rowan?'

'Nora was just leaving,' she answered, but didn't look at him.

'Come and join us, James,' said Nora. Her voice was mocking. She beckoned him into the room.

James didn't move. 'I don't know what's going on here, but if Rowan wants you to leave I suggest you do.'

Nora sauntered towards him and stopped an arm's length away. 'But I have some news to share. Aren't you even a little bit interested?'

'I don't care what you have to say. I think it's best if you leave now.' He stood to one side of the doorway.

'Oh you do, do you?' Nora laughed. 'It's pathetic. You really have no idea, do you? Take a ringside seat before I prove that Tom loved me.'

In direct contrast to the confrontational atmosphere he'd walked in to, Bing Crosby and David Bowie began to sing a melodious Christmas song. He couldn't take his eyes off Rowan who was looking ashen and exhausted by the hostility.

'It doesn't matter why you're here,' he said to Nora, 'but I think it's best if you go now.' He stood to one side of the doorway, leaving space for her to pass by him. 'Leave. You've done enough damage.'

Nora swung round and glared at him. '*I've* done enough damage. What about *her*? She came between me and Tom and spoilt something precious.'

'What? You and Tom? What do …?'

Before James could continue, Rowan interrupted while pointing a finger close to Nora's face.

'You had a pathetic sordid affair; nothing more than a regrettable fling on Tom's part. Don't try to reinvent the past by pretending it was something precious. Give me my key and get out.'

It suddenly began to make sickening sense to James.

After initially being taken aback, Nora smirked. 'It's far from over. Tom and I had been seeing each other for nearly three years and he was going to leave you.'

James saw Rowan flinch.

'Liar,' yelled Rowan. She strode towards the door. 'I don't have to listen to this.' She paused, momentarily speechless. 'My earrings. You're wearing my earrings. It was you who hid my jewellery on top of the wardrobe and stole some earrings. I knew I wasn't going mad.'

'Don't be stupid,' said Nora. 'You gave me these. We've established that your memory isn't your strongest point.'

'You're a thief. Why shouldn't I just pick up the phone and call the police now? My God! Tom's car. You were at the funeral and scratched his name in the paintwork.' She held up her hand. 'Don't answer! I don't want to listen to you any more. You're lying about the earrings and about being with Tom for three years. If he was going to leave me, he had the perfect opportunity when we'd sold the flat in Wilmslow and before we'd bought this place.'

'But he needed your grandmother's inheritance to afford this place. He couldn't buy it by himself and knew that when everything was divided, this place would be a lot more money than the Wilmslow place. Your apartment there wasn't up to much, as far as I could see.'

James watched Rowan's hand go to her mouth. He took a few steps towards her and put his arm around her shoulder. He could feel her shaking beneath his hold.

'You … you went to our Wilmslow apartment? He told you about Grandma's money?'

Nora sniffed. 'You were away at your parents and we had a long weekend there.'

James couldn't bear to see Rowan suffer any more. 'Okay, you've said what you came to say. I hope you're feeling good about yourself. Now get out.'

'You've no right to speak to me like that. By rights I should be your landlady and I wouldn't have been such a walkover as her.' Nora pointed at Rowan. 'She lets you shack up in her house with that air-head when I'd have had you both out on the streets weeks ago.'

'Helen and I aren't in a relationship.' He let go of Rowan and guided Nora firmly towards the open doorway.

Nora shook herself free from him. 'I hate you and I hate this place. Here, have your glass back.' Nora kicked several of the largest pieces shards into the apartment. One fragment flew towards Rowan and caught her ankle. A small drop of blood appeared.

'Enough,' shouted James. 'Rowan, call the police. We're not letting this go on any longer.'

Rowan looked coldly towards her ex-tenant before reaching for the phone and lifting the receiver. She pressed 999 and waited a few seconds.

'If you don't want Tom's daughter to go into care, I'd put the phone down if I were you.'

Rowan turned as if in slow motion.

'Emergency. Which service, please?'

'Look at Tom's photograph,' said Nora. 'Recognise the smile? The eyes?'

Rowan replaced the receiver. 'I don't believe you.'

'We met on Primrose Hill and agreed to call our baby after it.'

'If you have one ounce of decency left in you, go now,' said James.

Nora turned, walked downstairs and slammed the basement door behind her. James went to Rowan's side. He felt her body spasm like a small bird in the mouth of a fox. For a few seconds they stood in shocked silence. The music had stopped. James directed her towards the sofa where she bent her knees and allowed herself to be settled on a cushion.

'Please can you pass me that photograph?' She sounded as if she was in a trance.

'Don't let her get to you. You only have her word for everything and I'm sure that's not very reliable.'

'Please,' she repeated, holding out her hand.

James passed her the photograph. He watched her absorb Tom's features. He looked over her shoulder. The man in the photograph had Primrose's green eyes and the little girl's dimple. The same smile gazed back from the photograph.

'It's true,' said Rowan. 'Primrose is Tom's. There was always something about her but I couldn't quite put my finger on it. It makes sense now.'

'You can't be sure,' said James.

'I'm sure.'

James sat down beside her. He pulled her into his arms and felt her shocked body sink in to his embrace. Her eyes stared sightlessly in front of her, her arms hanging limply by her sides.

Chapter Thirty-Nine

Rowan walked over the bridge at Camden Lock, glimpsing sideways at the grey water below. As she exhaled, a white cloud of breath drifted into the frost-scented air before dissipating. The icy chill stabbed at her extremities and she pushed her gloveless hands deeper inside her coat pockets. It wasn't the perfect day for perusing the market stalls, but she'd had to escape Magnolia House and its convoluted mixture of unrequited love and byzantine ex-friends, if only for a few hours.

A night ravaged with bad dreams and wakeful episodes had made Rowan wake early and consider her future more seriously. Over an early morning pot of coffee, Jet's company and even more tears, Rowan had written out a rough plan on the inside of the back page of the latest novel she was reading. Her list included what needed to be achieved before moving to France. She's decided that she'd live with her parents for a few months in order to create business links for her jewellery. Once they'd been established, she'd set about looking for a small place to buy. She still hadn't decided whether to put Magnolia House on the market or to keep renting it out. What troubled Rowan was that if she kept it on, she'd have to return several times a year. Wasn't the whole point of leaving the country to start a new life and not look back?

Tom had died leaving her shattered, but nothing could have prepared her for the emotional abandonment she'd subsequently felt having discovered his infidelity. Even the memories that he'd left behind were now distorted by lies and mystery.

Libby and David's marriage was on an even keel again,

with renewed hope for conceiving a baby in the future. Ace was in love and there'd been murmurings about him moving in with Alan. Nora ... Rowan didn't want to think about Nora. She'd played and replayed yesterday's scenario in her mind and each time she was left feeling more confused and upset. Nora had disorientated her and left her feeling insecure and lacking in confidence. She'd invested emotionally in their friendship and had trusted her story. She'd believed that what she'd told Nora had been accepted in amity and confidence. Now Rowan felt as if her judgement had been knocked sideways by a wrecking ball. The edges of whom she could trust in the future had been blurred.

Passing a stall selling chestnuts from the hotplate, Rowan stopped, tempted by the sweet aroma. She bought a bag and wrapped her fingers around the paper, luxuriating in the comfort she found in its heat. She puffed out white clouds through her open mouth to cool the hot chestnut she was chewing.

And then there was James and Helen, thought Rowan. James had said that they weren't in a relationship, but surely that couldn't be true. Helen was often in Ace's apartment with James. She closed her eyes momentarily wishing it were true, but quickly berated herself. Surely it was wrong to think of James romantically after only sixteen months. What was the time limit for falling in love again after bereavement? Who set the rules?

Rowan crossed the road to the underground station. Maybe James had just felt pity for the young widow upstairs. She shivered, partly due to the icy chill and partly due to relief. At least he didn't know how she really felt about him. For her sanity and to save herself from having to watch his growing love affair with Helen, she had to leave. She wouldn't call it running away because her parents lived there. She'd call it rejoining the family. As she reached the steps to Camden Town underground station, her mobile rang.

'Hi, Libbs.'

'Where are you? It sounds noisy.'

'I'm just about to go down into the underground. I came for a wander around Camden Market. How're you feeling?'

'Much better, thanks. Are you busy or can you pop round?'

Rowan felt instantly relieved not to have to go straight back home. 'I was going to call you. I've got something to tell you. If you're sure you're up to a visitor, I'd love to come round.'

'Great. You sound a bit fed up.'

Rowan stamped her feet to keep warm. 'I'll tell you about it when I get there. Put the kettle on. I'm freezing.'

Libby clicked off her mobile phone and pushed her empty soup bowl across the kitchen table. Although she still ached, she could move more easily and her small scars were healing well. She'd phoned Rowan the previous evening to tell her about the new opportunity that had arisen for her at Ace's shop, but her sister-in-law's mobile had gone straight to answerphone. She stretched gingerly in her chair, pleased she'd be telling Rowan face to face.

Rowan arrived half an hour later and Libby could see that she'd been crying. She'd made an attempt to cover her red eyes with a little make-up, but it didn't hide the swelling.

'Tea, or something stronger?' asked Libby.

Rowan smiled, weakly. 'Tea's fine, thanks.'

Libby busied herself filling a pot of tea before carrying it to the kitchen table. 'Shall we stay in here? David lit the wood burner before he left for a meeting. It's much cosier.'

Rowan crossed to the table. 'Yes, it's lovely and warm. I'm beginning to thaw out.'

Libby watched her sister-in-law pour some milk from the jug and fill her cup from the teapot in silence.

'Rowan, what's happened? You look awful.'

Rowan took a sip of tea. 'I've found out who Tom was having an affair with.'

'No! Who?'

'Nora.'

'Nora? Not Nora downstairs? You don't mean Nora who lives with you?'

Rowan nodded.

'How do you know?'

'She told me.'

'But the texts were from E.'

'Nora's short for Eleanor.'

'Bitch!'

'Exactly.'

Libby leant forward, holding her stomach. 'When did she tell you? What did she say?'

'James came up to see me because he'd seen paper cuttings in her kitchen. She'd stuck some letters onto a piece of paper just like the anonymous messages I'd been getting.'

Libby gasped. 'Nora sent those notes? I don't understand.'

Rowan continued. 'I couldn't get it out of my mind and I knew I wouldn't be able to sleep, so I went to speak to her. I thought she'd be mortified that I'd found out about the notes, but she didn't seem to care. She asked me to leave.'

'She asked *you* to leave?'

Rowan nodded and sipped her tea. 'She asked me to leave a room in my own house.' She looked up, her eyes sparkling with tears. 'She asked me to leave Tom's studio.'

Libby stood up gingerly and moved around the table, where she wrapped her arms around Rowan. 'I can't believe it. What a hard-hearted cow. But what about the affair? How did she tell you?' Libby sat down next to her.

'She was eager to tell me that her name was Eleanor with a capital bloody E.'

Libby covered her mouth with her hands as if in prayer.

'She said that they'd loved each other,' continued Rowan. 'She'd rented his studio to be closer to his memory.'

'Shit. What did you do? Did she say how long they, you know—'

'It doesn't matter how long. It happened. But that's not the worst of it?'

'It gets worse?'

'Primrose is your niece.'

Libby heard the words but she couldn't make sense of them. She turned to face Rowan and frowned. 'What?'

'Primrose is Tom's baby.'

'No!'

Rowan looked at her and confirmed her statement with raised eyebrows and a slow nod of her head.

'No! She said that? You don't believe her, do you?' said Libby.

'Now I know, it's obvious. She has Tom's smile. She has his eyes. I couldn't understand why I felt so close to her. I thought it was because I lost our child. I suppose on some subliminal level I must have known because … because I loved her.

Libby was stunned. What could she possibly say to her sister-in-law to make things better? She couldn't. It was impossible. Her brother had deeply hurt her best friend and nothing she could say or do would undo that.

'I'm so sorry,' said Libby. 'I don't know what to say, but I'm so sorry Tom did this to you.'

'I think I could deal with it better if I didn't know who she was or if he was still here and I could speak with him.

287

I could rage at him or leave him. Instead my imagination is killing me because I can't ask him for the facts. Can you believe I'm staying away from my own house because my husband's mistress is living in our marital home?' Rowan held her head in her hands, leaning her elbows on the table. 'It's such a mess.'

'I still find it difficult to believe that Tom did such a thing. It seems so out of character. I'm sorry he's caused this nightmare for you. What can I do to help?'

Rowan reached out and touched Libby's hand. 'It's not your fault and you just need to rest and get better. This is something I've got to sort out for myself. I've asked her to leave but even that makes me feel guilty because poor little Primrose is being uprooted.' She paused, fiddling the handle of her cup. 'I'll miss her. She's such a sweet little thing.'

'She's not your worry, though. Primrose will be fine. Nora might be an awful friend but she's a good mother. My God, I can't believe she's my niece.'

'Libbs, I've thought about it all night and I'll understand if you want to keep in touch with her ... you know, because she's Tom's. She's your family.'

'This is crazy.' Libby slowly shook her head, still trying to comprehend the situation. 'I can't even think about that at the moment. Shit, I'll have to tell mum and dad they have a granddaughter.'

A piece of wood in the log burner cracked and hissed. They both turned distractedly to watch the yellow flames licking at the glass front.

'Anyway, let's change the subject,' said Rowan.

'It's okay. You can talk as much as you want to. I'm so angry with Tom too and if you want to vent your rage to me, I'll listen.'

'No, my head's spinning with it. I've thought of nothing else since I found out and I'm sick of it,' said Rowan. 'Talk to me about you. Have you heard when your op's going to be?'

'No. They said I should expect a letter with an appointment in a week or so. Rowan, we can't change the subject. It's too huge to push aside.'

'Pushing it aside is the only control I have over the bloody situation. Honestly, it's helps to talk about something else.' She swallowed another mouthful of tea. 'It's such a relief that you have a diagnosis for your pain and something can actually be done to help.'

'It is. Understanding the problem is half the battle. How was Camden? Busy?'

'It was fairly quiet, actually. It's so cold outside that the water in the lock was starting to freeze in places.'

'I'll be glad when Christmas is over and we can start counting down the days until springtime. Do you want to hear a bit of good news?'

'I'd love to hear some good news.'

'Ace rang me. He's giving up the lease on the shop and is going to work with Alan. And guess what? He's offered me the lease so I can open my own flower shop.'

A genuine smile spread across Rowan's face. 'That's amazing. You'll be so good at that.'

'I could decorate it, set up a delivery service—'

'Choose your own hours, be your own boss.' Rowan leant back. 'Thank goodness something's going right for one of us at least.'

'Remember I'm here for you, won't you?'

Rowan touched Libby's arm. 'I know. Thank you. Now, have you got anything sweet? We need to celebrate your new career with calories.'

Libby walked to the fridge. 'I'm determined to make a great success out of it so I can make David proud as well as earning the money to pay back what I owe.' She took out half a packet of chocolate digestives. 'It's a proper chance to make amends.'

'Good for you. Did Ace say he was going to move out?'

'He mentioned moving into Alan's place.'

Libby watched Rowan close her eyes and sigh. 'That means, with Nora and Ace gone, I'll be sharing a house with the lovebirds until I leave for France.'

'You're still going then?'

'Apart from you, what is there to stay for? The house holds no warmth for me now and I've hardly made inroads with my jewellery. I sell to two small shops that wouldn't pay the bills if the two apartments' rents weren't added to my income.'

Libby smiled sympathetically. 'I'm very proud of you and you should be proud of yourself. It's been a hellish eighteen months.'

'Thank you. It has.'

'We just need to get through Christmas and try to enjoy ourselves as best we can, then take a fresh look at things in the New Year. Deal?'

'Deal.'

'And you will come for Christmas, won't you?'

'That's really kind of you, but I was thinking of spending it quietly in France with Mum and Dad. Besides, you two need a bit of space.'

'If you change your mind, we have a spare room and we'd both love to have you.'

'Thanks.'

Chapter Forty

David returned home from work later that evening. He walked into the living room carrying a newspaper and his car keys.

'Hello, love. How's your day been?' he said, walking towards the sofa and kissing her.

'Eventful, to say the least.'

'Are you okay? You look pale.'

'Rowan's been over.'

'Is she okay?'

'Far from it. She found out yesterday that Nora's full name is Eleanor. It's Nora who's been sending the anonymous notes and you won't believe this, but Primrose is Tom's daughter.'

The colour drained from David's face. He dropped the newspaper and keys on the coffee table and held his head in his hands.

'God, no. Fucking hell.' He paced up and down behind the sofa. 'Shit, shit, shit.'

Libby frowned. 'What? That's a strange response?'

He pinched the top of his nose and squeezed his eyes shut. 'You don't understand. Fuck!'

Libby gingerly stood up. She took a few steps and stopped in front of him. 'Are you saying that you knew?' Her features were twisted with incredulity.

'It's not as simple as that, Libbs.'

'Did you know or not?'

'Yes, but—'

Libby laughed, sarcastically. 'I'd love to hear the *but*, David.' She followed him as he walked into the kitchen holding his head in his hands. 'We have a niece and you never bothered to tell me?'

'It was the last promise I made him. What was I supposed to do?'

'Tell *me*, that's what.'

'You were grieving. Rowan was grieving. We all were.'

'We still are and will be for a long time to come, but this isn't something you keep to yourself.'

David raised his eyebrows at her.

'Don't you dare compare this with me keeping a secret about debt,' said Libby. 'I had depression. It's an illness. It's not the same as keeping a huge family secret. This makes Primrose a relative and you thought the right thing to do was keep it from me?'

'I didn't know Primrose was Tom's. This is the first I knew about it. Bloody hell, I can't believe this.'

'I'm confused. You said you knew.'

'I knew he'd had a fling with someone called Eleanor and she'd got pregnant. Tom needed someone to talk to but swore me to secrecy. I told him it was unfair and out of order to ask me to keep it a secret but he was in a state. You should have seen him. I'd never seen this Eleanor woman so when I met Nora, I didn't know it was her. Of course I'd have said something then if I'd known. I've only just found out now that she's this Eleanor woman. Christ, what a mess. I thought it had gone away and no one would find out.'

'That's naïve, David. Things like this don't just go away.'

David dragged a kitchen chair out from the dining table and sat down heavily on it. 'I know, but I didn't want to rock the boat. The damage had already been done and I honestly thought it was best not to mention that Tom had a child.'

Libby scraped the chair out opposite him and sat down, her hands upturned pleadingly in front of her. 'Can't you honestly see that it was wrong to keep this from Rowan and me?'

'God!' he exclaimed, looking up at the ceiling as if seeking answers there. He met his wife's gaze. 'Yes and no. I know she should have been told but why cause her more pain and heartbreak? She might never have found out that Tom had fathered a child. And how could I have told you? Our silences were lasting longer and longer and when we did talk, we usually argued. When was I going to bring up that Tom had a maniac stalker that he couldn't lose?'

Libby frowned. 'What do you mean?'

'That I didn't know how to tell you?'

'No, I mean about the maniac stalker. Are you telling me that they weren't still seeing each other?'

'Christ, no. They'd had a brief fling for a few days. Tom ended things but he kept receiving pleading letters from her, threatening to tell Rowan about the affair if he didn't see her again. Then she wrote and told him she was pregnant but he didn't believe her and tried his best to ignore her. The last straw was when she turned up at their apartment in Wilmslow with a tiny baby in her arms. It was sheer luck that Rowan just happened to be in France with her parents. Tom told me everything but swore me to secrecy. The excuse he gave Rowan to move to London was for his new business, and partly it was, but the main reason was to escape this Eleanor woman and the letters. He had to move himself and Rowan somewhere she didn't know about. He hated himself for abandoning his daughter and for what he'd done to Rowan and was terrified that she'd find out about the affair. I think the added pressure along with the tension of building a new business and coping with the house move, made him stressed and put a strain on his heart.' David wiped a tear from his cheek. 'None of us knew he had a heart condition and couldn't cope with the stress and anxiety.'

'But something doesn't add up. Rowan said that Nora

knew about her grandmother's inheritance. How can that be?'

'Tom telephoned the day after Eleanor had turned up with Primrose, in a panic. He said his door key was missing. He had to break the kitchen window to get in. Papers were strewn everywhere and drawers had been opened so he was pretty sure it was Eleanor who had taken the key. She must have rummaged through the house for information. Nothing had been stolen and there was some valuable electronic and photographic equipment on show. He found a letter on the floor about Rowan's grandmother's money and the new address in Clapham. It's all a bloody mess.'

'I'm sorry, but I've got to phone Rowan back and let her know that Nora has a vivid imagination and that Tom deeply regretted the short affair. And you know I'll have to tell her how I found out, don't you?'

'She'll hate me.'

'She'll be relieved, David.' Libby stretched her hand across the table and laced her fingers through his. 'It must have been awful for you to keep such a secret, but I guarantee you that she'll be comforted to know that Tom made a dreadful mistake which he regretted immediately.'

Chapter Forty-One

James lay on his back with his hands behind his head on the lumpy sofa bed in Ace's lounge. The luminous green digits read 03.12 and cast an ethereal glow across the room. He punched his pillow and tried to find a more comfortable position. He preferred to sleep in a dark room but Ace's lounge never seemed to achieve that state. The television and DVD player's lights were constantly glowing and the light from the lamp post across the road poured in through a gap in the curtains, painting the walls with a pale orange flare.

Life had been so much simpler in California, he thought. He'd teach from eight-thirty in the morning for six hours, meet his friends on the beach in the afternoon and in the evenings he'd occasionally go on a date with a pretty girl. Now, here he was squatting in his brother's flat with six inches of snow on the ground outside and he still hadn't found a second opportunity to tell Helen their silly non-relationship was over. To complicate matters further, he knew he was falling in love with his widowed landlady who was living upstairs.

He turned angrily onto his stomach and pulled the pillow on top of his head to block out the lamplight. Despite the darkness beneath his pillow, his thoughts continued to bombard him with problems. Was it considered rude to flirt with a widow eighteen months after her husband's death? Was there a bloody manual somewhere that would enlighten him as to when to make a move?

James threw the pillow onto the floor and sat up. 'Make a move?' he said out loud. Did he really just sum up his desire to get to know Rowan more intimately as, 'making a move?' It sounded as if he was playing a game of chess instead of sorting out his life. But thinking about it, maybe the analogy was perfect. Life needed planning, you're surprised by unexpected twists and turns, sometimes you win and sometimes you lose.

Ace's bedroom door opened. 'Who're you talking to?'

'Myself.'

'First sign of madness.'

'Tell me about it.'

'What's the matter?'

'I'm figuring out how to capture my queen without pawns getting in the way.'

'Okay. Do it quietly, please. I need a pee.'

James heard him stagger towards his bathroom and had no choice but to listen to his brother aim directly into the water bowl ensuring that he made the most noise possible. He got off the sofa, switched on a lamp, walked into the kitchen and poured some milk into a pan. He lit the gas ring as Ace walked in scratching his cropped hair while yawning.

'Want some?' asked James.

'You know I don't do dairy. Except Frank the milkman. I met him in The Pink Feather last year at a fancy dress.'

James guffawed despite his low mood.

'Why're you up? I thought you had your queen, or has she done a bunk again?'

James stuck his finger in the milk to test its heat and sucked it. 'How many times? We're not dating. We're getting to know each other again. Although now I know it'll never work.'

'Allelulia!'

'I know. You told me so. Maybe I have someone else on my mind and don't want to risk losing the chance of making a go with her.'

Ace opened the fridge door, unfolded a parcel of silver

foil and ate several pieces of roast chicken left over from the previous evening's dinner. 'Spill the beans. Who?'

'It doesn't matter.'

'If it wakes me up from my beauty sleep, believe me, it matters.'

'Just someone I can't get out of my head, that's all.'

Ace began singing, 'Can't Get You Out Of My Head' before closing the fridge door. 'God bless Kylie. She has all the lines. Right, if you're not going to tell me, I'm going back to bed. I've got to sort out a dodgy ballcock with Alan at eight-thirty – and then we're going to work, boom boom!' Ace was walking out of the kitchen, before stopping and turning. 'If it's a certain landlady you want to make your queen, then make your move, bro. I've heard through the grapevine that she's taken quite a shine to you.'

James turned and faced his brother. 'What've you heard?'

'Just that she likes you. A lot.'

'Who told you? When?'

Ace drew a line across his lips as if he was closing a zip.

'Oh, no you don't,' James said, dizzy with hope. He walked towards his brother and playfully backed him against the kitchen door. 'You don't tease me with that sort of information and then keep schtum.'

'I can't say. Libby'll kill—'

'Ha,' said James. 'Gotcha!' He stepped back from Ace. 'What did she say?'

'Look, I shouldn't have said anything. She just mentioned that Rowan was a bit upset when you started dating … seeing … whatever you're doing with Helen. I don't want to burst your bubble though, mate, but Libby also said that Rowan was leaving to live in France.'

'What?'

Ace held up his hands. 'Don't shoot the tired messenger. I'm going to bed.'

'Don't you dare go back to—'

A hissing noise distracted James from pursuing Ace to his bedroom. 'Shit!' He hurried to the hob to remove the pan of milk that had bubbled over.

'Ace! Wait!'

Two days after Rowan had told Nora to leave, she sat by the lounge window on the first floor of Magnolia House, watching Nora carry bulging carrier bags and boxes from the house before throwing them into the back of a VW Campervan. Rowan had never seen the van before and didn't recognise the two women who were helping her to pack and move.

She stood up from her vantage point on the arm of a chair and walked to the phone. She felt alone and in need of support that only her mother could give at this moment.

'Hi, Mum.'

'Hello, darling. How lovely to hear from you. How are you?'

Rowan bit back tears on hearing her mother's reassuring voice. 'Not great. I've had a fall out with Nora, one of my tenants. She's packing up and leaving at this very moment.'

'Oh dear, that's awful. What did you fall out about that was so bad she felt she had to leave?'

'I asked her to go, actually. She wasn't paying her rent.' Rowan didn't like being untruthful to her mother, but neither did she want to worry her about nasty notes or Tom's infidelity. There was time enough for that in the weeks to come.

'Then you had no choice, did you, darling? How's everything else?'

'Okay, I suppose. Ace and James both have new partners and Libby's recovering well. I told you that she should be able to have children in the future, didn't I?'

298

'Yes. What a relief for her and David. I'm so glad they got to the bottom of her stomach pains with such a positive outcome.'

'How are you both?'

'We're fine. Your dad's well and is enjoying fishing and playing cards with the local men folk. I'm keeping busy at the shop and Fabrice sends his best wishes to you. His wife's expecting their fourth child so I may get a few more hours work in the near future. They're having another girl.'

'That's lovely news. I was thinking of coming out to see you at Christmas. Will you be there?'

'Of course, that'd be lovely. We'll be here and it would make your dad's day to know you were joining us.'

'That's good.'

'You sound a bit down. Are you sure there's nothing else the matter apart from the fall out with your tenant?'

'The weather's awful too, but you get used to it here, don't you?'

'I suppose you do. How's work going?'

'It helps pay the bills, but I could put more hours in if I was more motivated.'

'How are you managing financially? We can't help a lot but I'm sure we could manage something.'

'Oh, Mum, it's not as bad as that. I can always put more hours into my work. Did you get the photo I sent of Jet?'

'We did, thank you. Your dad has stuck it on the fridge. We had a good laugh at him looking so sorry for himself in the bath with his ears hanging like wet socks on a washing line.'

Rowan laughed and looked over to where Jet was lying asleep under the coffee table.

'He knows not to go swimming in smelly duck ponds.'

'We miss him. You must bring him at Christmas.'

There was a pause. 'Mum?'

'Yes, darling.'

'If I wanted to stay a little longer than a fortnight, would that be all right?'

'You know you're always welcome. How long were you thinking of?'

'I was thinking of moving there permanently.'

Chapter Forty-Two

The morning of 16th December was glorious. A fresh layer of snow lay on the ground and the azure sky was cloudless. The sun was weak in strength but its appearance after weeks of granite-grey days had brightened Rowan's mood. She lay fully clothed on her bed listening to the house creaking and sighing as if it were breathing. Occasionally radiators would click or she'd hear the sound of taps being turned on or off in the kitchen below. Earlier she had walked Jet on the common and was just catching her breath.

It had been an immense relief to receive a phone call from Libby, explaining that Tom had felt shame and remorse for a short-lived affair that had resulted in a child. It had helped incalculably to know that the relationship hadn't lasted long. Also finding out that Nora knew about their personal details due to theft and not through Tom having divulged private information was some comfort. The thought that he'd deceived her so brutally still stung, but now she sensed that she'd achieved some sort of inner peace. She supposed that it had helped that his deceit and duplicity had been drip fed to her over the months. He'd been unfaithful. Nora had been the mistress. He'd fathered a child. Better to learn that her husband had been a cheat and a liar in small doses!

She had explained to everyone that she needed a few days to herself to heal in peace and solitude and was grateful that everyone understood and had given her reflective space. She'd had many imaginary conversations with Tom during this time. Countless times she had cursed him quietly under her breath for fear of James or Ace hearing her and thinking she was losing her mind. She was powerless to understand why his ghost was the antithesis of her memories of his living self. As the days passed, Rowan had come to believe that a tarnished past wouldn't spoil her future. She felt cushioned by the support she knew she could rely on from her family and friends. Surely that was the first stepping stone to a fresh start?

Rowan reached out for what used to be Tom's pillow, inhaling into the cotton and feathers before positioning it lengthways beside her. She was surprised to realise that she felt some sympathy for him now. She conjured the sensation of his body lying alongside her as she lay with her arm draped around the pillow, but as her contact with the cool pillow warmed to her touch, she pulled it closer as visions of James filled her thoughts. She squeezed it and closed her eyes.

As she lay there she knew she had to tackle a list of things that needed sorting, one of which was to clean the vacated basement apartment. But Libby had texted while walking Jet, asking to meet her at a particular bench in Hyde Park. The text had also said to pack a small picnic and that sounded, although a little odd at this time of year, also a lot more fun than cleaning or a trip to the supermarket.

Before long Rowan stood fastening her coat, watching Jet eat his breakfast. His bowl scraped on the oak boards, moving slightly each time his nose nudged it while eating. She picked up her bag containing a picnic of ham and Emmental cheese sandwiches, a small bunch of grapes and a flask of tea. Pulling on her woollen hat, she told Jet to be good and left her apartment.

The tube was packed with Christmas shoppers and tourists, all carrying bulky carrier bags full of festive gifts. There wasn't a vacant seat so she'd been jostled and squashed for the whole journey while hanging on tightly.

By the time Rowan had escaped the confines of the underground system, a few clouds had appeared like blemishes. She took simple pleasure in crunching unspoilt snow beneath her boots and exhilarated in the open air while walking towards bench T108, on the north of Hyde Park's Serpentine. This bench, Libby had informed her on their previous picnic here during the summer, was used for clandestine meetings in the iconic film, *The Ipcress File*. Rowan was eager to find out why Libby had suggested a winter picnic at this isolated spot. Maybe she had some exciting information about the shop.

Rowan found the bench and brushed powdery snow from its seat. She tucked her coat beneath her bottom and perched on the edge, trying to keep her jeans dry. She looked along the length of the path in both directions but Libby was nowhere to be seen. Rowan glanced at her watch. It was a few minutes before midday. She pulled up her fur-lined hood and sat watching the wild birds swimming and swooping on the patterned, breeze-blown surface of the water. The clouds were expanding in the sky but a fragile heat still shone directly onto Rowan's face, making her feel more relaxed at this moment than she'd felt in a long time. The silence was a panacea.

Five minutes later, footsteps approached from behind the bench. Rowan's face remained upturned, her eyes stayed closed and a slight smile played on her lips. Libby was here.

A man's voice surprised her.

'What's this all about then, Libby? Why all the mystery?'

Rowan sat up quickly and spun round, her hood falling off. James stopped walking and looked equally surprised to see her.

'Hello,' he said. 'What're you doing here?'

'Waiting for Libby. What are you doing here?'

James looked bemused. 'The same.' He lifted a blue plastic bag in one hand. 'She asked me to bring a picnic,' and then raised a tartan throw in the other, 'and a blanket.'

Rowan looked at him standing in front of her with both arms raised. His hair was pushed back away from his eyes, which were narrowed in confusion. His thick padded jacket hugged his body tightly and his jeans were tucked inside chunky boots. He was gorgeous without trying and she could feel her heart racing at this unexpected meeting.

He walked round to the front of the bench. 'Mind if I wait with you?'

'Don't be silly. Of course not.' She swept away more snow from the bench with her gloved hand.

'Jump up and I'll put the cover down to sit on.'

Rowan stood up and watched James arrange the blanket.

'There you go.' He smiled, directing Rowan with a flourish of his arm.

'Thank you.'

James sat beside her. 'So, what do you think she wants to tell us?' he asked, bending to place his plastic bag on the ground. 'And why here of all places?'

'I've no idea what she's up to. We've been here several times in the summer, but never to picnic in the winter.'

The sun disappeared behind a grey cloud, the tenuous warmth from the sun vanishing in an instant. She leant forwards rubbing her gloved hands together and blowing warm breath into her cupped palms.

'I've made some hot chocolate. Would you like a cup?' said James.

Rowan thought that chocolate sounded much better than her flask of tea. 'Yes, please.'

He reached for his bag, pulled out a thermos flask and poured two plastic cups full of steaming chocolate before handing one to Rowan. The other he placed on the arm of the bench while he screwed the lid back on. When he lifted his cup from the wooden arm, it had melted a perfect circle in the snow. James sipped from it twice and hugged the hot cup with his fingers. Within seconds of each other, their mobile phones received a text.

'It's from Libby. She says she can't make it,' said Rowan.

James was reading the screen on his phone and then turned it to face her. It was the identical message from her sister-in-law. 'I think we've been conned. I don't think she ever intended joining us.'

Rowan was confused. 'Didn't she? Why?'

She noticed James look down at his cup and was sure that his face flushed pink. Suddenly it dawned on her and a blush warmed her own face too. Libby had set them up. She'd made sure they were alone somewhere quiet and scenic with a blanket and picnic; a secluded romantic rendezvous in the snow. Perhaps this was Libby's way of proving that she was okay about her moving on from Tom, but Rowan would much rather she'd just told her it was all right. Besides, what had Libby been thinking? She knew that she was leaving in the New Year and that James was seeing Helen. Rowan sipped her sweet chocolate, giving herself time to think. Surely James didn't think that she'd planned this with Libby. That would be so embarrassing. She'd have to put him straight.

'I'm really sorry you've wasted your time. I thought she was meeting me to get some fresh air and talk about Ace's shop.'

'I haven't wasted my time.' He paused. 'I hear you're thinking of leaving?'

Rowan lowered her chin and played with a loose thread on one of her gloves. She looked up and met his gaze. 'I just think that maybe it's time to move on. I was going to tell everyone in the New Year.'

James leant back against the bench, causing a waterfall of snow to sprinkle onto the ground behind him. 'Why such a drastic move?'

She shrugged. 'The house doesn't hold any happy memories for me. I thought it was going to be a home where Tom and I lived happily ever after. That's what should happen when you get married, isn't it?' She stretched her legs out straight in front of her, resting her boots on their heels. 'I thought our children would grow up there. That Tom's business would take off. But I couldn't have been more wrong, could I?' She frowned, her lips parted in disbelief as if the lunacy of the situation had only just dawned on her.

'I'm sorry you've had such a tough year. It's a lot to deal with.'

'Thanks. It happens. Others have it far worse.'

A breeze whipped around their ankles and shook the branches of nearby trees, causing snow to fall to the ground with a thud. They both turned at the sound.

'Why France? Why not just move house?' said James.

She noticed a fallen eyelash resting on his cheek and longed to gently wipe it away. 'Mum and Dad live there.'

'So?'

'Isn't that a good enough reason?'

His head tilted to one side as he chose his words carefully. 'Maybe for a holiday, but I remember you telling me that you didn't speak fluent French.'

The silence of the settled snow engulfed them during each pause in their conversation.

'They say the best way to learn a language is to live in the country itself.'

'Maybe. But what about your business?'

'It's not growing and I can't find the motivation to develop it further.'

'And you think you'll find that in the depth of the French countryside?'

She didn't answer. Perhaps she should just come out with

it and tell him that she had fallen in love with him. That if she moved to France, she'd miss the feeling of calm she felt in the knowledge that he was close. She'd miss the tingle of anticipation each time she left her apartment, just in case she met him in the hallway. She'd miss the electricity she felt when he touched her, his smile that revealed one slightly crooked tooth and she'd miss the smell of bergamot and spice from his aftershave. If he felt something for her, it would give him the opportunity to speak up.

She glanced sideways at him, watching as he scraped away snow with his boots to reveal the frozen grass beneath. His expression was downcast. Could she really dare to hope that he might genuinely be upset at the thought that she was leaving? He looked so sad; so deep in thought. She'd do it! She'd tell him. Nothing too dramatic or cringeworthy. Just enough of a hint for him to open up. She breathed in deeply, preparing to turn towards him with her declaration. But before she could speak, he faced her with an accusation.

'I think you're running away from your problems,' he said. 'You're only going to find yourself isolated in the French countryside trying to sell your work in local markets. It's not sensible. You need to establish your business here in London. It's where the money is.'

Rowan blinked in surprise. She'd dared to imagine that he'd ask her to stay because he'd miss her, not that she should focus on her financial prospects while insinuating that she was being impractical. She shivered, angry with herself for allowing her fantasies to blur reality and for so nearly telling James how she felt. Her disappointment made her snap.

'Who are you to accuse me of running away?' She stood up and brushed herself down briskly, all the while staring furiously at James who was sitting wide-eyed looking up at her. 'What do you call flying off to California to escape a broken heart? Isn't that running away? Or was that just a grand romantic gesture on your part? Don't point an accusatory finger at me when you've done exactly the same thing.'

James stood up and reached for her hand. 'I left because I couldn't be with someone I'd wanted. Why are you leaving?'

His question was so unexpected that she was left flustered for a few seconds. She was leaving for exactly the same reason. She felt his fingers rub her hand through her gloves and her longing to wind her fingers around his and hold him tight was almost painful in its intensity. But he'd made it clear, hadn't he? He was concerned about her financial welfare and was back with the girl he'd left the country for. Now she needed to protect herself from yet more heartache. The past eighteen months had taken its toll emotionally and she knew she wasn't strong enough to cope with more disappointment. She needed to bring up a barrier between them, no matter how painful it might be.

'There's nothing here for me to stay for.' She removed her hand from his. 'I really must get back now and clean the basement. Thank you for the drink.' Rowan picked up her bag, turned and started to march as quickly as her dignity would allow along the slippery path. Snowflakes began to fall. She walked away from him, stumbling on tree roots that had twisted across the path.

'Rowan!' James caught up with her. 'Rowan, please stop.'

She turned and looked into his dark eyes, cross with herself for feeling immense relief that he'd followed her. It had started to snow more heavily and snowflake crystals decorated his hair and coat.

'It's just that I'll—' He sighed. 'I'm not good at this.'

Rowan didn't answer, but wiped away a tear that was tickling her face. 'I need to get back. I know, you've already said. I'm being pathetic and running back to my mum and dad. But I've got plenty to run away from, don't you think?'

'Actually, no I don't. You've had a tough year and a dreadful loss, but you've accomplished a lot.'

'Oh please, don't list my achievements,' she snapped. 'Yes, I've survived my husband's death, a miscarriage, news of his affair and finding out Tom fathered a child. But everyone's moving on and I feel like I'm a spectator.'

Rowan's tears took her by surprise as she thought of her lost baby. Her body still ached for the little person who had once shared her body and it was only standing here on this snow-covered path, that she realised why life seemed such a struggle. Tom may have been deceitful and selfish, but the baby who'd been growing inside had been innocent, vulnerable and already deeply loved. The pain of losing her baby had been pushed to one side while her grief for Tom had engulfed her.

Rowan felt herself falling towards James. It happened too quickly at first to realise that he'd taken hold of her shoulders and had pulled her towards him. She held him tightly, crying into the thick padding of his jacket, feeling him stoke her hair and comforting her with gentle whispers of support.

Rowan looked up, their arms still loosely draped around each other. 'I'm sorry. Can we forget about the last half an hour? It's been a bit of a disaster.'

James shook his head. 'Not possible, I'm afraid. How could I forget sharing a hot chocolate with you in the snow and holding you in my arms?'

'Don't, James. It's not fair.'

They stood facing each other. Rowan looked into his dark eyes, the amber flecks in his pupils noticeable at such close proximity. He moved a strand of hair that had fallen from her woollen hat across her face, and he smiled. Slowly, he began to move closer towards her. The snow fell silently around them as she leant towards him.

'You bastard!'

Rowan and James snapped apart. They turned to see Helen striding comically towards them in high-heeled boots, occasionally slipping while holding her arms out to her sides at right angles for balance. Her long blond waves hung like wet shoelaces, sodden by the falling snow. Rowan took a step back as Helen pushed herself in between the two of them.

'You liar.' She slapped his face. 'You said that you had a meeting with that frumpy Libby.'

James answered in monotone. 'She cancelled. And I've never called her that.'

'*I'm* calling her that. Why did you think I let you go?' She raised her voice. 'Why did you lie to me?'

Rowan felt very uncomfortable and began to shiver. The snow on her clothes was melting and sinking into her coat and gloves.

'Firstly, you didn't *let* me go. I told you I was going. Secondly, Libby couldn't make it and Rowan was here to meet her too. But, more importantly, what are you doing here? Have you been drinking? I can smell alcohol.'

'I followed you and it seems my instincts were right. And who do you think you are? My dad? I can have a drink if I want one.' Helen wiped snow from her eyelashes, smudging mascara across her face.

'Like I said, I was meeting Libby and I thought she wanted to ask me for a favour in private. To be honest, I thought she was going to ask to borrow some money for her new business.' He pulled out a small bundle of notes from his jacket. 'I've got four hundred pounds here that your dad gave me for making his garden furniture. I was going to loan it to Libby.'

'It all sounds a little bit too convenient to me. And what were you doing with your arms around her?' she said, jerking her head in Rowan's direction.

'It was my fault,' said Rowan. 'James was just comforting me. I was upset about something.'

Helen swung round to face her and sneered. 'Like what?'

'It's private.'

'Yeh, I bet it is. Not private enough to share it with my boyfriend.'

'I'm not your boyfriend, Helen.'

'This "see how it goes until Christmas" thing is ridiculous,' she snapped. She mimicked him. 'Let's just take it slow. Let's not rush things. Look around you, James. It's snowing. It's Christmas now.'

Rowan was looking at James. He'd said he wasn't Helen's boyfriend. If they weren't dating, did that mean they hadn't slept together? Could she dare hope that this was the case? Helen rounded on her again.

'Come to think of it, weren't you also upset about something the day James had been looking after Primrose? You got a hug from him then, too. Is that your tactic? Cry and be comforted?'

Rowan's mouth was dry and she was now shivering from cold. She wished she'd never agreed to come. It was like a bad dream.

'That's enough,' said James, raising his voice. 'Go back to the apartment and get changed and then go home to your parents. I'll phone you later.'

Helen swung back round to face James. 'Did I ruin your romantic walk in the snow?' She turned to face Rowan again. 'You should be ashamed. I thought you were recently widowed. I bet he's turning in his grave.'

James stepped forwards. 'Shut up, Helen. Go now and we'll speak later.'

311

Rowan felt as if the air had been punched from her lungs and sensed her legs weaken.

'How dare you?' She spoke to Helen through clenched teeth. 'You don't know anything about me.'

'I know you were standing with your arms around James. I heard you were going to France. Why not book a flight this evening?' Helen made an attempt to push Rowan, but slipped on the snow and fell to the ground. She stayed there, not attempting to get up. She looked up at James, her chin quivering. 'How am I supposed to make it back home in these by myself?'

Rowan looked at Helen's high heels and turned to James. 'I'll be fine,' she said. 'Thanks for your support but I'll be okay by myself. You help Helen get home.' She tried not to meet Helen's eyes, although she felt them boring into hers. She could see from James' face that the last thing he wanted to do was take Helen home, but she also knew he was too much of a gentleman to let her struggle alone.

'No, we can all—'

Rowan shook her head and turned. 'I'm fine, honestly. You help Helen.'

Rowan crunched through the snow back through Hyde Park, not glancing behind her once to see if they were following. She couldn't feel her fingers and even her toes were going numb with the cold. Thankfully the snow was now falling more lightly. The park looked so beautiful draped in white that she actually appreciated the scenery despite her chattering teeth and the past awful hour.

As Rowan sat on the tube train on her way back to Clapham, she had time to think over what had happened. One particular moment kept replaying in her mind. It was when James had turned serious, looked into her eyes and was slowly leaning towards her. She felt a bubble of excitement in her stomach. Had James been about to kiss her?

Chapter Forty-Three

When Rowan reached street level at Clapham, she called Libby on her mobile.

'Hello.'

'Libby, what were you thinking of by setting us up? I can't believe you did that. It was so embarrassing and Helen turned up and she completely lost it.'

'She didn't spoil it, did she?'

'Libby! That's not the point. Why did you do it? I was mortified. I bet he thought I'd asked you to set us up. Oh, why did I go?'

'Listen, I'm sorry if I embarrassed you. Ace was saying that James wasn't happy with Helen and wasn't going to take the relationship any further.'

Rowan crossed the main road. 'Well, I shouted at him anyway, so it's all a mess.'

'What did you say?'

'He accused me of running away from my problems and started sounding like my accountant. He was telling me to stay because the money was in London.'

'Of course he was telling you to stay, but not because he's worried about your earning potential. It was just the excuse he used.'

'It didn't sound like that.'

'The poor guy was asking you to stay because he'd miss you and you yelled at him.'

'Then he should have said that.'

'He's a man, Rowan. Nothing's straightforward with men. He has to think of excuses for you to stay, rather than take the risk of being ridiculed if he said that he'd miss you.'

'The truth is, I think I was angry with him because what

he was saying was too close to home. I'm scared of being alone again, so if I'm with Mum and Dad, I won't be. But I can't, can I?'

'Can't what?'

'I can't run back to Mum and Dad just for company, can I? They've got used to living by themselves and they rub along nicely with the locals and being part of the community. They have their little routines and if I turn up with a van full of furniture and clothes, it wouldn't be fair on them. And as for selling my jewellery out there, seriously, who am I kidding?'

Rowan had reached her front door and tried to find her key while resting her mobile between her ear and cheek. 'I'm home now. Damn! My fingers are so frozen I can't pick my keys out of my bag.'

'Are you in later? I need a moan. David's working at home today so I could borrow the car and drive over.'

'Yes, I'm in all day now. I'm locking my door to everyone but you. Anyway, what have you got to moan about now you're about to become a florist?'

'I'm not sure the shop's going to happen, but you get warm and I'll tell you all about it when I get there.'

Rowan struggled with the keys in the door. 'Okay. The first thing I'm going to do is have a hot soak. I'm frozen to the bone. Give me an hour to thaw out and then I'm all ears.'

Fifty-five minutes later, the intercom sounded and Rowan buzzed Libby in. She opened her apartment door as her sister-in-law reached the first floor.

'You look cosy,' said Libby. She kissed Rowan on the cheek.

Rowan looked down at her pale blue, fluffy dressing gown. 'I was so cold. A hot bath has never felt so good. I just thought I'd lounge about in comfort for an hour or so. Do you fancy a drink?'

'No, thanks,' said Libby, taking off her coat. 'When David works from home, he tries to drown me in tea every half an hour. My bladder's in overdrive.'

Rowan watched Libby bend and make a fuss of Jet who was burying his head between her knees and wagging his tail. She sat on a settee next to her sister-in-law and tucked her feet under her bottom. 'I think he was going to kiss me.'

Libby stopped stroking Jet and looked up at her. 'Who?'

Rowan grinned. 'I honestly think James was going to kiss me.'

'You mean my plan nearly worked? What stopped him?'

Rowan shook her head. 'Helen did. It all happened so quickly. I was upset, he hugged me, he moved my hair out of my eyes, he leant in towards me and then Helen appeared from nowhere and swore at him.'

'What was Helen doing there?'

Rowan leaned her head against the back of the settee and stared at the ceiling. 'She followed him because she didn't believe he was meeting you.'

'Hmm. There's an insult in there somewhere.'

'No, it's just her possessiveness.' Rowan looked at her. 'She was shouting and crying and even slapped his face. I think she'd been drinking.'

Libby leant forwards hanging on her every word. 'No. What did James do?'

'He was calm until she started accusing me of stuff.'

'What stuff?'

'She was bringing Tom into the conversation and accusing me of wanting James.'

'Well you do, don't you?'

'Libby!' She laughed and leaned forwards. 'James denied being her boyfriend. It sounded as if they'd given each other until Christmas to decide whether to make a go of it or not.'

'You're kidding.'

'That's what it sounded like.'

'You mean they're dating platonically for a set amount of time? God, that sounds a bit old-fashioned.'

Rowan grinned. 'I was lying in the bath trying to remember when I'd seen Helen leaving the house in the morning for work. I usually take Jet about eight to half past, and I can't ever remember seeing her car outside, nor did I bump into her at a time she would have left.'

'Now you mention it, they were never lovey-dovey when we saw them together. It was more a case of Helen giving a keep-your-hands-off-James sort of look whenever we were around.'

'My head's spinning with broken relationships; Helen and Nora. Tell me about the shop. What do you mean that it might not happen?'

Libby flopped back against the cushions and looked despondent, fiddling with the fringe on her scarf. 'I've done the sums for the business plan and frankly the bank manager will have a good laugh when he sees it. It's the bloody repayments on my cards that have spoilt everything. They say what goes around comes around, don't they? It's payback, come-uppance, karma; whatever you want to call it. I frittered and spent too much money and now I don't have enough to finance my dream.'

'Can't you consolidate your debt with a nought per cent interest account?'

Libby laughed. 'Now *you* sound like an accountant. David's helped me to do that already. I can afford the rent on the shop but there's no way I could afford the decoration, advertising or the website. And I'll need a website.'

'But won't money come with sales?'

'Yes, but I can't afford the initial stock. I won't get far with a flower shop that doesn't have any flowers to sell.'

'There must be some way. What about sponsorship? Perhaps you could ask the local paper for some coverage. I bet they'd promote a new small business. I could help you decorate it and I'm sure Ace and Alan would too.'

Libby closed her eyes. 'Maybe in a few years' time. When we've paid off the loan. In the meantime I'll have to look for a waitressing job or something.'

Rowan squeezed Libby's hand. 'I'm so sorry. I wish I could help but now that Nora's rent has stopped …'

'It's all right. Sorry to be such a misery, but I'd let myself believe it was possible and pictured the layout and even the shop name. Libby's Lobelias.'

Rowan pulled a face.

'What?' asked Libby. 'Don't you like it? It's a play on the L's and B's.'

'It's terrible. And it'll be a pretty boring shop if you're only going to sell Lobelias.'

'It's better than Ace's idea. He said I should call it Dead Stuff as Lifestyle Accessories.'

'But he loves flowers,' Rowan said, laughing.

'I know. He was just being silly. Anyway, it doesn't matter now.'

'The main thing is that you're sorting your health and finances out. As you say, maybe in a couple of years things'll look better. At least you know what your dreams are. You want children and a flower shop and both are achievable. Some people reach their forties and fifties and still don't know what they want to do.'

'True.'

Rowan stood up. 'It's nearly three and I fancy an early glass of wine. Are you having one? I won't tell if you don't.'

'A small one. I'm driving and I can't stay too long because I've got dinner to sort out.'

Rowan walked across the room and into the kitchen. She took two glasses from the cupboard and lifted a bottle of white wine from the fridge. As she poured wine into the glasses, she tried to think of a benefactor who could help Libby. Perhaps she could go into business with someone else and share the expense; someone who was looking for an outlet for a home-based business.

Rowan stopped pouring the wine. She placed the bottle on the worktop as if in a trance. Her mouth fell open into a half gape and half smile, then she walked slowly back into the lounge.

Libby turned her head. 'Are you all right?'

'I'm fantastic.'

'What have you done?'

'I've thought of an idea that'll make us both happy.'

Libby twisted in her seat. 'What d'you mean?'

'How do you fancy a business partner to share the costs?'

'Who?'

'Me.'

'You?'

'Yes.'

'You mean it?' Libby's eyes watered. She faced Rowan. 'What about France?'

'Like I said, it wouldn't be fair on Mum and Dad. And James was right. What's the point of setting up a jewellery business in rural France when I live in the capital of England? I could sell my jewellery and you could sell your flowers.'

Libby put her hands together and rested her fingers on her lips. 'Seriously?'

'Seriously.'

Libby squealed and they hugged tightly. Their embrace

318

turned into jumping up and down with a mixture of laughter and tears.

'Business partners,' yelled Rowan, as she held her palm up in the air.

Libby slapped it. 'Oh my God, I can't believe it.'

'There's just one thing,' said Rowan, more seriously.

'What?'

'We'll have to change that awful shop name.'

Chapter Forty-Four

James turned the shower on and helped Helen out of her wet clothes. He'd considered running her a bath but having found a half empty bottle of gin in her coat pocket, he thought better of leaving her alone in a tub full of hot water. When she was standing shivering in her bra and pants, James gathered her wet clothes together.

'Leave the door open in case you slip. I'll put these in the wash.'

She didn't answer but he heard her removing her underwear and stepping into the shower. He crossed the living room with the damp bundle and crouched down in the kitchen beside the washing machine. Shoving the clothes inside the drum, he threw in a washing tablet, slammed the door shut and turned it on. He then slid onto the floor and sat with his back leaning against a kitchen cupboard. That must have been one of the most stressful, unpleasant, exhausting, exciting hours of his life, he thought. He didn't know where to start to decipher it all.

James absent-mindedly looked at the nails on one hand and nibbled an uneven cuticle. Why had he accused Rowan of running away? What he'd really wanted to tell her was that he'd miss her. That she was the first person he thought about when he woke up in the morning. He squeezed his eyes shut, remembering the moment when he was going to kiss her just before Helen had arrived. 'You stupid, stupid idiot,' he said out loud. He pressed his closed fists against his eyes, remembering that she'd just mentioned her miscarriage when he'd tried to kiss her.

'Idiot. Idiot.'

James glanced through the circular glass door of the

washing machine at Helen's clothes rotating in bubbles of water. He placed his splayed fingers on the warm glass and felt the machine's vibrations. He had to be decisive. He had to tell Helen that he didn't want to take their relationship any further and then he had to speak to Rowan again.

'You're not an idiot,' said Helen. She was standing at the kitchen doorway. She had a towel twisted into a knot on her hair and a bath sheet wrapped around her body. 'You just made the wrong decision.'

James looked up at her. 'What?'

'Meeting up with Rowan.'

'I told you, that's not what happened. I'm glad you've calmed down. How do you feel after your shower?'

'Much better, thanks. I see you found the bottle of gin. I didn't drink it all this morning, you know? I'd already started it.'

'As you said earlier, I'm not your father.'

'Why are you sitting on the floor?'

James shrugged. 'Seemed like as good a place as any.' He groaned as he stood up. 'You can grab a shirt of mine from my cupboard. Your clothes are on a quick wash so I'll tumble them in twenty minutes.'

Helen put on a squeaky childish voice and wore a feigned sad expression. 'Are you still angry with me?' She walked toward him and ran a finger seductively from his neck, down his chest, past his stomach and towards his crotch.

He stopped her hand. 'No.'

She frowned. 'What's the matter with you? You're no fun.'

'Perhaps we just have different ideas of what fun is.'

Her face softened and she tried again. 'I know one sort of fun we both used to enjoy as much as each other.'

She grinned and untied her towel, letting it drop to the floor.

'Helen—'

'Just call it an early Christmas present.'

James walked past her and out of the kitchen. 'I'll get you that shirt.'

He reached the bedroom door as Helen caught up with him, grasping the towel to her body.

'What's your problem, eh? Have you any idea how many men would love to see me drop my towel in front of them?'

'I don't doubt it.'

Helen lurched forwards and punched him in the chest. 'I hate you.'

His body jerked with the force of the punch. He threw a shirt at her. 'Get dressed, Helen.'

She snatched it. 'How dare you ignore me,' she screamed. 'Perhaps we should stop seeing each other if you don't find me attractive any more.'

He faced her, calmly. 'I think you're right.'

She stood open-mouthed at the bedroom doorway. 'What?'

'I said, I think you're right.'

'But I don't mean it. I'm just angry.'

He walked past her into the living room. 'But I do, Helen. It's not working. I don't want us to become a couple again. I think it's best if we call it a day while we're still speaking civilly to each other. We've both changed in the past couple of years. I'm not looking for a life of partying or drinking any more.' He heard her getting dressed.

She shouted, from Ace's bedroom. 'Neither am I.'

James sat down at the small dining table because it seemed more appropriate to have this conversation there, rather than on the folded sofa bed.

Helen came out of the bedroom door. 'Did you hear me? I said, neither am I.'

James watched her sit down next to him at the table.

'Listen to yourself. You've only just sobered up. What if you'd fallen and sprained an ankle in Hyde Park? You'd be lying in the snow and God knows when you would have been found.'

'See. You do still care.'

'Of course I care about you, Helen.'

She smiled.

'But that's not enough. I'm looking for more. I'm eleven years older than you and although that doesn't necessarily matter in ten or twenty years' time, I think it does now. You're twenty-two.'

'But I love you.'

'I'm not sure you do. You came back to me when your footballer boyfriend left. Would you have come back otherwise? He lived your fantasy life. Travelling, partying, drinking. Lavishing you with gifts. You have to admit you've been moaning about staying in watching films. And you'd rather go out than have me cook for you. I don't have the astronomical wages that footballers have, in fact, I've got to get my act together and start earning.'

'I enjoy watching films with you.'

He smiled. 'I enjoy that too, but the truth is, I'm not in love with you any more. I was heartbroken when you left me, but I've moved on. I thought I could recapture that feeling again when you came back, but—'

'I broke your heart?'

James saw how immature Helen really was. She needed to feel that she was gaining some emotional ground back by acknowledging that she'd hurt him in the past. If it gave her the confidence to move on, thought James, that was fine.

'Yes. You hurt me more than I'd ever been hurt by any woman before. I even left the country to get over you.'

Helen's eyes grew wide. 'You left because of *me*? Wow. It's like a romantic film script.'

'But without the happy ending.'
'We still could have.'
James shook his head.

Helen had left after James cooked a final meal for her. She appeared much calmer, having accepted that their relationship was over and had even been looking forward to contacting a friend to go out to a wine bar and then dancing later that night. It even crossed James' mind that his decision was actually as much as a relief for her as it was for him.

He'd taken a shower after she'd gone. It had only been early evening, but he felt as if he needed to finally rinse away any pain or regret he'd felt when she'd left him previously. He'd mistakenly taken the first step to rekindle their relationship but it had enabled him to move on too. Standing beneath the pummelling jets, he'd closed his eyes and raised his face to the spray. He'd opened his mouth, taken in mouthfuls of hot water before letting it drain from his lips time and time again. As he lathered his body with bubbles he washed away images of false nails, hair extensions, fake tan and layers of make-up. He daydreamed about Rowan, who had looked beautiful without the use of synthetic additions. In Hyde Park she'd clung to him tightly in the snow. It made him smile to himself.

The following morning, James woke up without the usual aches and pains from the springs in the sofa bed. He'd recently been sleeping in Ace's bed because his brother had all but moved in to Alan's house. Ace had agreed to this under the proviso that James was to 'sod off' back to the sofa bed when he occasionally returned to Magnolia House.

The sun was streaming in through the vertical blinds, criss-crossing the walls like latticework. He'd slept soundly all night and couldn't even remember dreaming. He felt relieved that he and Helen had gone their separate ways without bitter recriminations or upset. He felt excitement for the future and was determined to speak to Rowan and be honest about how he felt about her. He felt energised with a new enthusiasm for finding work – his own carpentry business.

By eleven o'clock, he had cleaned the apartment and was working at his computer designing a website for a new business he'd decided to set up. He'd had a few enquiries from people who had seen the garden furniture he'd made for Helen's parents, so he decided to put the photographs he'd taken on to a ready made website template. He bought an online image of an oak leaf and designed a small logo for Oakland Garden Furniture.

Finally, he was organising his life and it felt good.

Chapter Forty-Five

It was nearly midday and Rowan knew what she must do. She put the pillow to one side, stood up and walked towards the wardrobe. Reaching on her tiptoes, she pulled a large case down from the top of it. Particles of dust danced in the air as she laid it on the floor and unzipped it. She pushed the lid back until it fell with a *thwack* on the floor. Next, she stood in front of the wardrobe and ignoring her reflection in the long mirrors on the doors, she pulled the left side open.

Tom's clothes were neatly hung and precisely folded. One by one, she removed the articles from their hangers and shelves and placed them in the suitcase. She fetched his photograph by her bedside, then the framed picture from the lounge and placed them on top of the packed clothes. Next she bent down and picked up the box where she'd found Tom's mobile phone. She pushed it into a corner of the case. The phone was lying upside down on the top. Rowan looked down at the bulging case before remembering one more article. She walked through the lounge, passing Jet who was asleep under the coffee table and into the kitchen. She pulled open a top cupboard and lifted down Tom's mug. It read *Keep Calm and Carry On*. She didn't need Tom or any silly message telling her what she already knew. She would make her own rules from now on. Carrying the mug back to the suitcase, she pushed it in amongst Tom's clothing and closed the zip before heaving it through the bedroom, across the lounge and towards the front door.

Yesterday, before Libby had left the apartment following their decision to work together, her sister-in-law had taken her by the hand. She'd apologised for taking the edge off their excitement but said that she needed to be honest about something. She and David were going to try and find Nora so they could make the first steps in having some contact with Primrose. They didn't want to hurt Rowan, but Primrose was Tom's daughter and, therefore, she was family. It hadn't come as a surprise to Rowan. In fact, she'd previously broached the subject herself. She understood and had given her blessing. Maybe Primrose would enter her life in the future, too.

As she was nearing the front door, Jet gave a half-hearted bark just before there was a knock at the door. Rowan opened it. It was James.

'Hello,' said Rowan.

'Hello.'

'Would you like to come in?'

'If I'm not disturbing you.'

Rowan shook her head. 'Not at all.'

'I wanted to help you overcome the idea of nasty notes. I thought I'd give you a friendly one.' He handed a piece of paper to Rowan.

Rowan looked at him questioningly and unfolded the paper.

Don't go. I love you. James X

'As notes go, it's very nice.'

James was bashfully trying to bite a smile from his lips. He looked down at Jet who was sitting next to a blazing red poinsettia, its waxy leaves splayed wide and green. Then his gaze moved from Jet to something sitting on the floor next to him. The smile slipped from his face when he saw the suitcase on the floor. 'You're leaving. Were you just going to fly to France and not tell me?'

'No.'

James shook his head. 'Don't go, Rowan. I can't stop thinking about you. I've been crazy about you since the first time you knocked on Ace's door. I've happily suffered sleeping on a lumpy sofa bed because I knew that you were just above my ceiling when I'm there.'

Rowan's heart was racing so fast that her fingers tingled with pins and needles. James Gregory Oakland was crazy about her.

'I've tried to give you time these past couple of days,' he continued, 'but I couldn't bear it any longer. I'll wait for you. Until you're ready. That's if you're interested. It's just that Ace mentioned you liked me and—'

Rowan watched his face crease with frown lines, his hands gesticulating in front of him as he stumbled over his words.

'I'm not going anywhere.'

'You're not?'

'No. The suitcase is full of Tom's things. I was going to drag them down into the basement for the time being, until I decide what to do with them.'

'Oh.' He rubbed the stubble on his chin before pushing away dark tendrils of hair that had fallen into his eyes. 'I've been worried about you.'

'I'm fine. Really. Hasn't Ace told you that I'm setting up in Mason's Closet with Libby? I'll be selling my jewellery alongside her flowers.'

He looked surprised. 'No, he didn't, but then again he hasn't been here much. He just dashed back for half an hour yesterday to grab some clean clothes. He's more or less moved in with Alan.' He laughed. 'That's an amazing idea. That's fantastic.'

Rowan listened to him speak. She wanted to reach out to him but felt too shy. She wanted to touch him, to smell him, to kiss him. She pushed Tom's suitcase out of the way with her leg and stood in front of him, willing her hands to stay still. His dark eyes were searching hers, staring so intently she felt her breath quicken. She recalled his words in his note. 'You wrote, I love you.'

His gaze didn't leave her eyes. 'I know.'

'You said you'd wait for me.'

'I will.'

'I'm ready.'

He swallowed. 'What for?'

'Not for Christmas, that's for sure.' She looked more serious, wringing her hands together. 'For you, silly.'

Still standing an arm's length away, she watched him lower his eyes to her knotted fingers, take a step forwards and gently unfurl them. His hands felt warm and large in hers. Her skin tingled as he ran his hands up her arms. He held her shoulders and pulled her towards him. She could smell his cologne. She could see his eyelashes, a freckle on his cheek, black stubble on his chin and a sprinkling of grey hair at his temples. She felt him move his warm palm up from her shoulder to her neck, her eyes involuntarily closing as she lifted her face to his. She felt his lips kiss her neck and a small gasp escaped her lips.

His warm mouth was now covering hers. His arms slid around her waist pulling her body towards his. She splayed her fingers, pushing them through his hair. He tasted of sweet orange juice as his tongue slid inside her mouth. His hand found the soft skin between her jeans and T-shirt, every nerve ending tingling at his touch.

Chapter Forty-Six

Four months later

Rowan hummed to herself as she made the bed, shaking the duvet and plumping the pillows that were indented from where she and James had slept the previous night. They hadn't slept apart for a single night since the day they declared their feelings, just before Christmas.

Today was the grand opening of hers and Libby's shop. The lease had been transferred, Ace and Alan had put in a new bathroom, cleared and decorated the premises and she and Libby had been working hard to arrange the shop fittings and fill it with stock. James had organised the local press to take photographs for an article in the following day's local paper and had also designed a website for them.

Libby and David, Ace and Alan and she and James, had spent many a tipsy and fun-filled evening thinking up names fit for a jewellery and flower shop. She could hardly wait to see James' winning suggestion hung above the shop later that day.

She and James had walked hand in hand across Clapham Common earlier that morning taking Jet for a walk. They'd recently interviewed two couples who were going to move into the basement and ground floor apartments and had talked about how relieved they felt to have found such nice people to share the house with, now that Ace had moved in with Alan. After they'd spent Christmas making love and planning their future together, they decided not to sell Magnolia House, but that James should move into her apartment and sell his place. With the equity of the sale, they'd buy a small place in France close to her parents' house, which they could stay in when they visited, or rent out to holidaymakers.

James also planned to set enough money aside to invest in buying a mountain of wood for Oakland Garden Furniture. He'd rented a small building on Wandsworth Road where the agency had described it as 'benefiting from retail fronting onto the road and backing onto a workshop space with lower ground office/storage.' It had been perfect for establishing his new business where he would take on a young apprentice to teach the trade of carpentry.

Rowan settled Jet into his basket and left Magnolia House, having arranged to meet James at the shop. He and Ace were to collect the shop sign and drill it in place before everyone arrived. She ran downstairs and through the front door before stopping outside to gasp in wonder. During the warm morning sunshine, the magnolia tree had burst into bloom. The bulbous, candle-shaped buds had opened to reveal hundreds of blushing blossoms, their white and pink frothing petals decorating the tree. After weeks of late nights planning her new enterprise with Libby and designing more jewellery, it had taken her by surprise.

'Dah-ling, how did the check-up go?' asked Ace, when Libby arrived at the shop.

'Good thanks.' She put the box full of triangular cellophane flower bags on the floor by the new cash desk. 'It's been eight weeks since my operation. Can you believe how time has flown?'

'Don't talk to me about time flying. Every time I look in the mirror I see less of Enrique Iglesias looking back and more of Julio.'

'Rubbish. You look gorgeous.'

Ace winked. 'I always said you had great taste. But

seriously, I'm relieved you're on the mend now they've removed those trees from your oasis.'

'Endometriosis, idiot.'

'That's what I just said.'

'I love you, Mason Clint Oakland.'

'Sorry, but I'm spoken for.'

Libby nudged him, amicably. 'Is Rowan here yet?'

'No, but she phoned James a quarter of an hour ago to say she was setting off. The press aren't here until two, so there's plenty of time. Where's David?'

'He's parking the car and will bring the champagne in. I must get the glasses out of the store room at the back before I forget.'

'Will you stop carrying stuff. You'll burst your stitches. I'll fetch them.'

'My stitches came out weeks ago.'

'All the same. Go and make sure Alan isn't breaking his neck up that ladder while I fetch the glasses.'

Libby watched him disappear into the back room that was now their kitchen and flower preparation room. The plan was for Rowan to continue making jewellery from Magnolia House as it was warmer, lighter and had plenty of space to store her equipment. Libby couldn't wait for her sister-in-law to arrive so she could share her excitement.

Once outside, Libby looked up at the shop sign that was now fixed in place above the display window, but hidden beneath a large sheet of material. James and Alan were both at the top of stepladders on either side of the sign, draping the material to hide every inch of its name. The locals and the press had no idea, so they were going to have a grand unveiling.

'How's it going?' she called up to them.

James turned and grinned down at her. 'All done.' He descended the ladder and hugged her. 'How're you feeling?'

'Great. Fantastic!' Libby laughed, rubbing her palms together in excitement. 'This day seems to have taken ages to arrive but I suppose we did start planning at Christmas when there was a thick layer of snow on the ground.' She looked around at the blossoming trees dotted along the pavement, full of new leaves unfurling. 'Now it's warm and sunny and everything's falling into place.'

'You both deserve it. I've got to say, you and Rowan have done a great job with the window display. It looks very professional.'

'Thanks. We had a lot of fun doing it.'

They turned to look into the shop window. Easter eggs were draped with gold, green and yellow beaded jewellery. Yellow tulips and daffodils stood proudly in pretty vases next to wicker baskets full of blossoming lemon primroses. The whole display sat on waves of rolling satin that shimmered in the sunlight.

'Here they are,' called Alan.

Libby turned to see David and Rowan walking towards them side by side, carrying two bottles of champagne each and grinning widely.

'I needed rescuing,' said David. 'Luckily Rowan was coming down the road from the tube just as I was about to drop a bottle.'

'Come on then. This way and we'll put them in the fridge.'

Libby disappeared back into the shop with David following close behind.

Rowan smiled at James, who'd stepped forwards to take the large bottles from her arms and kiss her on the lips.

'Hey, gorgeous.'

'Hello. I see the sign's up,' she said. 'It's so exciting.'

'It's firmly fixed in place. A hurricane wouldn't blow that down.'

'Thank you, darling. I can't wait to see it revealed to the world.'

'Not long now,' said James, looking at his watch. 'Another twenty minutes and the press will be here.'

Rowan followed him into the shop where the perfumed aroma seemed almost visible in its intensity. Flowers of all shapes, colours and sizes decorated one half of the shop, sitting in large vases. She turned and moved towards her display cabinet on the opposite side. It was lit with miniature spotlights that shone on her handmade beaded earrings and necklaces.

'Rowan!' Libby hugged her.

'I can't believe it, Libbs. It's happening.' Rowan kissed her cheek.

'Me neither. Hang on. I'll be back in a minute. I must just make sure I've put my business cards in my handbag.'

Rowan watched her scurry off into the back room. It was so lovely to see her sister-in-law happy after the terrible couple of years she'd had. She seemed like a new woman now that she'd had her operation and the constant nagging pain in her stomach had gone away.

Rowan turned to look inside a tall glass cupboard. Inside was a revolving circular shelf where bracelets and necklaces hung from intricate curled pieces of driftwood. She watched her designs pass in front of her eyes and disappear to the back as the shelf rotated.

The next moment she felt arms enfold her waist and a warm body press against her back. That familiar scent filled her senses as James' cheek pressed against hers.

'You should be proud of yourself. They look amazing.'

'Thank you. I didn't think it was possible to be this happy.'

He squeezed her a little tighter in reply and kissed her hair.

'The press are here,' shouted Ace. 'How do I look? Where's a mirror? Check my teeth, can you? I had a poppy seed bagel this morning.'

Rowan and James turned to see Ace displaying his teeth for approval.

'Anything?' he asked.

'No.' Rowan giggled. 'You look adorable.'

Ace grinned back at her, before his attention turned to two men standing outside. One man was holding a camera and the other a microphone. Everyone was introduced as curious members of the public began to congregate on either side of the shop.

'Right, shall we begin with a group photograph?' asked the photographer.

'How about a photo of us popping the champagne open?' suggested Ace.

'Perfect. Perhaps if you all held a glass?'

Rowan stood in the middle of her group of friends, with one arm wrapped around James' waist and the other holding a champagne flute. She looked to one side where Ace and Alan were laughing like schoolboys as they prepared to pop a cork. They'd moved in together and AA Plumbers & Son was doing very well. Their *son* was waiting patiently for them at home. They'd called their tiny Chihuahua puppy, Son, and were planning an autumn wedding in which Son would carry the rings at the ceremony around his neck on a pink ribbon. They'd all been invited and had already spent a couple of hilarious evenings polishing off several bottles of wine while they planned their forthcoming nuptials.

Rowan then looked to her left. David and Libby were holding hands, deep in conversation. She saw David wipe a smudge from Libby's cheek and plant a kiss on her nose. Counselling had been a great help for her sister-in-law. She was now happy and confident and would much rather spend time designing bouquets and flower displays than buying pointless items in shops. Laughter filled their time together and now that Libby was pain free, she'd lost a stone in weight due to the fact that she wasn't comfort eating.

To loud cheers from the assembling crowd, corks were popped and sparkling bubbles were poured into the proffered glass flutes. As hiccups mingled with cheers and laughter, Libby and Rowan each pulled on the corners of the material that hung from the shop sign. Applause rippled and the camera flashed as the sheet billowed gently to the floor, revealing the shop's new name.

The Buds And The Beads.

Thank You

Dear readers,

Thank you for choosing to read *Magnolia House* out of the thousands that merit reading. I loved creating all my characters and was surprised at how much I missed them when I'd finished my story.

If you loved *Magnolia House* and have a minute to spare, I would really appreciate a short review on the page or site where you bought my book. Your help in spreading the word is hugely appreciated. Reviews from readers like you are invaluable and make a huge difference in raising a book's profile. It makes authors very happy to see that you've enjoyed our books.

Thank you

Love Angela x

About the Author

Angela Barton was born in London and grew up in Nottingham. She is married with three grown up children. Passionate about writing both contemporary and historical fiction, Angela has won and also been shortlisted for several writing competitions. She reads avidly, makes book-related jewellery and loves a nice cup of tea. Angela is a member of the Romantic Novelists' Association and Nottingham Writers' Studio.

For more on Angela visit:
www.angelabarton.net
www.twitter.com/angebarton
www.facebook.com/angela.bartonauthor

More from Angela Barton

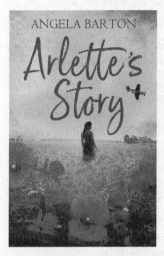

Arlette's Story

One woman's struggle to fight back against the enemy in order to protect the ones she loves.

When Arlette Blaise sees a German plane fly over the family farm in 1940, she's comforted by the fact that the occupying forces are far away in the north of the country. Surely the war will not reach her family in the idyllic French countryside near to the small town of Oradour-sur-Glane?

But then Saul Epstein, a young Jewish man driven from his home by the Nazis, arrives at the farm and Arlette begins to realise that her peaceful existence might be gone for good …

Visit www.rubyfiction.com for details.

You've Got My Number

Three isn't always a magic number ...

There are three reasons Tess Fenton should be happy. One, her job at the Blue Olive deli is dull, but at least she gets to work with her best friend. Two, she lives in a cosy cottage in the pretty village of Halston. Three, she's in love with her boyfriend, Blake.

Isn't she?

Because, despite their history, Blake continues to be the puzzle piece in Tess's life that doesn't quite fit. And when she meets intriguing local artist Daniel Cavanagh, it soon becomes apparent that, for Tess, love isn't as easy as one, two, three ...

Visit www.choc-lit.com for details.

More from Choc Lit

Why not try something else from the Choc Lit selection?

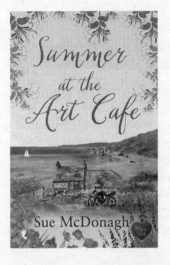

Summer at the Art Café
Sue McDonagh

From watercolours and cupcakes to leather jackets and freedom …

If you won a gorgeous purple motorbike, and your domineering husband said you were too fat for leathers and should sell it, would you do as you were told – or learn to ride it in secret?

Artist and café owner Lucy Daumier intends to do just that – but learning to ride is far from easy, especially under the critical eye of prickly motorcycle instructor, Ash Connor.

But gradually she gets the hang of it, and in the process re-discovers the girl she used to be. So starts an exciting summer of new friendship and fun – as well as a realisation that there is more to Ash than meets the eye when she is introduced to his seven-year-old daughter, Daisy.

But can Lucy's new-found happiness last when a spiteful family member wants to see her fail?

Watch for Me by Twilight

Kirsty Ferry

Hartsford Mysteries series

The past is never really the past at Hartsford Hall …

Aidan Edwards has always been fascinated by the life of his great-great uncle Robert. A trip to Hartsford Hall and an encounter with Cassie Aldrich leads him closer to the truth about Robert Edwards, as he unravels the scandalous story of a bright young poet and a beautiful spirited aristocrat in the carefree twilight of the 1930s before the Second World War.

But can Aidan find out what happened to Robert after the war – or will he have to accept that certain parts of his uncle's life will remain forever shrouded in mystery?

Visit www.choc-lit.com for details.

Escape to the Little Chateau
Marie Laval

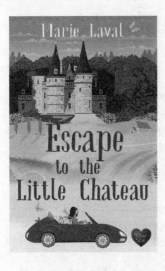

Will Amy's dreams of a Provençal escape come true?

There are many reasons Amy Carter is determined to make Bellefontaine, her farmhouse hotel in the French countryside, a success. Of course, there's the time and money she's put in to making it beautiful, but she also has something to prove – particularly to people like Fabien Coste.

Fabien is the owner of the nearby château, and he might just be the most arrogant, patronising man Amy has ever met ... unfortunately, he's also the most handsome.

But as rumours circulate in the local community and secrets about the old farmhouse begin to reveal themselves, Amy quickly sees the less idyllic side of life at Bellefontaine. Could Fabien be the man to help prevent her Provençal dream from turning into a nightmare?

Visit www.choc-lit.com for details.

Introducing Choc Lit

We're an independent publisher creating
a delicious selection of fiction.
Where heroes are like chocolate – irresistible!
Quality stories with a romance at the heart.

See our selection here:
www.choc-lit.com

We'd love to hear how you enjoyed *Magnolia House*.
Please leave a review where you purchased the novel
or visit **www.choc-lit.com** and give your feedback.

Choc Lit novels are selected by genuine readers like yourself.
We only publish stories our Tasting Panel want to see in
print. Our reviews and awards speak for themselves.

Could you be a Star Selector and join our Tasting Panel?
Would you like to play a role in choosing which novels
we decide to publish? Do you enjoy reading women's
fiction? Then you could be perfect for our Tasting Panel.

Visit here for more details …
www.choc-lit.com/join-the-choc-lit-tasting-panel

Keep in touch:
Sign up for our monthly newsletter Spread for all the
latest news and offers: www.spread.choc-lit.com.

Follow us on Twitter: @ChocLituk, Facebook:
Choc Lit and Instagram: ChocLituk

Where heroes are like chocolate – irresistible!